FANNY AND
THE REGENT OF SIAM

By the Same Author

Fanny Knox

FANNY
AND THE REGENT
OF SIAM

by

R. J. Minney

COLLINS
ST JAMES'S PLACE, LONDON

FIRST IMPRESSION   JANUARY, 1962
SECOND IMPRESSION   MAY, 1962

For

HETTY

© *R. J. Minney, 1962*
Printed in Great Britain
Collins Clear-Type Press
London and Glasgow

CONTENTS

ILLUSTRATIONS

ILLUSTRATIONS

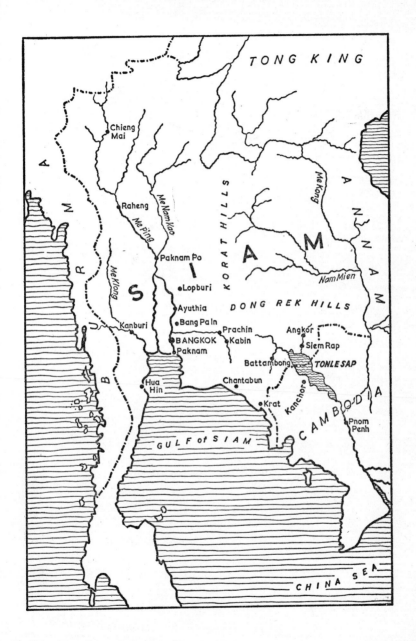

FOREWORD

THIS IS the story of Louis, the son of Anna Leonowens, the English governess in *The King and I*, and of the two beautiful daughters of Sir Thomas Knox, the English Consul General in Bangkok. Louis had been in love with the elder of these girls, Fanny, since his childhood.

This narrative thus takes Margaret Landon's famous book *Anna and the King of Siam* one generation further. The King here is the boy Anna taught and many of the people so dramatically involved in this story were well known to Anna. The book begins eight years after Anna left Siam. Louis has recently returned to the country and is in the service of the King.

The story has been compiled from official documents, private diaries and letters, many talks with those familiar with the incidents and with the people involved or closely related to these families, and also a careful examination of the newspapers of the period in England, France and Bangkok. It is therefore based substantially on fact. All the main incidents occurred and are supported by records and papers. A narrative form and dialogue are used in order to provide a more vivid continuity. It would be as true to say of this book as Margaret Landon said of *Anna and the King of Siam*, that 75 per cent of it is based on fact.

I went to Siam and the adjacent countries, visited the towns and villages concerned and was fortunate in having as my guide on all my journeys either direct descendants or very near relatives of the chief persons who figure in this story.

The assembling of material for this book began in the autumn of 1930 when two Englishmen sat talking in a garden on the outskirts of Bangkok. The rains were over, but the sun was still hot and blinding.

Dr. M. Carthew, who had been in medical practice for many years in that city, said to his guest, Mr. W. S. Bristowe, a visitor to the country: " Not five years ago, in that very chair in which you are now sitting, one of the most remarkable women I have ever known used to come and sit and tell me of her life and work.

" Her name was Fanny Knox. She was very lovely as a girl and set many hearts aflutter. Princes used to come to the British Consulate in their boats to serenade her. Her life was exciting yet deeply moving. . . ."

Bit by bit, he unfolded her story and the story of her sister Caroline and of Anna's son, Louis Leonowens. All this was told nearly fifteen years before *Anna and the King of Siam* was published, twenty-six years before Anna's story was given to the world in that enchanting film *The King and I*.

Mr. Bristowe, on returning to his hotel, made notes of what Dr. Carthew had said. To these he later added details supplied by other residents in Bangkok, who had known Fanny Knox and Louis. These notes Mr. Bristowe was kind enough to hand to me. But a considerable amount of research had still to be undertaken and in this too he most eagerly aided me.

I made a close study of the Foreign Office files at the Public Record Office, where the official documents relating the dramatic developments are preserved in three large volumes. In this I was greatly helped by Prof. B. R. Pearn, of the Foreign Office Research Department. The inter-departmental notes exchanged between Lord Salisbury, Secretary of State for Foreign Affairs at the time, and his Assistant Under-Secretary, Sir Julian Pauncefote, written by each in his own hand, are the basis of the dialogue I use in these scenes. Similarly most of the other conversations are based on letters, diaries and on the personal memories of those familiar with the events.

I list the chief sources from which my facts are drawn:

THE KNOX FAMILY—Debrett and Burke record Sir Thomas Knox's link with the Earls of Ranfurly. His daughters Fanny and Caroline and their marriages are mentioned, but hardly anything is said of their descendants, who are now living in Canada and Guatemala.

Fanny's first cousin, Sister Blanche, a daughter of Sir Thomas Knox's brother, the Rev. Charles Knox, who is a nun in the Anglican convent at East Grinstead, had, although in her ninety-fifth year, very clear memories of Fanny. Mr. Ian Madden, of New Zealand, another cousin, descended from Clara Knox, Fanny's aunt in Ireland, was kind enough to supply extracts from the diary of his cousin, also named Clara, and other useful family information as well as photographs.

A file of personal papers belonging to Fanny's father, Sir Thomas Knox, are in the possession of M. Duplantier, a lawyer in Pau, where Sir Thomas was living until the eve of his death in 1887.

I am greatly indebted to Mrs. C. E. Brewster of Peaslake, near Guildford, also descended from Fanny's Aunt Clara, for much information about the family and for many photographs, including the photograph of Fanny.

Miss Gertrude Bindloss, who was a governess to Fanny's children and took them out to Siam to join her, kept a diary, which her nephew, the Rev. Dudley Hiam, has most generously placed at my disposal. I am indebted to Mom Sribrahma Kridakara for indicating this source.

Of the older residents in Siam who knew Fanny I have to thank Mr. W. A. R. Wood, C.I.E., C.M.G., who was British Vice-Consul in Bangkok and later Consul at Chiengmai: he has been in Siam for sixty-five years and has been of immense help in supplying details of the life in that country in the old days; Mr. C. H. H. Monro, of Bangkok, who also knew Fanny well and is a close friend of the family into which she married; and Dr. Malcolm Smith, medical attendant at the Court of King Chulalongkorn, who knew Fanny too.

Louis T. Leonowens—His grandson, who bears the same name Louis T. Leonowens and now resides in Guatemala, very kindly sent me information about the family and supplied photographs of his grandmother, Caroline Knox, and his great grandmother, the famous Anna. Mrs. R. Monahan, of Quebec (née Anna Leonowens, a daughter of Louis), Mr. W. Mottershead, general manager of the firm of Louis T. Leonowens at Bangkok at the time of my visit, as well as members of the London offices of that firm, in particular Mr. Basil Cleaver, Mr. C. T. Cox, a former manager in Bangkok, and also Mr. W. Bain, Mr. H. G. B. Garrett, Mr. K. Gairdner and Mr. William Elder of the Anglo-Thai Company, all of whom knew Louis Leonowens in Siam, have supplied details of immense value.

Mr. A. C. Pointon, of the Bombay Burma Company, and Mr. T. C. Martine of the Borneo Company supplied details of the teak concessions on which Louis worked.

THE KING OF SIAM—His Royal Highness Prince Chula of Thailand, who was in Siam during my visit, talked to me of King Mongkut and of King Chulalongkorn, who was Anna's pupil. Prince Chula also arranged for the Lord Chamberlain to escort me through the Royal Palaces and temples in Bangkok so that I might see the settings of some of the scenes in this book.

Other members of the Royal family who helped me are Princess Chula, who gave me an Englishwoman's impressions of life in Siam; His Highness Prince Dhani; His Serene Highness Prince Prem; and Princess Poon, the daughter of Prince Damrong, who figures in this book. Princess Poon supplied many important details about Fanny and the attitude of the King towards Fanny and her husband Phra Preecha.

THE REGENT OF SIAM—His direct descendant, Miss Suvari Bunnag, who bears the same surname, has been of the utmost assistance to me, not only in connection with matters relating to her family, but much else. Her aunt, Chao Chom Liam, a granddaughter of the Regent who married King Chulalongkorn, as is stated in this book, very kindly supplied the photograph of the Regent. Miss Bunnag also harnessed the aid of others and accompanied me on most of my trips. Further information was obtained from a contemporary book *The Land of the White Elephant*, written in 1871-72 by an American visitor, Frank Vincent.

Fanny's husband, Phra Preecha Amatyakun, and his Family—His Excellency Dr. Manu Amatyakun, Thai Ambassador in Moscow, a great nephew of Phra Preecha, escorted me to Prachin, where Phra Preecha was Governor, showed me round the district, took me to Government House, and introduced me to priests and others who remember the story of Fanny's marriage and its consequences. Through him I saw the memorial to Phra Preecha which is now a place of pilgrimage.

Miss Vong Thavil Amatyakun, a direct descendant of Phra Preecha, being the granddaughter of Trakun his daughter, was also extremely helpful and supplied the photograph of her great grandfather. Phya Pattipan Amatyakun and his son Nai Tri Amatyakun, of the National Institute of Culture and the National Library in Bangkok, were also of immense help.

Others: Some information about Henry Alabaster was supplied by Sir Grenville Alabaster in addition to that collected from other sources; about the Knoxes' stay at Biarritz and Pau— Mr. J. Labord, Dr. A. Bellairs, and Mr. M. H. Carter; about Saigon M. Rene de Berval, editor of France-Asie; His Excellency, the French Ambassador in Cambodia, and Mr. D. F. Elliott, of the British Embassy in Cambodia, for details about that country.

My thanks are also due to Sir Richard Whittington, British Ambassador in Siam, Dr. Reginald leMay, Mr. Robin Penman and Mr. Vadhana Isarabhakdi, who was a judge at Prachin for many years and accompanied me on some of my tours: he is now Thai Ambassador to Australia and New Zealand; Capt. Douglas Gregory of the Naval Intelligence department at the Admiralty; Miss Rose Wood; Mrs. Ousa Weys; the P. & O. Shipping Company; the Messageries Maritimes; Mr. M. Willson Disher; the Ministry of Works for the photograph of the old British Consulate in Bangkok, and the Public Record Office for permission to quote from the documents and for photostat copies of some of the documents. Mr. Henry Fearon supplied information about Mr. Theodore McKenna, who was the grandfather of the actress, Virginia McKenna. Sir Victor Brooke was the father of Lord Alanbrooke.

FOREWORD

Siamese names of people and places are not easy to render phonetically. Even in the Thai versions they vary greatly. There is the further complication that the letter given as "l" in English is pronounced as thongh it were an "n." To be consistent I have spelt such words as they are pronounced. I have also tried to avoid the confusion that would arise with changes of name when new titles are conferred. I have kept to the one name throughout the book. I have also omitted, since they are not pronounced, the final letters "se" in the name of the Regent, for example, which is spelt Suriwongse in Siamese, and in other names of that kind. Though family names were not adopted for general use until later, I have found it more convenient to refer to the Amatyakuns and Bunnags in this book in order to indicate those who belonged to the same family.

R.J.M.

BOOK ONE

The Laughing River

Chapter One

AT THE first sight of the feathery attap palms her heart leapt. She gazed at the mangrove swamps, the tall coconut trees and the even taller betel palms behind, the monkeys swinging from bough to bough, the flashing colours as the birds darted in the thickets, the muddy red-brown river. Fanny shut her eyes and raised her face towards the sky, golden and blinding in its glare. She was home.

It had been a long voyage. First the large and comfortable *Verona*, the P. & O. steamer they had boarded at Marseilles on the 24th March, 1875, then the change at Singapore to this small, shabby *Alligator*, in which they had rolled and tossed for four days in the Gulf of Siam. After they had crossed the bar at Paknam, the vast salt marshes could be seen stretching into the distance from both shores. Then the river began to narrow. She saw again the coloured houses, pink and blue and yellow, built on tall stilts or floating on rafts, and the pretty little temples, like dolls' houses, with their gilded *narks*, rising from the roofs like serpents, to ward off the evil, wandering spirits.

The river wound tortuously. From the fishing boats men waved their greeting. Now the ship was steaming past the larger, slower rice boats, then the lorchas came into sight, with their great mat lug sails, the chugging paddles of the steam launches with trails of frothing water behind, the towed barges, the sailing dinghies, the long, low canoes—the river was getting very congested. Her face alight, Fanny caught sight of Bangkok again, just ahead.

From one of the many small boats, rising and dipping as they approached, she could see three men waving excitedly. She took the glasses from her father and leaned across the rails. Her yellow, flowered muslin frock set off what remained of her pinkness after six weeks of travelling through the tropics. Her pale brown hair, long now but bunned and chignoned, gave her a grown-up air which her mischievous hazel eyes belied. For all her nineteen years she was still tiny, scarcely more than five foot high.

" It looks like Louis," she said, turning to her father.

Louis was the son of Anna Leonowens, who had been governess at the court of King Mongkut of Siam. He was fourteen when his mother resigned her post in 1867 and took him with her to England and then to the United States. The King Anna had served died a year after she left and he was succeeded by his eldest son King Chulalongkorn, who was only fifteen at the time. Louis and the new King were of the same age and had played together as children.

" I forgot to tell you," Knox replied. " Louis returned some months ago. Then he went off to Australia to buy some horses for the King—there aren't any in Siam, only ponies in the North, from the Shan States. They have a Household Cavalry at the Royal Palace now."

She waved her hand in response. " Is his mother back too? "

" Oh, no. Anna's doing much too well lecturing all over America after the success of her book telling them how she taught the King of Siam to speak English."

Fanny looked through the glasses again. " And that's Nai Dee, isn't it? "

Knox nodded, his dark beard blowing in the wind.

Nai Dee was the favourite grandson of Somdetch Sri Suriwong, the Prime Minister of Siam. He had been appointed Regent by the dying King and still retained the position, although the young King had by now come of age.

" Surprising," Fanny said. " Aunty Anna and Nai Dee's

grandfather used to hate each other. How have those two come to be friends? "

" Anna was a little unkind to the old Regent in her book. I don't think she was very fair to him. He's a great man really. He is doing so much for Siam. I bet you don't know who the boy is with them."

Fanny looked through the glasses again. The boat was much nearer now. But she still couldn't tell.

" Prince Damrong, the King's brother," Knox said. " He was only four when you last saw him. Nine years make a lot of difference."

A great cluster of little boats gathered around the *Alligator*, cutting off Louis and his friends. The air was filled with hollering and shouting and much laughter. Along the banks she could see the busy wharves piled high with bales of merchandise. From the sawmills and rice mills rose thick clouds of black smoke. The British consular launch, painted an official red, its brass-work gleaming, the Union Jack fluttering, gave two warning snorts and tore forward. Knox could see his deputy, Gould, standing for'ard. They saluted each other.

The little boats tried to make way. The consular launch came alongside. " Glad to see you back," Gould called.

The ship's ladder was lowered. The Captain came up to bid them farewell. For Fanny he had a large bouquet of flowers.

Chapter Two

As THE launch neared the red landing-stage of the British Consulate, Fanny could see Mamma and Caroline hurrying across the lawn. The large attractive wooden house, raised high on stilts, a flight of steps leading up from the lawn to the spacious veranda with its panels of close-meshed lattice, the winding garden path, the tall mango trees filled with monkeys, the bushes of hibiscus and oleander, the canal flowing at the side below Papa's bedroom and hers . . .

Mamma was blowing kisses and in a few moments they were locked in each other's arms. " My ! My ! How you've grown," Mrs. Knox said. " You're not a child any longer."

" I'm not much bigger than you are," Fanny laughed.

Mrs. Knox was Siamese. The daughter of the Duke of Somkok, she had from the age of fourteen been a lady-in-waiting at the court of the Second or Deputy King, a younger brother of the late King Mongkut. He was wholly western in his outlook and his way of life. English was spoken in his home and he had so great an admiration for both England and America that he named his eldest son, who had now succeeded him as Second King, George Washington. When Knox had arrived in Siam in 1848, after serving with the Indian Army in the China Wars, he had been persuaded by the Second King to undertake the training of his own small army. It was then that Knox and the pretty young lady-in-waiting had met and married. She was seventeen. There was no British Consulate in Siam at that time. It was established in 1856, a few months after Fanny was born. Knox joined the Consulate shortly afterwards as an interpreter and within two years was appointed acting Consul, many said through powerful family influence, for he was closely related to Lord John Beresford and to the Earl of Ranfurly. In 1864 Knox was made Consul. Anna Leonowens had sought his help constantly because of her recurrent quarrels with King Mongkut.

Mrs. Knox, with such a background and upbringing, not only spoke English fluently, but was completely westernised in her outlook. Her younger daughter Caroline, two years Fanny's junior though she towered above both her mother and her sister, scarcely bore any resemblance to Fanny. Her complexion was a pale olive, her hair jet black, her eyes a deep brown. She looked Spanish or even Greek, whereas Fanny was unmistakably Irish. In temperament too they were different. Caroline was the quiet one, she preferred to remain with Mamma and not go "gallivanting all over Europe in quest of an education," as Mamma put it. Her health was not robust, which was another reason why she stayed at home. Younger than both girls was their brother Tom, who was still at school in England.

Knox gave instructions about the grand piano Fanny had brought out with her from Paris. He then turned and embraced his wife. He had been away six months to fetch Fanny. With his arm linked through his wife's they walked together across the lawn.

The residence was raised above a bare open space. The garden stairway led up to the first floor where Knox had his study, alongside the main reception rooms. The bedrooms were on the floor above. At the back, in bungalows of assorted sizes, lived the staff—Gould, Newman, Alabaster and two young student interpreters, all Englishmen. Beyond were the quarters of the Indian staff, the clerks on one side, the domestic servants on the other, beside the small gaol. A gate led out into an alleyway at the back which in turn led to the New Road, the only road in Bangkok; all the rest of the traffic went by water. The only post office in Bangkok stood alongside the consular landing-stage.

A flock of servants, male and female, headed by Singh, the tall, turbanned Sikh, stood salaaming at the foot of the garden stairway. Two large dogs came bounding forward.

Tea had been set out in the veranda.

" Oh, the wonderful smell of it all," Fanny exclaimed, looking at the great line of floating houses across the water; the lofty spire of the Wat Arun, the Temple of the Dawn, blue-grey in the sunlight; the glittering tops of the Palace's golden pagodas; the vast Chinese bazaar which separated the Palace from the Consulate. She listened to the murmur of voices and the laughter on the river, the singing of the boatmen, the cry of the birds, and watched the antics of the monkeys in the tall trees.

" I've missed it all so much," she said.

Across the lawn she saw Louis and Nai Dee and Damrong coming towards them. With Caroline she raced down the stairs to greet them.

" Any excitements while I was away ? " Knox asked, pulling up a chair for Gould at the tea table.

Gould, short, slightly bald though still in his thirties, mopped his brow. " I go all hot and cold when I think of it."

" Who did what ? " Knox demanded in his blunt manner.

" I've never been able to find out. It didn't concern us at first. A fire broke out in the main Palace of the First King. That happened on the 27th December last, very early in the morning. The Second King noticed the fire from his Palace and sent his soldiers to help put it out, but this was misunderstood by the officials at the main Palace. They saw an army advancing and they called out the First King's troops to repel them."

" Good God ! " Knox exclaimed. " Was there a fight ? "

Suriwong Bunnag, Regent of Siam—from a painting

Anna Leonowens in her sixties
—from a painting

" No, sir. Just as shots were about to be exchanged the Second King fled in alarm and took refuge in the British Consulate."

" Here? In the Consulate? "

" He appealed to me for sanctuary and, in view of your close relations with the Second King's family, I thought you would approve of my granting it."

Knox scratched his chin. " How did the Second King get here? "

" Before the opposing troops could reach his Palace, His Majesty managed to escape in disguise through a window at the back. He arrived here with his leg badly injured and had to lie up in his tent . . ."

" Tent? "

" Yes, sir. We had a number of tents all over the lawn here. His Majesty brought a great many retainers with him."

" I'm surprised Mrs. Knox told me nothing of this in her letters."

" I asked her not to, sir. I felt that by the time you heard of it in London it would all be settled."

" How did you settle it? You went to the Regent, I suppose."

Gould nodded. Mrs. Knox came up and joined them. Gould went on:

" The Regent was appalled. He said the officials in the main Palace should *not* have called out their army. The Second King was only trying to help put out the fire."

" That's what I expected the old devil to say," observed Mrs. Knox.

Knox said: " Let Gould go on, dear."

" There have been no end of rumours, sir," Gould added. " It was said that the fire at the main Palace was a put-up job . . ."

" What do you mean? " Knox asked.

" That it was started on purpose."

" For what purpose? " asked Knox.

Gould flicked his eyebrows.

" Princess Chandr is convinced . . ." Mrs. Knox began. Princess Chandr was the Second King's sister.

" Princess Chandr fills my wife's head with nothing but gossip," Knox said sharply.

The Princess's friendship with Mrs. Knox was close. They were about the same age and had been drawn together when Mrs. Knox was a lady-in-waiting.

" Princess Chandr is convinced that the Regent was behind the whole thing," Mrs. Knox said.

" What would he want to start a fire for? " asked Knox.

" What he wanted," his wife explained, " was a clash between the two Kings. It was his way of telling Chulalongkorn that his coming of age was not going to make any difference, and that unless he minds his p's and q's a new King will take over."

Knox fell silent. He knew that King Chulalongkorn, a spirited young man, had been restive ever since he came of age quite recently. His head was full of plans and with the Regent still in control he felt fettered and frustrated. How long could this situation go on? Would the Regent be prepared to replace the King if His Majesty tried to get his own way?

Knox shook his head. " I doubt it. The Regent wouldn't go as far as that."

" Wouldn't he? " said Mrs. Knox. " That old devil will not stop at anything. You don't know him as I do. My father's sister was married to a cousin of his . . ."

" Another thing, sir," Gould said, " perhaps I ought not to mention this, but one of our own staff, Henry Alabaster . . ."

" What's Alabaster been up to now? " Knox interrupted. " We're always having trouble with that fellow."

" He's mixed up with this in some way."

" With the fire? "

" With the intrigue that led up to the fire, I understand—at least that is what I heard from the French Consul, M. Garnier. He says Alabaster is always crossing the river to see the Regent."

" Why? "

" We don't know, sir. M. Garnier says if Alabaster were a French subject, he'd have packed him off home."

" Have you discovered any specific fact this time, Gould? "

" No, sir. We can never get hold of anything specific. But everything Alabaster does is odd and suspect."

" He's a snake in the grass, that Alabaster," said Mrs. Knox. " He works like this through the undergrowth." She indicated it with her hand.

" I'd better have a word with him after tea," Knox said. " Where are the girls? Call the others, dear."

Mrs. Knox patted her husband's cheek, saying, " You poor darling, after London and Paris, back again in this jungle of intrigue and revenge and vendettas, and so long as that old Regent's alive . . ."

Knox rose irritably. " Sometimes you say the most appalling things, dear. We've got his grandson Nai Dee here." He went to the veranda rail himself. " Come on, Fanny and Caroline; all of you. Tea."

They came up the stairs. The boys shook hands formally with Knox. Mrs. Knox showed them where they were to sit, but Damrong peered into the drawing-room.

" I've never been in here before," he said, then, pointing to an enormous painting on the wall, remarked, " Is this a picture of you, Fanny? "

" Oh, no," she laughed. " That's a copy of Reynolds' famous picture of the Three Graces."

" So that isn't you? " He pointed to a woman half-kneeling on the left.

" That's Papa's grandma, Barbara Montgomery."

Night fell suddenly while they talked. The lamps were brought in and placed on the tables. In the garden four lighted lanterns swung from tall posts, two others lit up the landing-stage and cast their glow on the river. Lights were to be seen everywhere now, shimmering in the waters of the thousand canals that led to the west and the east and the north. A light in every boat, in every ship anchored in the river, in every mat-masted junk and barge. A fairyland of light, with the music of guitar and flute drifting over the waters and the laughter of young men and women. Fireflies began their dance. The monkeys had ceased their chatter and the birds too had said their good night, and had gone off to bed. The murmur of the bazaar was clearer in the night air. Mingled with it was the *tchik-tchik* of the cicadas and the burbling croak of the water frogs.

Caroline noticed that Louis had eyes for no one but Fanny, and saw that from across the table Nai Dee was looking intently at her too. She had come back prettier than ever. Ah, well, perhaps Louis might be a brother-in-law. Mamma, watching the girls, had much the same thought. Fanny would be more suited to Louis, with her splendid education and her western ways—London, Brussels, Paris. Caroline—possibly Nai Dee? It might not be a bad idea to link their family with the Regent's.

" It was odd," said Fanny, " to find when I got to England that they have no Second King there. I used to wonder who could be Second King to Queen Victoria."

" Mr. Disraeli, of course," Mamma suggested.

Knox laughed. " Lord Beaconsfield now," he corrected.

" You have heard, I suppose," Gould said, " that the Regent always speaks of you as the Third King."

" Yes, I've heard him say so," Knox replied.

" I wonder what he means," said Mamma. Curious the way

the Regent's mind worked. Behind that smile of his he was always up to something. It was his men, many of them relatives, all of them closely dependent on him, who occupied the chief places in the Government. Yes, it might be better to be linked with him than to have him against you.

Chapter Three

After Mamma had gone to bed, Caroline slipped into her sister's room. " Aren't you going to unpack? " she asked. " What have you brought for me? "

" One or two pretty dresses. I'll unpack in the morning." Fanny stretched and yawned in her bed.

" How lovely! " Caroline began to fiddle with the trunks. " Please, Fanny."

" Oh, Caroline, it's been such a long, tiring day." But she climbed out and began to unpack. She held up a pale-blue dress, with frills down the sleeves and the skirt. Caroline took it from her, hugged her sister excitedly and began at once to try it on.

" Paris? "

Fanny nodded. " It's a bit big at the hips, I see. The women in France need quite large chairs to sit on. You can get that taken in. I wasn't quite sure of this one." She held up a bright yellow dress with an enormous bustle.

" It's beautiful! " That was tried on too.

" What are Frenchmen like? " Caroline asked.

" Oh, nice. They tease rather. But I teased them back."

" You must speak French well."

" I ought to. But the voyage to Singapore, Caroline . . ." She screwed up her nose and shut her eyes.

Caroline, seated on the bed in her underclothes, leaned eagerly towards her sister.

" There was a young man from the Foreign Office, Edward

Lambton. He's huge, about six foot two or more. Good-looking, light reddish hair and a fetching smile."

" With Papa there . . ." Caroline began.

" Oh, Papa didn't interfere. He read most of the time. Besides, he liked Edward. They used to talk about the Foreign Office together."

" I suppose the ship was much bigger than the *Alligator*."

" Much. About ten times the size. A vast deck, about half a mile long."

" Half a mile? "

" Well, perhaps not quite half a mile. But we used to play deck tennis and quoits and dance, and go to the far end at night and stand under the stars and talk. And once when we were having a sherry in the saloon by ourselves, I tried to smoke a cigarette."

" Oh, Fanny! Papa would be furious."

" I didn't like it," she said. " It made me cough. But the sherry was not bad. Tastes odd at first."

" Where's Mr. Lambton? In Singapore? "

" No. He went to Japan on a tour for the Foreign Office. He's coming here, though, on his way back."

Looking at her sister in a puzzled way, Caroline said: " You aren't a flirt, are you, Fanny? "

Fanny considered the question. She did enjoy the attention she received and the compliments the men paid her, but she never took the initiative.

" No. I'm not a flirt," she said. " They flirt with me."

Fanny awoke very early next morning. The room was already filled with sunshine. She lay in bed listening to little sounds that brought back so many childhood memories. Suddenly she leapt out of bed. Papa had bought her a horse, she remembered. She dressed quickly in a silver-grey whipcord habit and dashed down to the stables.

Papa was there already. He pointed to the dun Australian gelding. Fanny, her eyes glowing with admiration and pride, flung her arms about its neck, then mounted it and together with Papa set off for their morning canter.

They were galloping along the New Road when Knox pulled on the reins. Ahead of them, riding towards the Palace, was a small group. Fanny saw that the young man in the middle was the King. He turned his head to look at them and, as they approached, greeted them with a wide, welcoming smile. He was small and slight and wore a thin moustache.

" They did not teach me how to curtsy on a horse, Your Majesty. I shall have to learn," said Fanny.

" Or better still, teach the horse to curtsy, for you'll be meeting His Majesty quite often on this road." It was Louis who spoke. She had not recognised him in his magnificent gold-braided uniform.

Knox, after the conventional gestures of homage, had engaged one of the others in conversation, a man in his thirties, not handsome, but strong and rugged.

" Your daughter? " the man asked.

" You can't possibly remember her," Knox said. " She was only ten when she left here. Fanny, this is Phra Preecha, Governor of the province of Prachin."

She remembered seeing him quite often at the Consulate as a child. The *Phra* was his title. He was a baron. He and Knox were good friends. In his eyes Fanny noticed just a hint of a smile, but they did not linger on her.

The King announced his intention of giving a party in honour of Fanny's return.

" Enchanted," she replied. It was a word she had learned in Paris.

With a quick bow His Majesty dug his heels into his horse and rode on, the others following. Knox turned and rode off too. But Louis stayed behind.

King Chulalongkorn, shortly after his accession

Official group taken during King Chulalongkorn's visit to Calcutta in 1872. Centre, the Viceroy of India, Lord Mayo—on his left, the King of Siam—on the King's left, Sir Thomas Knox

The British Consulate in Bangkok—from an old photograph

On the parade ground opposite the Palace the Royal Household Cavalry were assembling.

" Oughtn't you to be there? " Fanny asked Louis.

" Not for a moment or two. I want to talk to you. Are you planning to stay in Bangkok? "

" For the rest of my life, I suppose. By the way "—she added, glancing over her shoulder—" who is Phra Preecha? I remember him only faintly."

" He's married and has two children. I should forget about him."

" Beast! " she exclaimed. " Don't be late for your parade— though perhaps I would like to see you shot."

The road, four miles long and built but recently, ran from the Palace to the foreign consulates, which were mostly grouped together.

Her groom had hung behind while she talked. Now he padded after her through the light traffic of rickshaws and ox-carts and pedestrians. The sun was already hot and blinding. Along both sides of the road were small stalls. The Sampeng market gateway on the right led to the Chinese bazaar. It had fascinated her as a child to wander with Mamma and Caroline amid the acrid smell of herbs and over-ripe fruit, with flies everywhere, to hear the intoned cries of the vendors, to see the bustle, the colour, the jostling, and catch glimpses through the heat-haze of the blacksmiths, the silversmiths, the weavers, the fortune-tellers, the letter writers, the quack doctors, the gambling booths with the pawn shops alongside, the story-tellers with their audience seated on their haunches, and to linger for a while at the open-air theatres.

All the shops faced the river and the canals. On the New Road, there were some single-storied dwelling-houses, a sprinkling of temples, each with three overlapping roofs, gilded *narks* curling defiantly above them. Swarms of pariah dogs hung about the open drains and scavenged in the mounds of refuse. At intervals the road crossed a canal, in which sepia children could be seen tumbling and playing, while women washed and gossiped and the boats drifted by.

Saffron-clad priests, smoking cheroots, stopped to stare at Fanny and she *wei*-ed a polite greeting. A Norwegian sea captain, lolling in a rickshaw, touched his cap as he passed her. Many whispered: " That is the English Consul's daughter." Some remembered seeing her as a child. She used to go about with Missy Anna and her son Louis and attended the school at the Palace, where Missy Anna taught. To those who bade her good day she replied in Siamese. It was as much her mother tongue as English.

Knox had got home early in order to see Alabaster. He was a man in his early forties, short and gaunt, with long side whiskers. His pale-grey eyes had a studious look, but they were shifty.

Knox motioned him to a chair and asked how he liked being in Siam.

" Very much."

" Made many friends? " Knox asked.

" Quite a number. They are an especially friendly people."

" I'm glad to hear you say that. You weren't well disposed towards them at first, Alabaster. I remember I had to reprimand you for your patronising and contemptuous attitude towards the people, which is not the sort of attitude we can tolerate at the British Consulate."

Alabaster shifted in his seat.

" You've abandoned that attitude, I imagine? " Knox remarked.

" All that was some years ago," said Alabaster. " I had not been long here—only a few months."

" I understand you see a great deal of the Regent. Is that so? "

" Ye-es. In a way."

" What do you mean by 'in a way'? " Knox asked.

" Well, I am translating the Buddhist scriptures into English, and I wrote and asked His Excellency if I might do some research in his library."

Knox sat up in his chair. " You wrote to the Regent? "

" I did not see any harm in that," said Alabaster.

" You did not feel you ought to ask my persmission before you wrote such a letter? "

" No," said Alabaster. " I did not think that what I did with my spare time concerned the British Consulate."

" Not concern us," Knox exploded. " It concerns us vitally. Only the head of the Consulate has any right of access to the head of the government here. You most certainly ought to have sought my permission before you did anything of the kind."

" You were not here," said Alabaster with an air of indifference.

" Don't quibble, Alabaster. In my absence you should have sought Mr. Gould's permission. Did you consult him? "

Alabaster was silent.

" Did you consult him? " Knox roared.

" No."

There was silence for a moment. Alabaster broke it by rising. " I had better resign," he said. " My letter will be in your hands within the next few minutes."

The insolence, Knox thought. Alabaster had not once addressed him as "sir."

" Your passage home will be arranged for by Mr. Gould," Knox said.

" I do not intend to go home," said Alabaster in an off-hand tone. " I mean to continue my work here, if not for the British, then for others. But I shall be glad if Mr. Gould would arrange for me to have the passage money, to which I am of course entitled."

Knox was in a great rage as Alabaster left. He rang for

35

Gould and told him what had happened. " It will not surprise me," he added, " if Alabaster decides to work for the Regent, with whom he has clearly been in the closest contact for some time."

" It may well be proof," said Gould, " that M. Garnier was right when he told me Alabaster had a hand in that fire. What part he actually played we shall never know, for he works furtively."

Chapter Four

WITH Caroline watching, Fanny took off her wide riding-apron, peeled off her breeches and flung them on her bed. Her zinc bathtub had been filled by one of the maids. Fanny stepped into the cool, scented water and stretched herself at full length. She was small and slender, but well shaped. Her skin was milk white, her pale-brown hair, with glints of gold in it, was bound in a sky-blue scarf. Her eyes, the liveliest feature in her expressive face, seemed at times more green than hazel.

All the doors were open as they always are in the East, but the thin flowered curtains were slightly drawn to show that one had to knock before entering.

Caroline's dark hair was cut close about her ears. She was attractive rather than pretty.

" You like Louis, don't you? " Caroline asked. " I mean ..."

" Go on, Caroline."

" He was always asking after you. I think he likes you."

A slight glow came into Fanny's face.

Fanny took off her scarf and tossed her head, letting her hair fall in its natural folds. " I met a most attractive man while I was out this morning. He isn't exactly good-looking, but he has a lovely face."

Caroline laughed. " How on earth can he have a lovely face if he isn't good-looking? "

" Well . . ." She began to gesticulate with her little hands. " There's a gentle—a spiritual quality in it. He has a far-away look as though he can see beyond the skies."

Caroline frowned in thought. "Do you mean Phra Preecha?"

Fanny nodded. " So you can see it too."

" Yes. He has that look. He's a nice man, but he's married."

" You and Mamma talk like the characters in Jane Austen's books. You've got marriage on the brain. I have no intention of getting married—not for a long, long time."

Just then Mamma came into the room, with a large bouquet of flowers. Though a dozen years younger than her husband, who had just turned fifty, her hair was lightly touched with grey. Her vivacity and her air of elegance could have made one think she was French. In fact, she had never left Siam, nor apparently ever had any wish to do so. That she had breeding was instantly apparent.

" Who are the flowers from? " Fanny asked.

" From the Queen." Mamma handed her the card on which was written " For dear Fanny. I hope she remembers me."

" She is Nai Dee's sister," Mamma explained and went on: " Now tell me, who doesn't want to get married for a long time? You, Fanny? "

" Yes, Mamma."

" Have you a reason? "

" Have you a reason why I should? " Fanny asked.

Mamma smiled at this turning of the tables. " By the time I was your age I was already married. It's good to marry young. Besides, if you have too many admirers, as I'm sure you will have—well, there's bound to be trouble. And did somebody say something about Preecha? "

" Fanny met him out riding this morning," said Caroline.

Mamma was thankful that he was married. Had he been free and had fate by some inscrutable design caused her daughter and Preecha to be drawn together, then trouble would undoubtedly have followed. For Preecha belonged to one of the oldest and most exalted families in the country. The only other family of equal importance was that of the Regent.

38

For some centuries, going back to the reign of King Rama the First, these two families had been predominant. But for the past quarter of a century, ever since the Regent had been instrumental in bringing Mongkut, the father of the present King, to the throne, it was he who had been all powerful. He was Prime Minister then, as his father had been before him. When Mongkut lay dying, with his heir still a minor, the Prime Minister was made Regent as well, and Suriwong Bunnag had held those dual offices ever since. All the reins of power in the State were in his control. He appointed ministers. He selected judges. Nobody dared defy him. The Amatyakun family, to which Preecha belonged, came under his domination. They did not like it. The rivalry between the two families had since grown into an enmity.

" Preecha's a nice man," Mamma said. " Good—almost saintly. Your father is very fond of him and so is the King. He has a fine brain. He found a gold mine in his province and presented it to the State. He is working it himself with machines and engineers. It brings a lot of money to the Government. Preecha is married," she went on. " He has two children, one aged four and the other two."

" I know," said Fanny.

Singh appeared in the doorway and announced that lunch was ready. The meal was served in the veranda. The venetian blinds had been lowered to keep out the blinding glare, but through the slats Fanny caught glimpses of the enchanting pageantry of the river.

They had barely risen from the table when suddenly all the servants in the veranda and on the lawn, fell on their knees and pressed their foreheads to the ground.

Turning towards the landing-stage, Fanny saw a long gilded boat with tasselled green awnings, and emerging from it, with an umbrella held above him, came the Regent Chow Phya Sri Suriwong. He was a little above medium height, slender, on the verge of seventy, and most handsomely dressed in a pale-blue *panaung* of thick silk, which fell in folds to his ankles; he wore also a bright-red jacket, with richly embroidered collar and cuffs, and gold buttons.

"Fanny!" he called, raising his eyes to the veranda and joining his palms in greeting.

"Your Excellency!" She too joined her palms together.

"I have come especially to see you," he cried.

He came up and put his arm affectionately about her. Knox had already hurried down the stairway to receive him.

"My dear friend," he said to Knox, his warm smile dispelling the normal sternness of his countenance, "I am so glad you have returned. Even a brief absence is an interruption. Let us sit here in the veranda where it is cool, and we shall talk."

Mrs. Knox and Caroline, having paid their respects, withdrew. But the Regent detained Fanny for a moment.

"You've been away too long, my little Fanny." He pinched her cheek affectionately. He used to do that when she was a child and she had never liked it. "Wait a minute. I have brought you something." He clapped his hands. One of his attendants came up the stairs and lowered his forehead to the floor. He was carrying two parcels. The Regent took the smaller one from him and handed it to Fanny.

His sharp eyes observed her as she undid the wrapping. A velvet box was disclosed. Inside it lay a small heart-shaped locket, covered with rubies and edged with tiny diamonds.

"When you open it you will find there is a place inside for a picture. One day you will decide whose picture you should put in there. Is it nice?"

"Very pretty indeed, Your Excellency. Thank you very, very much."

Bowing, she left to show her present to her mother and sister.

" And this I have brought for you, Tom," the Regent said, handing Knox the larger parcel. It contained a gold cigar box.

" Your Excellency is far too generous. My little gift to you is extremely modest." He called to Singh, who brought a small Sèvres figure of a seated shepherdess. By her rustic stool a small clock had been let in. " I got it for you in Paris."

The Regent held it to his ear. " It goes," he exclaimed. " This will be a great joy to us in my home."

The servants brought cheroots and brandy and the two sat talking for some time. When the Regent rose to go, he turned to Knox with a warm smile.

" I want to say one thing more, my friend. Have you ever thought how nice it would be if our two families could be linked —not now perhaps, but one day." He smiled again, baring his even, white teeth. " Fanny, I see, has flowered wonderfully. She was always a pretty child."

" Your Excellency is most kind. Some seem to think she is pretty. As her father it is difficult for me to judge."

" You say nothing about the alliance. I recognise that she is young by the standards of your country. But Nai Dee is ripe now. In a few days he will be twenty-one."

" I greatly appreciate the compliment Your Excellency is paying us."

" It would link our families, even our two countries, because of the marriage between Nai Dee's sister and the King."

" It is indeed a great honour." Knox paused.

" But——? "

" I feel—and I hope Your Excellency will appreciate that it is only natural—I feel that Fanny must be consulted. She has a will, you know."

" This she gets from you."

" Possibly. But in England girls now make up their own

41

minds. Marriages are no longer arranged for them. So she must have her say."

"I know. I know. I realise it is too early yet. All I am saying is—one day, perhaps. You talk to her. Sow the thought in her mind. We must let it grow there. It will take time, of course."

He held out his hand in farewell.

Chapter Five

FOR MANY hours after the Regent had left, Knox found it difficult to think of anything else. He kept going over it in his mind. A link between our two families—and our two countries. What was behind it? The Regent generally had a purpose of some kind. True he had always been fond of Fanny and he had known her well ever since she had been born. Nai Dee was his favourite grandson—he had been indulged and spoilt. Anything he wanted the old man always got for him. If Nai Dee wanted to marry Fanny . . . But that, Knox reasoned, was not a sufficient explanation. There must be more to it.

Knox's mind went back to the talk he had with Gould about the fire at the Palace and the manœuvres of the Regent to retain his hold over the restive young King who had just come of age and wanted to be free. Arranging a marriage between Nai Dee's sister and the King had fitted into this pattern, for even though she was not the King's only wife, it introduced an influence which could be exercised during the King's hours of relaxation. But marrying Nai Dee to Fanny—what purpose would that serve? How could it affect the King's position, supposing the Regent was trying to checkmate the King? Suddenly an explanation flashed into his mind: such an alliance, by establishing a close link between the Regent and Britain's chief representative in Siam, would align not only Knox personally, but might appear to align the might of Britain behind the Regent's power. This seemed to him to be the answer. But would it be right for him to encourage it?

Looked at solely on a personal basis, it was a matter for Fanny alone to decide.

Knox decided to discuss the matter with his wife before he gave Fanny even a hint of it. Mrs. Knox, because she was Siamese, understood the Siamese mind and was able to interpret the twists beneath its seeming simplicity. She claimed to possess intuitive insight. This he doubted. It was a claim most women made. His mother and his sister Bella had called it Celtic foresight and said they had inherited it from their Highland ancestors. The fact was that women had a great deal more time to think. Mrs. Knox was addicted to analysing everything that was done or said. She gnawed at even trifling incidents as a dog does a bone.

Now he heard Fanny at the piano. It had arrived that afternoon and had been placed under the large Reynolds picture in the drawing-room. She played well, but what was she playing? Some music-hall air—*The Ratcatcher's Daughter*. Her father was a little startled. . . . And this was followed by *Polly Perkins of Paddington Green*. Where on earth had she heard them? Possibly, while she had been staying with his cousin, General Knox, in Great Cumberland Place, near Marble Arch: he might have taken her to a music-hall.

Anyway, it was time to change. They were going out. Even though it was really too hot to get into a dinner-jacket, he put on one of black alpaca with satin-gin trousers tied with a red cummerbund.

They dined at the German Consulate. The dinner was good, but the rest of the evening was dull.

On their return home Knox went to his wife's bedroom in his dressing-gown and talked to her while she undressed. She was greatly surprised by what he had to tell her, for she did not think the link with the Knoxes could possibly mean much to the Regent. Perhaps it was his way of flattering Knox. But if it were serious, she felt that it might well be of advantage to

Fanny, and possibly even to all of them, if she married Nai Dee.

" Then Suriwong Bunnag would be definitely on our side and it's better to have him with us than against us."

" The Regent's just on seventy and he won't live for ever," said Knox. " The important thing is that Fanny should be happy. She may not want to live here. She has spent half her life in the West. Just now she's excited about being back, but when this wears off, she may hanker to go back to Europe."

" If she decides to go back," said Mrs. Knox, cracking a peanut—she kept jars full of nuts and sweets in her bedroom, for she liked nibbling—"then we might as well forget about Nai Dee. He'd be like a fish out of water there, just as I would."

" That's nonsense. You've never tried. Anyway, I'm not sure Nai Dee is the right man for her. What have they in common? "

Mrs. Knox laughed. " A lot of people said that when you wanted to marry me."

He smiled and walked across to her. " You were pretty— you still are."

" Are you going to talk to Fanny about it? " she asked.

" I'll have to tell her. But I don't intend to influence her; my own feeling is that she ought to marry an Englishman."

" Why? " she inquired.

" Because she's completely English in her thought and out-look. Caroline is different. She'd be much more suited to a marriage of this kind."

" Then why not talk to Caroline as well? "

" No. The Regent wants Fanny, not Caroline. Besides," he added in his cold, reproving manner, " one can't do that sort of thing. You surprise me sometimes. You're westernised in many ways and yet so primitive about this sort of thing."

" Only my head and shoulders have emerged, dear," she said, " my feet are still deep in Siamese soil."

" It's your head that's full of all this nonsense," he laughed.

45

" You know, I have a feeling . . ." Mrs. Knox began.

" You and your feelings! "

" I feel," she went on, " that if he doesn't get Fanny, there'll be trouble."

" Trouble ! " Knox exclaimed.

" If Fanny's going to say ' No ' to Nai Dee, it would be best for her to leave the country."

" Fanny is a British subject," Knox said with slow emphasis.

" I wouldn't put it past the old man's cunning to think of some way . . ."

" He can do nothing," Knox barked, and he turned and walked to the door. " We must give the girl time to settle down. The Regent himself said there's no hurry. She only knew Nai Dee as a child. Until she sees something of him we can hardly expect her to make up her mind."

" Do you know, Tom," she asked, " if there is anyone else— someone in London, or Paris, or on the ship . . .?"

" There's Lambton. He was on the ship with us. I don't know how serious that is. A nice fellow. Tall, good-looking, reddish-gold hair. You'll see him. He's stopping here on his way back from Japan."

" I knew it. There's something going on there. He's coming here to see Fanny."

" He's coming here," Knox said sharply, " because it's part of his tour for the Foreign Office. Fanny has nothing to do with it. It is possible, of course, that he'll be glad to see her again."

" That makes two," Mrs. Knox said, " Nai Dee and Lambton. And Louis, I feel, is interested in her too "

" Stop arranging marriages. Stop being like Queen Victoria. Go to sleep and leave Fanny to me."

Chapter Six

FANNY AND Knox went riding every morning. The King was often out too, but Preecha was very rarely with him and when he was, he merely bowed politely to Fanny and turned to exchange a word or two with Knox. It seemed as though he were intent on avoiding her. This puzzled her. She wondered whether it would be possible to draw him into conversation, without appearing to be forward. But after a week or so she no longer saw him.

"I suppose he has gone back to Prachin," she said to Caroline. "He must have a busy time as Governor of such a vast province."

"You seem tremendously interested."

"I think he *is* interesting. He has that strange, spiritual look in his eyes—with, just round the corner, a dancing sense of fun. I'd like to know what goes on in his mind. But he won't talk —not to me at any rate."

Caroline laughed. Fanny glowered at her sister.

"I wish you wouldn't be so silly, Caroline," she said, and walked out of the room. But the mood passed quickly.

She went out with Caroline on her many tours of rediscovery. Occasionally Mamma went with them. They took one of the smaller consular boats, rowed by only one man, who stood in the stern dressed in short Chinese trousers, with a scarf thrown round his bare shoulders. With a single oar he manœuvred the rudderless boat in and out of the canals, while the three women peered out from under their gay parasols.

Fanny was struck by the tremendous growth of Bangkok. There were many new shipyards and the rice and timber mills had multiplied greatly. To the north, just beyond the American mission centre with its large girls' school, new houses of brick were being built.

Their boat skirted the floating houses against the banks which stood, four or five deep, on rafts moored to posts, rising and falling with the tide. Some of them were shops, but most of them were lived in by large families. From time to time they unhitched their homes and drifted downstream or poled their way to the north.

Beside the cluster of golden pagodas in the vast grounds of the Royal Palace, Fanny saw a group of houses, built of brick and stucco, around three central courtyards. In the large surrounding park there were tall palms and many lovely shrubs, their brilliant flowers glowing in the sunlight. Pavilions, with tip-tilted Chinese roofs, all of them tiled, supplied a distinctive symphony of colour.

" I seem to remember that place," Fanny said; "whose is it? "

" It belongs to the Amatyakuns," Mamma explained. " Phya Kesab lives there."

" Phya Kesab? "

" He is Phra Preecha's father," Caroline added, with a smile.

" Which is Preecha's house? " Fanny asked.

" Oh, one of them," Mamma said, dismissing it.

Facing this, on the opposite bank of the river, stretched the even larger estate of the Regent. Thus, across a span of water not half a mile wide, the rival families confronted each other.

Fanny knew the Regent's Palace well, for she had often been there as a child. Its landing-stage was at the side, on a canal or *klong*, known as Regent's Canal. Beyond it was the estate of the Regent's half-brother, the Foreign Minister. Nai Dee and she used to play in both gardens as children.

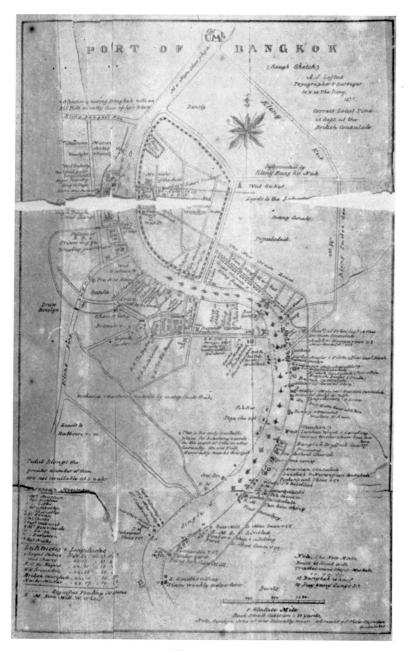

Map of Bangkok in 1878

Phra Preecha

One day Fanny learned from the French Consul that Preecha's wife was very ill. She felt deeply sorry for him, as she knew they were devoted to each other. When she could, she asked news of her: it was always "worse."

One morning they climbed with Mamma to the top of Wat Arun, from whose lofty tower they could see all Bangkok spread out beneath them—Thonburi, with the Regent's Palace on this side, the Royal Palace enclosure, a square mile in extent, as large as the City of London, with elephant stables by the main gate, the white elephant stalls by the temples, and beyond them the extensive women's quarters, where in a hundred houses, separated by streets and parks and a sprinkling of shops, the queens and princesses lived, protected by a police guard of Amazons in daffodil-coloured uniforms.

From this height they could see the vast sweep of rice fields beyond, parched now and awaiting the rains. Beyond these was the jungle, stretching for mile upon mile across the plains, and striving always to edge its way back into the city. Mamma remarked that all life was like that. The jungle kept fighting to get back.

" How the place has grown," exclaimed Fanny.

" It's the Regent's doing," Mamma said, " he has encouraged these foreign firms to come here. He is responsible for the new houses, the hospital, the shipbuilding. We are also to have roads."

" I hope he isn't going to rob us of our lovely canals? " Fanny asked.

" No," said Mamma. " New canals are being cut and the old ones are being constantly dredged, so that boats may reach the remoter villages. There's to be more irrigation too. The Regent is doing a lot for agriculture."

As they descended from the tower of Wat Arun, the pilgrims at the Wat drenched them with water, for it was the Songkran festival, which takes place just before the rains.

That evening Nai Dee came to the house with a large syringe and squirted water at the girls amid much laughter and a scowl from Knox.

Nai Dee, though short and squat, was six inches taller than Fanny. His square face was strikingly like his grandfather's, but less stern. He laughed a great deal, but memories of their childhood reminded Fanny that he was also capable of being cruel—to animals chiefly. His silly pranks with the monkeys, the tormenting of dogs and cats, who used to slink away when they saw him, came to her mind. But doubtless he had outgrown all that. Anyway, she hoped so.

Louis came even more frequently than Nai Dee. If the girls happened to be out, he would call again. Often he was there at the same time as Nai Dee. The two men watched each other like hawks and each tried to anticipate the other in doing something for Fanny. Sometimes this became a little uncomfortable for Caroline, for she felt certain that Fanny preferred Louis and would marry him.

The next day Fanny heard that Preecha's wife had died.

Chapter Seven

THE RAINS started and men, women and children were busy in the rice fields.

Fanny rose from the dining-table with some letters, and tripped down the stairs and across the lawn to the small post office by the river.

" Fanny! "

She saw Nai Dee manœuvring his canoe towards the landing-stage.

" Hallo! "

" I heard you at the piano as I went by this morning. Will you play for me? "

" Of course."

He tied his boat and sprang out.

" What would you like me to play? " she asked.

" What were you playing this morning? "

" Chopin."

" I liked it." He turned and smiled at her.

When they came up to the veranda Nai Dee bowed deferentially to Mr. and Mrs. Knox. A fan flapped overhead. It was hot and sticky.

" Nai Dee has developed a sudden passion for western music," Fanny announced.

" Not sudden," said Nai Dee. " You forget, I spent two years in England."

Her fingers were already touching the keys. Then, instead of playing Chopin, she played the popular music-hall tune " Diddle Diddle, Dumpling."

Nai Dee's face lit up. "I know this," he exclaimed, and supplied the line "Went to bed with his trousers on."

Fanny went on to "Oh where, oh where is my leet-el wee dog? Oh where, oh where can he be?" Knox took it up and sang the chorus lustily. Next she played "Champagne Charlie."

Mrs. Knox, standing in the doorway of the drawing-room, raised her eyebrows. "Tom! Where did you learn such songs?"

He did not pause to tell her.

Fanny was playing something French now. It was gay and lively.

"Look," cried Nai Dee, pointing to the river, where the lights were already coming up. Boat after boat had pulled up by the landing-stage. Many men and women had alighted and were seated on their haunches, grinning as they gazed up at the house.

"Go on! Go on!" they called in Siamese.

Instantly Fanny began to play some Siamese songs she remembered and Mrs. Knox joined in the singing. Nai Dee waved his arms to the spectators and urged them to sing too.

"This is something new," said Nai Dee. "With Fanny's homecoming, everything has changed here."

Then, leaping across from one boat to the next, came Louis. His face was flushed and happy. But his expression changed as his glance alighted on Nai Dee. Nai Dee, however, was warm in his greeting. "Sing, Louis, sing with us," he urged and after a brief hesitation, Louis joined in too.

Along the alleyway, leading to the Consulate from the New Road, came the French Consul and his wife. They brought a mandolin with them. A moment later the Portuguese Consul arrived with a drum he had bought in the bazaar.

"We heard that you were playing French music," Madame Garnier called out as she climbed the stairs. "So here we are."

" I came to listen to Chopin," said Nai Dee. " But this is much better."

Fanny played some Irish songs. The crowd on the river bank stayed on, grinning and chattering, waiting for a return to something familiar.

The large canvas punkah flapping overhead had to be supplemented by immense palm-leaved fans which the servants waved in various parts of the drawing-room and the veranda. Other servants brought trays of ice-cold beer and set out a cold buffet.

The music and the singing went on far into the night.

Chapter Eight

THE PARTY the King had promised Fanny was held some weeks later on the eve of His Majesty's departure for his country palace at Bang Pa In, forty miles farther up the river.

It was a formal reception. The King, in uniform, wearing all his decorations, stood by the golden throne, which was shaped like a boat and had a pagoda in the middle of it. Beside him, in the great Amarindr Hall, stood the Regent. All the nobles and officers of state were present, including Phra Preecha. Fanny had not expected to see him here, since his wife had died so recently. She looked at Preecha with the deepest sympathy, as she waited in the queue to be received by the King.

His Majesty held Knox's hand for a moment while he talked to him. Then the Regent whispered: " Have you said anything to her yet? "

" Not yet," Knox replied. " As you so wisely said, these things must take time." Detecting not even a flicker in the Regent's inscrutable face, he added, " But I will."

" Good," replied the Regent, and turned to Mrs. Knox. " I am glad you have come too. So often you stay at home." Fanny he welcomed by placing his arm about her shoulders.

" My little Fanny! "

Saucily she curtsied to him too and moved on. As she turned, Fanny found herself beside Preecha. She held out her hand.

" May I offer you my sincerest condolence," she said. " It

is very sad and terrible for your children, who are very young,
I hear."

"My daughter Trakun is four, my son Arun only two.
Thank you." He bowed and walked on.

She saw Louis coming towards her. He was dressed in a
cream tussore suit with wide silk lapels. There was a swagger
in the way he walked. For her he had a warm smile.

Not far away was Nai Dee. He, too, came up and a moment
later Caroline joined them. She pointed out Captain Christie.
"He used to be with Captain Orton on the *Chow Phya*," she
said.

"Orton brought you and your mother out here in his ship,
didn't he, Louis?" Nai Dee asked.

"Yes. He has retired, I hear." And with a smile, he added:
"He wanted to marry my mother."

"Why didn't she marry him?" asked Fanny.

"She was too devoted to my father's memory," said Louis.

"You won't find many women like that to-day," Nai Dee
said.

Fanny looked reproachfully at him.

Behind a screen, able to look on but themselves invisible, sat
the Royal women, the only women in Siam who were kept in
purdah. One could hear their ceaseless chatter, the tinkle of
their bracelets, their laughter, rising occasionally almost to a
shout. There were dozens of them there—wives, sisters, aunts,
nieces, sisters-in-law of the King. With them were their
ladies-in-waiting. Women in uniform guarded the entrances.

Mingling with the other guests in the hall were more than
forty Siamese women, some married to Europeans, many the
wives of Siamese nobles.

Prince Damrong was with his brother Prince Naret. Fanny
had met them a number of times in the preceding weeks, for
Bangkok, though large, had at its core a small, closely-knit
community who constantly saw each other.

55

Prince Naret drew a passer-by into the group. "Fanny, I don't think you know Pet Pichai, do you?"

They bowed.

"He is Phra Preecha's brother." She noticed a slight resemblance.

The family name was rarely used and titles caused the greatest confusion, for with each rise in rank came a change of name. In that family the father was a duke, another brother was a count, Preecha was a baron. Most of them had been educated in England, and Preecha had studied engineering in Scotland.

Henry Alabaster drifted by. He greeted the others, but merely stared at Fanny and walked on.

"A sour man," said Louis.

"Translating the Buddhist scriptures should have purified him," said Naret. "I don't like him either."

With a smile the King came up to Fanny. She had noticed how serious he had become, for as a child, though not as boisterous as his younger brothers, he was full of fun. He used to tear out of the class-room when Anna released them, and joined in most of the mischief. But now he rarely laughed. He was striving to understand and to learn, just as his father, King Mongkut, had done.

The King said: "Tell me, Fanny. Are you making plans?"

"You are most kind to be interested. What sort of plans does Your Majesty think I ought to make?"

"You were always quicker and cleverer than the rest of us. You could do almost anything." He paused. "Are you thinking of a career? I don't mean as a governess. You would be wasted as a governess. Of course Anna was pretty too— but you are too pretty." He smiled.

Then he went on: "You were so determined, even when we were children. . . . You are not the placid kind. You won't be pushed into a back room somewhere over there "—he waved his hand towards the harem—" and be left to provide a new offspring every year. It will be interesting to see what you do."

Smiling, she replied: " Perhaps I shall marry and have children."

" So you have a plan. And until you make your choice, many of my male subjects will have heart attacks," he chuckled.

Chapter Nine

EVER SINCE Preecha's wife had died, Mrs. Knox had been uneasy. She sensed Fanny's interest in him. But as yet he did not appear to be interested in her, and she hoped he would never be. She shuddered at the very thought, for that would rouse the Regent to frenzy. A member of that hated family to be preferred to his! And, besides, it would mean an alliance with a close friend of the King's. One of the things that had intensified the Regent's dislike of the Amatyakuns was the King's constant association with Phra Preecha. Probably it suggested to the Regent that His Majesty had begun to strengthen his position by allying himself with this powerful family.

Mrs. Knox felt they should do everything they could to prevent it happening. The best thing would be to get Fanny married as quickly as possible to Nai Dee, if that was what she wanted, otherwise to Louis, or better still, to Lambton, for that would get her out of the country and out of the Regent's reach.

Greatly agitated by these disturbing thoughts, she decided to discuss them with her husband. He merely laughed at her fears.

" Why are you so frightened of the Regent? He's not a cobra," Knox said.

" He's worse," she replied, " much, much worse."

Knox disagreed. " He's not. He's fighting hard to bring this country up to the standards of the West—and he's succeeding."

" In material things—yes," she said. " But, Tom, the

Regent's not just the polished, civilised person you see. There's quite a different person inside him—hard, cruel, ruthless. I know what he's really like when he's roused. You remember what he did to Phya Brusa's nephew. The boy was kidnapped. He was tortured. They extorted a false confession from him, then they put him on trial—a secret trial to which no one was admitted. . . . It's no good shaking your head, Tom. I know what happened. It was in my village—at Somkok."

" The boy ran off with a Chinese girl they had found for the Regent's harem—or so it was said."

" But that's not what he was tried for," said Mrs. Knox. " They invented all sorts of other charges. He was executed. His father's house was sacked. His mother and his sisters were kidnapped and were kept in prison for years. I don't suppose you believe any of that."

" No," he said. " A man in the Regent's position is bound to have many enemies. They say vile things. They'll believe anything."

" And you think I'm like that—I believe anything——? "

" That's the side of you I can't understand," he said.

" I am telling you only of things I know. I know, Tom. You don't believe it because you don't come in contact with any of it. You deal only with British subjects—you try them yourself. You have no idea what goes on outside your jurisdiction."

" In any case," he said, " all this has nothing to do with us. Fanny is English. She is not under the Regent's authority and never will be."

" Not if she married Preecha? "

" Certainly not," he said. " Besides the Regent—even if he were as you say, which I don't accept—wouldn't dare do anything. He'd have me to reckon with."

" Still, I'd be happier if we could get her married. Have you talked to her about Nai Dee? "

" Not yet." He had been deferring it. He wasn't sure of the right opening. She'd wonder why Nai Dee had been singled out.

" Well, it's time you talked to her—and you'll have to tell her about the Regent," Mrs. Knox went on. " She has got to know the tremendous pressure there is behind it."

" You expect my daughter to marry through fear? " he asked angrily. " She'd refuse at once—and I wouldn't blame her."

" Tom," she began in her mollifying voice, but he interrupted her.

" It won't do any good rushing at it. I'll find a way when the time comes."

She tried a different approach.

" She's had some postcards from Lambton. The last one was from Manila. He says he's coming, but he doesn't say when."

" Still reading your daughter's correspondence? " He smiled and shook his head. " Manila—that means he has left Japan and is now on his way back. He ought to be here in the next month or so."

He saw the look of hopefulness on her face. They were going to the American Consulate for dinner and he went up to change.

It was a long and pleasant evening.

Knox was tired when they left and then they had a long journey ahead, all the way upstream, with only two men at the oars. Nevertheless he lay awake in bed, turning over in his mind what his wife had said about talking to Fanny of the Regent and Nai Dee.

He had only just fallen asleep when he was awakened by the strumming of a Siamese guitar under his window. A man's voice was singing softly to it. He was able to catch the name Fanny. Her bedroom was alongside his and both overlooked the canal.

He got out of bed. In the boat below was Nai Dee.

Knox was angry at being awakened, but, seeing that Nai Dee had come to plead his cause so romantically, he smiled.

After a time Fanny came laughing to her window and threw a handful of coins into the boat.

"Come earlier next time," she said. "This is much too late."

Next morning Knox came down whistling to breakfast. He was trying to whistle what Nai Dee had been singing, but he couldn't quite recapture it.

Now he had found a way of talking to Fanny. He had intended to avoid raising the subject while the others were still at the table, but Caroline gave him an opening.

"Fanny, you were being serenaded last night. Was it Nai Dee?"

"Did you hear it on your side of the house?" Knox asked.

"N-no," she replied, and glanced at Mamma. So those two had been talking of it. Knox rose irritably. "Come along, Fanny. Swallow your tea. We are late for our ride."

Fanny looked up in surprise. Then helping herself to a final mouthful of toast and marmalade, she rose from the table.

As soon as they were on their horses, Knox began: "Making a din at that hour of the night."

"He wasn't making a din, Papa. He was singing quite softly—and sweetly, I thought."

"Is that how you feel about it?"

"Well, it was fun. Like the old stories one reads. A casement window and a man singing to his girl."

"Do you like Nai Dee?" he asked bluntly.

"Yes. I do—very much."

That was a help. "Do you like the life here or would you prefer to live in England?"

61

" I've been away so long that I'm loving it here."

" Would you like to live here always, I mean? "

" I haven't thought of that." She saw that he was driving at something. " Do you mean would I like to marry and settle down here? "

" Well, would you? "

" It's too early to tell. You weren't thinking of my marrying Nai Dee, were you? " she added.

" I just wondered. I think the old Regent would be delighted if you did."

" What makes you think that? Has he said something to you about it? "

" N-not exactly. He did once mention that it would be nice if our two families could be linked."

" Perhaps he was thinking of Caroline."

" I don't think so. Well, look at the way he behaves towards you. His arm about your shoulders at the King's reception and always ' My dear little Fanny.' "

" I see."

They rode on for a while in silence.

" How would you feel if Nai Dee——? "

" Oh, I don't know. Serenading doesn't mean anything. It's just fun. If every man who did a bit of serenading was expected to marry the girl . . ." She did not finish the sentence and he felt it was best not to pursue it. He had planted the thought. Now they would have to wait and see what followed. Nai Dee would come serenading again and that might help.

That evening it was not Nai Dee who came, but Louis. He arrived early and waited at the mouth of the canal until he saw the lights go out at the Consulate. Then he moved his boat along the canal until he was under Fanny's window. He had brought with him two boys, one at the drums, the other with a flute. He himself played the guitar. But his voice was not as soft or as melodious as Nai Dee's.

Fanny came to her window laughing. Undiscouraged, Louis sang louder, the musicians played with greater frenzy, and the dogs began to bark.

Knox, half undressed, moved towards the door, then to the window, not sure which noise to stop first, the dogs or the music. Then with sudden decision, he appeared in his undervest at the window and saw it was Louis.

" Go away," he shouted. " Stop that blasted row."

But Louis went on with undiminished vigour.

" Singh! Singh! " Knox bellowed. " Will you keep those wretched dogs quiet."

At that moment he caught sight of Nai Dee coming along the canal with his guitar. " My God," he groaned.

Caroline and Mrs. Knox, who had joined Fanny at her window, were enjoying it hugely. Nai Dee, signalling in vain to Louis to be off, began an independent serenade, but as his voice was drowned by the din, he eventually decided to join forces.

Soon Mrs. Knox and her daughters joined in the singing.

Knox now came to their window. " I give you five minutes to finish and go home," he called down.

But, back in his room, his anger passed and soon he began to sing too.

The next evening neither Louis nor Nai Dee came. But there was another boat under Fanny's window. Prince Damrong and his brother Naret were in it, strumming their guitars and singing.

Knox, on his way to the window, picked up the water jug from the washhand stand and with a vigorous swing emptied it on the young princes.

" What are you doing? " shouted Naret.

" I've done it," Knox cried. " You two ought to know better. Go home."

63

In the morning, after his ride, he went to the Sampeng Market and bought a horse-whip. He tried it at the stall. The lash was not long enough to reach down to the canal. So he had it extended. Thereafter, with the whip by his bed and the water jug near at hand, he was ready to deal with all who dared disturb his night's rest.

Chapter Ten

LAMBTON arrived in the middle of November.

They were at tea in the veranda when Fanny, with a gasp of pleasure, saw his long, lean form walking across the lawn.

Knox called out, " Hallo, Lambton. I'm delighted to see you. But why didn't you let us know? "

" I didn't want to put you to any trouble, sir."

" Edward," Fanny greeted him with a warm smile. " This is a lovely surprise."

" My wife, my daughter Caroline. Mr. Edward Lambton," Knox said. " Where are you staying? "

" At a hotel called Falcks'. It isn't bad."

" One can hardly call it a hotel," said Fanny. " Just a billiard saloon and a bowling alley—with a shakedown at the back for marooned seamen."

" Will you be comfortable? " Mrs. Knox asked. " We could easily put you up, you know. Mr. Gould has plenty of room in his house by the Chancellery."

" I'll be quite all right, thanks."

Mrs. Knox was fascinated by Lambton's great height, he was even taller than Singh, and by his reddish-gold hair. . . . She could hardly take her eyes off him. Caroline too found him extremely good-looking. He talked well and was amusing at times in spite of that earnest look in his eyes. He addressed most of his remarks to Fanny.

" I'm hoping you will show me something of the town," he said.

While they talked the lights came on and sparkled in the

river and the canals and the voices of the boatmen drifted to them from the junks and sampans.

Mrs. Knox asked Lambton to stay to dinner and he accepted with alacrity. Her mind was already busy making plans. If Fanny didn't want Nai Dee, then she would have to make a life for herself outside the country. There was no point in inviting trouble. Tom would retire in five years and he talked of settling in Biarritz, where the winters were not so cold. She didn't think she was going to like it there, still, they would be near to England and to Fanny if she married Lambton.

" How long are you going to be here? " she asked Lambton.

" I'd like to go on to Angkōr," he said, " if that could be arranged. Have you been there, sir? " he asked Knox.

" Yes. A number of people have been there in the dozen years since Mouhot discovered the magnificent ruins there."

" I thought it might be easier to go from Bangkok than from Saigon."

" Much easier from here," said Knox. " You go through Prachin. The Governor, Phra Preecha, is an old friend of ours. He has helped quite a number of people from England and France—and more recently from America too—to get there. I will invite him to come here one evening and you two can go into the details together." Mrs. Knox glanced quickly at her husband, then at Fanny, then at Lambton.

" The French, incidentally," Knox went on, " get all the credit for this really remarkable find. True, Mouhot was a Frenchman. He fought his way through the jungle with his camera and took some fascinating photographs. But the expedition was financed by English societies of archæologists and explorers."

" I had heard that. Few know it, though. We are much too reticent about ourselves," said Lambton.

The talk went on in this serious vein through dinner. Later Louis arrived.

"And now, let's add to Mr. Lambton's more frivolous education," suggested Fanny. "I think you'll enjoy the entertainment booths in the bazaar, Edward."

Mrs. Knox thought this was a very good idea. "Let's all go," she said. She wanted Fanny to see more of Lambton and obviously the two could not go out alone together at that hour.

At the landing-stage they divided up into two groups. Louis wanted Fanny to come in his boat, but she got into the consular boat with Lambton and Papa. Caroline and Mamma went with Louis.

The bazaar was fairly full even at that hour. Very few of the shops were shut. Some were dimly lit by small kerosene lamps, others had bright naphtha flares and attracted the crowds, who stood in groups watching the tumblers and jugglers or listening to the story-tellers. Children chased each other and darted through Lambton's long legs. In the jostling throng there were pig-tailed Chinese, Malays, Burmese, Laotians, Cambodians, Annamese, Polynesians, and Indians, all of them in distinctive dresses, which though workaday, were full of colour and grace.

Mrs. Knox bought a saucer of sea urchins and dumplings from a Chinese stall and munched as she walked on, then stopped for some pink ice-cream from a man with a small rotating barrel. She bought peanuts in paper cones, dried fish delicacies, and laughed when the others teased her.

From the stalls they called to Knox: "Excellency! Excellency! Come in here. We sell you cheap." The air was filled with the acrid smell of powdered spices and of raw hides. Drums could be heard. Flutes piped. A drunken French sailor lurched by, singing to himself.

They passed Mrs. Hunter, the Siamese wife of the Regent's English secretary. She was followed by three young girls, her servants, who had been brought to carry her purchases. Hunter was just behind. They stopped. Knox introduced Lambton and suggested that the Regent might find it interesting to meet him.

" I feel sure he will," said Hunter.

Mrs. Knox whispered to Fanny: " I have found a nice little girl to be your personal maid—Oun, she is half-Chinese and only fifteen. You'll like her."

Fanny raised her eyebrows. " Thank you, Mamma. I'm delighted. When is she coming? "

" She is consulting the astrologers. They will tell her the right day to start."

Women were seated on their haunches by the booths, smoking long cheroots, while their children skipped and hopped around them. The night was hot and sticky. Lambton noticed that most of the Siamese girls had their shoulders bare and some had one breast exposed. They looked lovely in their bright silk jackets and *panungs*, chattering and laughing, as they went by. Priests with shaven heads, some in their early teens, walked past in their saffron robes. At little tables, a few yards from each other, sat solitary Chinese wearing spectacles, with piles of yellow lottery tickets in front of them.

Fanny, slipping her arm through his, led Lambton to the fighting fishes.

Louis promptly went to her other side.

" Oh, look," he said. " A ventriloquist. Let's listen to what he has to say."

The entertainer was a short, fat Dutchman. He knew no Siamese and gave his performance in broken, guttural English, which not many of his audience were able to understand. So after some moments they began to drift away.

" Silly man," said Louis. " I suppose he's on his way to Java and thought he'd pick up some money in the booths here. He won't get much. Yet a small fortune can be made with the right show."

" Are you in business here? " Lambton asked.

" He's in the Royal Household Cavalry," Fanny replied.
" You are a captain, aren't you, Louis? "

" Major," he replied, swelling a little.

Louis would make a good showman, she thought. At school
he used to stand on a chair and wave his arms about, attempting
to instruct the young princes and princesses, imitating his
mother.

" I'd like to be in business," Louis said. " For there's not
much money to be made in the Household Cavalry."

" Ah, but there's the attractive uniform," said Fanny.

" Come on," he replied. " Let's go and see the dancing."
And he drew Fanny away from Lambton, whispering, " I
want to talk to you."

" What about? "

They were jostled by the passing throng. An American
missionary stopped and greeted Louis, then went on to talk to
Knox. While Lambton was being introduced the rest of the
party waited.

" No, no," said Louis as Fanny began to linger too. He
hurried her along the nearest alley towards a flower stall where
a woman was covering up the flowers with long strips of wet
muslin.

" It's the first time you've ever bought me flowers," said
Fanny.

He looked flurried. " What would you like? The others will
be here soon. Take these." He seized the nearest bunch of
marigolds, thrust them into her hand and flung some coins on
to the counter.

" Oh, it's a private talk, is it? "

" Very private," he answered. " Fanny, do you remember,
before you left for England, we were sitting together by the
edge of the river, dangling our feet in the water . . .?"

" We did that many times."

" But this was a special occasion. We said a private good-bye—do you remember? "

She laughed. " Yes, of course—it was my tenth birthday and you kissed me for the first time."

" The *only* time. You're not helping at all, and here are the others. Fanny "—he was breathless now—" we said that when we grew up we'd get married."

" I did? It was you who said that, Louis."

" Well, whoever it was——"

" Hallo," called Lambton. " Buying flowers? " And he insisted on buying flowers too. But he bought them for Caroline and for Mrs. Knox. " Obviously you won't want any more," he said to Fanny.

" The dancing is on the other side," remarked Mrs. Knox. " I don't know what made you and Louis turn into this alley, dear."

They retraced their steps. On a small stage a troupe of girls in bright dresses and jewelled hats, shaped like pagodas, danced, their hands fluttering, their arms quivering. Lambton looked at Fanny. During their voyage out he had been enchanted by her lively gestures. He noticed now how closely the animated hands of the dancers resembled hers.

" Why are you staring at me? " she asked.

" The dancing is lovely," he said.

" Then look at it."

Chapter Eleven

Knox accompanied Lambton on his visit to the Regent. They crossed the river in one of the consular boats and turned into Regent's Canal, where, entering through a low water gate, they reached the imposing landing-stage, with its red-and-gold awning.

There they were confronted by two large stone figures of Chinese mandarins mounted on horseback and painted in brilliant colours. Crossing a wide courtyard paved with slabs of stone, they passed on the left a green-and-gold pavilion which His Excellency used as his private theatre. On the right was the Palace, with its sweeping, semi-circular façade. Beyond lay the Regent's private estate, the size of a small town. The houses, separated by streets and surrounded by lovely gardens in which fountains played, were painted cream and blue and pink, and had loggias and piazzas. Knox used to come to one of these to see Anna Leonowens and Louis, until another house was found for them.

At the entrance to the main palace they were briskly saluted by two barefooted sentries. Hunter, the Regent's secretary, hurried out to greet them and escorted them through a series of luxurious salons. The ornate candelabra and the French furniture blended a little uneasily with the more grotesque Chinese vases, the hideous grinning statuettes and the immense burnished brass chalices.

At the open doorway of the Regent's office, Hunter announced the visitors and withdrew. The Regent's welcome was warm.

71

Taking both Lambton's hands in his, he poured out an elaborate greeting.

They talked for a while of Lambton's travels. Drinks were brought in. Then abruptly the Regent rose. " I have delayed my journey to the North," he said, " because I especially wanted to meet you. But, if you will forgive me now . . ." He shook hands.

At the door he slipped his arm through Knox's and detained him for a moment.

" Have you any news for me? " he asked.

" I've talked to her," he replied.

" Yes? " The smile was expectant.

" I've told her of your feelings. I have sown the seed, as you advised. We shall have to see how things develop."

" Of course! Of course! It should not take long now."

" I think it may, Your Excellency. She has to weigh things up, to try to adjust herself . . ."

" What is there to adjust? "

Knox hesitated.

" What you are saying, my friend, is that she cannot make up her mind. Is that right? "

" Yes," said Knox.

" Ah-h-h! " The smile deserted the Regent's face. " Better, is it not," he said, " that we, who are older and understand these things better, should make up her mind for her? "

" Older people may think so, but would she agree, Excellency? After all, it is she who will have to live by her decision—for fifty years or more, who knows? "

The Regent chuckled. " You are an old fox." He gave a wink, and stroked the ends of his thin moustache. " You are right, we cannot hurry it," he added. " She is not easy to manage. She has fire. That is what Nai Dee likes about her and I like too. But work on her, Tom, in your clever, foxy way. . . ."

" No," said Knox bluntly. " It cannot be handled in that way."

The Regent chuckled again. " Persuade her then—a word to-day, another to-morrow. In time it will work. You will see."

As they emerged from the office together, Knox saw pretty girlish heads, with flushed cheeks and flashing eyes, peering through the curtains. Embarrassed at being caught, the girls burst into peals of laughter, and there was a tinkling of bracelets and bangles as they began to scamper away. Beckoning to them, the Regent drew them out and presented them one by one to Knox. This happened every time Knox called. The Regent had only one official wife, Koon Ying Phan, a stout woman in her early fifties, with kind and gentle eyes. The girls were his concubines.

Knox exchanged a joke or two with them, waved through a window to Koon Ying Phan, who was busy in her garden, and rejoined Lambton and Hunter in the entrance hall.

Chapter Twelve

PHRA PREECHA's father, Phya Kesab, when told by Knox that Lambton needed his son's advice about the trip to Angkor, said: " Preecha will be here on Thursday. Come and dine with us, all of you. They can discuss it then."

Kesab was in his late sixties. He had a gentle face, soft grey eyes, a little tired through his insatiable love for reading, and a drooping white moustache.

The houses on his estate were built in the Chinese manner round a series of spacious courtyards, each filled with flower-beds and trees, statues and fountains. The property ran along-side the tall white walls of the Royal Palace and, though the house overlooked the river, the landing-stage was in a wide canal at the side.

On the evening fixed for the dinner, Lambton, seated under the striped red-and-white awning of the consular boat, said: " I see they live directly opposite the Regent. I suppose they must be close friends."

" Enemies," replied Mrs. Knox quietly.

" You shouldn't say that," Knox chided her. " They may not be friends, but I wouldn't call them enemies. Though of course the two families have been rivals for centuries."

" Do they resent the Regent being in the ascendant? " Lambton asked.

" It's the other way," muttered Mrs. Knox.

" The Regent," Knox explained, " has given all the plums of office and preferment to his relatives and friends. All he had

74

left for Phya Kesab, who is a man of brilliant ability, is the job of Superintendent at the Mint."

" He should have refused it," said Fanny.

" He wanted," Knox remarked, " to help in the regeneration of his country. He spent some months at the Mint in London, mastering the details."

" It's the Regent who is resentful," said Mrs. Knox. " Those he favours kowtow to him. Kesab's family is just as rich and aristocratic, but they don't make a fuss of the Regent and that's what he doesn't like."

Phya Kesab and Preecha were on the landing-stage waiting to receive them and both Preecha's brothers, Pet Pichai, whom Fanny had met at the King's reception, and Aphilla, came to dinner with their wives. Phya Kesab being a widower, one of Preecha's sisters acted as hostess. Fanny had heard that Preecha's two children were living with Pet Pichai.

The house, the largest on the estate, was simply and well furnished. There were flowers everywhere. In the long dining-room, dimly lit by candles, the meal was served by a dozen Chinese girls, dressed in emerald-green jackets and tight three-quarter length trousers the colour of ripe maize. The food was Siamese, though with a strong Chinese influence.

During dinner Preecha turned to Lambton.

" Now, Mr. Lambton, let us talk about this trip. I understand you want my advice and help. I propose to go part of the way with you. We could set out from here, and travel in my houseboat as far as Prachin. From there I will take you to the borders of the jungle in the heart of which Angkor lies. You will need coolies. You will have to take all your stores with you—for yourself and your coolies. How do you plan to travel? By elephant? "

" If that's the best way."

" It is," said Preecha. " Elephants are able to clear a way through the jungle with their trunks. Horses cannot do that."

" I gather it will be through rough country."

" Rough, yes," said Preecha. " But it's wild, enchanting country. Unbelievably beautiful orchids will hang above your head from the branches of gigantic trees. Birds of breath-taking variety—with gorgeous tails and tufted heads, will fly around you and you will hear the tantalising call of the mocking birds. Butterflies, like coloured flakes of enamel, will alight on your wrist. And in the evenings you will see millions of fireflies flickering in the dark, silvering the leaves of the trees with their light, and almost turning night into day."

As his words poured out Fanny listened entranced. His enthusiasm was infectious. He was sparing in his gestures, but his eyes lit up his tanned face, which was strong in every line. She wished she were going on the journey.

Caroline's eyes were fixed on Fanny. She had never seen her sister so interested in any man. Poor Louis, she thought.

After dinner Fanny asked Preecha about his children. " They are with my brother." He pointed to Pet Pichai. " His wife is looking after them. They miss their mother deeply. Lamai was gentle, kind, understanding. I have known no other woman like her."

He talked of her influence, of the way in which she had moulded his character. " I used to be eager, thrusting, quarrel-some, pugnacious, in the way that men who strive to achieve anything have to be. She altered all that. She smoothed out, not the ambition, but the pugnacity. She changed all my values, they were altered for the better."

Mrs. Knox helped herself to a chocolate. She had been silent for some time. Knox saw the look of concern in her eyes.

The next day Knox was putting away his papers when his wife came into his study. She had a bustle in her hand which she had found in Fanny's room.

" I was thinking of trying it **on**," she said. " It must be most uncomfortable, sticking out behind like that. You could never sit back and relax."

" No woman should relax when she's dressed."

They both laughed.

" But I haven't come to talk about this. I just thought it might put you in a good mood."

" What is it now? " he asked.

" Fanny," she said. " I didn't like the way she kept looking at Preecha last night."

" Now don't go jumping to conclusions. It doesn't mean anything." He cleared his throat. " He's an attractive fellow, and he's intelligent. But he's too old for her. There must be a dozen years between them at least."

" That didn't stop us, did it? " She held out the bustle again. " I think it's a pity the crinoline went out. It was so graceful and elegant."

" Are you trying to tell me that Fanny would have been married by now if the crinoline was still being worn? "

" What I'm trying to tell you, Tom, is that you should have a word with Lambton."

" Lambton? Propose to him, do you mean? " He threw his head back and laughed. " I know. I'll say ' Look here, me lad, I think you ought to marry our Fanny.' "

" And why not? She can't do the proposing."

" That won't do." His voice was serious and abrupt. " It wouldn't be a bad match, mind you. But—well, we don't yet know how they feel about each other. Besides he's going off in a day or two, and they can't be expected to go honeymooning on the back of an elephant."

" At least they would be alone."

" Except for the coolies and the mahout—and Preecha for the first week or so."

" Yes, Preecha. He's the one man she must not marry."

77

" There's not the remotest sign," he said with emphasis, " that she has made any impression on him."

Mrs. Knox was silent for a moment. They heard Fanny's voice in the garden. Who was it she was talking to? They discerned a figure, half-hidden by the trees. A moment later he was visible.

" There's another possible solution," said Mrs. Knox.

" Louis? "

" Yes. He's been following her about like a dog. You know, Tom, you ought not to discourage her suitors by pouring jugs of cold water on them and threatening them with a horse-whip."

" They shouldn't do their courting so late. There seem to be swarms of them," he went on. " Nai Dee, Prince Naret and Damrong, and the other night still another brother of the King's—Bhanurangsri—came along. I gave him a good drenching."

" He hasn't been seen since. He's probably in bed dying of pneumonia. I see Louis and she are going off together in a boat. Now about Louis . . ." she began.

" Stop making up her mind for her."

Meanwhile, Louis was taking the oars as Fanny settled down at the tiller.

" At last I've got you alone," he remarked rather breathlessly. " What about it, Fanny? And don't say ' What about what? ' You know exactly what I'm talking about."

She smiled. " I like you very, very much."

" But——? "

" I didn't say but."

" But a 'but' is there, or you'd have answered my question."

" We're both very young, Louis."

" I'm not. I'll be twenty-two in a few weeks and I'm going into business. I've made up my mind. I'm going to make a lot of money. We'll be rich one day—very rich."

" How exciting! "

" I'm doing this for you, you know."

" Tell me."

" In the North there's a lot of teak. I think I can get concessions from the King. I'll fell the teak, float it down the river
and export it. There's a fortune in it. I'll have to work with
one of the big export firms at first. Perhaps they can help me
to get started—by financing me. One day I'll have a firm of
my own, with my name right across the waterfront—Louis T.
Leonowens. You'd like to be rich? "

" I would, but——"

" But what? "

" Money isn't everything."

" You mean you don't love me? "

" I think I could love you, but I don't yet."

" For heaven's sake! I've known you for nearly thirteen
years, and that's most of your life."

" You've known Caroline even longer. She was here while
I was away."

" What has Caroline got to do with it? "

" Haven't you noticed anything? "

" No."

Fanny laughed.

" Did she say anything to you? " he asked irritably.

" Not directly. But she's desperately anxious to have you as
a brother-in-law."

" That only means that she'd like *you* to marry me. She and
I are in complete agreement about that."

" And about a lot of other things as well, you'll find."

He frowned. " I'm not in love with her. She's a nice girl.
I'm sure she'll make a nice wife. . . ."

" What else do you want? "

" How many ways has a girl of saying ' No '? This is the
second time you've turned me down."

" Let's be sensible, Louis. I'm rather unsettled. I need somebody strong and stable to keep me in check. . . ."

" Like that fellow? "

" What fellow? "

" Lambton."

" Oh! "

" Does that ' Oh! ' mean that he's out of it? "

" I don't do the proposing."

" If you did, who would it be? "

" That would be telling."

" When you said ' Oh! ' like that, whom did you think I meant? Nai Dee? "

" Oh, no, he's as wild and unstable as you are."

" After I've been telling you of the new career I've planned and the money I'm going to make."

" Caroline would suit you much better. She is the quiet, settled kind."

" Why shouldn't I wait until you make up your mind? "

" That would not be fair," she replied.

" Not fair to whom? " he asked.

" To Caroline. To you. At least you two might be happy."

" And what about you? "

" I'll be all right."

He looked at her for a moment. " There *is* someone, isn't there, Fanny? "

" I'm not sure."

" That means he's not sure."

" Maybe."

" Who is it? "

" There's no point in going into it, Louis. It's too vague." She laughed.

" I love you, Fanny."

" And I love you too, Louis. But not enough."

" If I married Caroline, it would only be because that's the nearest I can get to you."

" Flattering, but I'd rather you married Caroline because of *her*. Think about it. Will you? Think of her nicely, Louis. I wouldn't like her to be hurt."

Chapter Thirteen

LAMBTON WAS away for more than two months. He did not return until the end of January. Then he called at the Consulate and about a quarter of an hour later Preecha arrived too.

It was Preecha's first meeting with Lambton since he had set out from Prachin on his journey to Angkor, and it was Fanny's first meeting with Preecha since the night of the dinner.

Lambton, looking tanned and thin, was warm in his praise of what Preecha had done for him and enthusiastic in his account of the ruined temples, the great range of crumbled palaces, the monumental gates, the temple of Bayon, with its tiers of galleries, the exquisite carvings, the superb sculpture, the bas-reliefs.

" I do hope," Mrs. Knox said, " that you will stay with us for a little while now."

" I'm afraid I can't," Lambton replied. " A ship is sailing to-morrow for Singapore and I am already some weeks overdue in London."

" When are we likely to see you again? " asked Mrs. Knox anxiously.

He gave a half-laugh. " A tour like this comes once in a life-time. I doubt if I'll have another chance—at any rate, not for many years. But perhaps you would be so good as to allow me to call on you and Mr. Knox when next you come to London."

" My husband will be there in two or three years' time. But Fanny may return before then."

" I hope you will come soon, Fanny," he said, with a warm smile. " When do you think that will be? "

" I can't say. I love it here. So it may be a long time, Edward. But I'll come."

" Perhaps you two will write to each other," suggested Mrs. Knox, " and Fanny may go to England much earlier than she thinks."

Knox glanced at his wife. He knew what was in her mind.

As the visitors were leaving Louis arrived. He came almost every evening in the hope of wearing Fanny down in time.

" I'm glad, Major Leonowens," Lambton said, " to have this opportunity of seeing you again. The Baron Preecha was telling me that you were responsible for bringing horses into this country. Won't you find it a wrench leaving your horses when you go into business? "

" Yes, but I haven't got very far with my plans. Everything moves so slowly in this country."

" Patience is the key to it all," remarked Knox. " In the end, with patience, people get their way."

" Always? " Lambton asked.

" Nearly always," replied Knox.

Soon after Lambton and Preecha had left, Nai Dee arrived. He, too, came almost every day, generally during the morning when he knew Louis would not be there, for he was aware that Louis was in love with Fanny and was concerned as to how far he had progressed.

The early morning rides, confined for so long to herself and her father and the King's party, became much more popular during the winter. Fanny was surprised that the American Consul, General Partridge, and his son often came out riding too. They lived so far from the road that a journey by boat, as far at least as the French Consulate, must have been necessary. She asked Louis whether they brought their horses with them. He explained that he had started a riding stable near Alloin & Co.'s general store, which was alongside the French Consulate. In addition to the Partridges, Mme. Garnier, the wife of the French Consul, kept her horse there, and a young Portuguese secretary, M. d'Almeida, was another customer.

" You *are* enterprising, Louis," Fanny exclaimed, " and how are you getting on with the teak project? "

" I've had a word with the King. I asked him if he could grant me teak concessions in the North. He said it might be possible. That was weeks ago. I've heard nothing since."

" The Regent is the man you should see," said Fanny.

" I would prefer it if the King talked to him. He may."

" He would have to—if you're to get your concessions."

" There are various Chiefs in the North, round about Chiengmai, who have certain rights . . ."

" The Regent could cut through all that with a stroke of his pen. Why not mention it to Nai Dee? "

" No," he said. " I'll have another word with His Majesty. But months go by before any decision is made. Meanwhile, I've found a company to handle the export of my teak—the Borneo Company. They are prepared to advance money so that I can get the labour and hire the elephants. I've got to get the teak to the river and float it down to Bangkok."

" That's a big move forward, Louis. You'll have to keep on at it."

" I certainly shall," he said. " I never give up."

That was what she liked about Louis—his determination.

Preecha went riding with the King's party only occasionally. He seemed to be away for weeks at a time at Prachin or at the gold mine at Kabin. But one morning, when her father was in bed with gout and she was out alone, she saw him riding with his daughter, a girl of five, who trotted beside him on a pony. He was very gentle with her, showed her the correct way to hold the reins and placed his hand on her arm when they galloped.

Fanny hung behind, watching them. When Preecha saw her, he waited for her to come up and introduced the little girl.

" My daughter, Trakun," he said, with a courteous inclination of his head. " This is Miss Fanny Knox, the English Consul's daughter."

" How do you do? " said Trakun, formally.

She was strikingly like her father.

" What a lovely shaggy pony," Fanny said. " Is this your first ride? "

" My first time on the road," said Trakun. " But Grandpa has taken me round and round all the courtyards. Only he would keep holding on to the reins."

Preecha smiled with pride.

" Now Papa is back," said Trakun, " I shall always come out with him, shan't I? "

" Every morning," he said.

" What's your pony's name? " Fanny asked.

" Lamai. It was my mother's name."

" We'll be going to Prachin for the summer," Preecha said. " It will be much easier for Trakun to learn to ride there."

" You'll like that? " Fanny asked.

" I will," said Trakun. " It's nice at Prachin."

For some weeks they saw each other every morning. Knox, out again after a few days, observed the easy relationship that had developed between Preecha's child and his daughter. At first it was " Miss Fanny," then once while cantering she called excitedly, " Look, Fanny, look. I can do it." After that Preecha too called her Fanny.

" You must all come to Prachin one day, Tom," Preecha said. " I think Mrs. Knox will like it there—and Caroline too."

" We'll try to arrange it," Knox replied. " It's some years since I visited that part of the country."

Chapter Fourteen

In April, after the Songkran water festival but before the rains, the Regent sent out invitations to a garden party, and Mrs. Knox, with the card in her hand, remarked: " This is unusual, Tom, he doesn't often give a party. I wonder if he is going to announce his retirement as Regent? "

" He'll never retire," Knox replied. " He loves power too much."

" Then perhaps," said his wife, " he expects to get an answer from you in time to make an announcement—about Fanny."

" I've told you, and I've told him, that I don't intend to rush Fanny," he answered irritably.

Mrs. Knox shrugged her shoulders.

The party was a brilliant one. Coloured lights were hung in all the trees and the pavilions were bright with Chinese lanterns, shaped like dragons and butterflies and pagodas. The King was there with all his brothers; for his wives and sisters there was a veiled pavilion. The Regent's own women moved among the guests, smiling shyly, curtsying, chattering.

In addition to the Second King, George Washington, whose father Knox had served as an Army instructor, and all the aristocratic families—"including *his* enemies," said Mrs. Knox as she pointed to Kesab and his sons—the richer merchants and traders, most of them Chinese and Indians and Malays, were present. And the European community seemed to be there in its entirety—consuls, business men, sea captains, doctors, a dentist or two, a photographer, missionaries, some governesses and even a few travellers from the hotels. It was an assorted throng, gay in its vast range of coloured silk dresses.

At the landing-stage there was a congestion of boats around the enormous royal barge, with its pink-and-gold figurehead. Two of Nai Dee's young sisters helped the attendants in guiding the boats in and out.

The Regent, with Nai Dee beside him, received the guests at the main gates. This seemed to confirm Mrs. Knox's expectation that it was intended to be Nai Dee's evening.

Mrs. Knox drifted early into the refreshment pavilion, where she nibbled dried fish and roast duck cut up in small squares. With her was Caroline, who ate hardly anything and kept glancing at the gate.

Louis was one of the late arrivals. He came in his gold-braided uniform and looked, Caroline thought, more handsome than ever. He gazed about him, as though seeking someone—she guessed it must be her sister. With an excuse she left her mother and went out into the throng, hoping he would see her. At last he called to her and she turned in simulated surprise, which did not conceal her obvious pleasure.

" I don't know where Fanny is," she said. " She was with Papa, talking to Phra Preecha—over there somewhere."

Louis smiled. " Come along," he said, slipping his arm through hers, " let's go and see that Japanese magician in the pavilion there. I'm sure we shall catch him out."

The magician was good and, even if he had not been, Caroline would have thought he was.

" You are enjoying yourself, aren't you? " Louis said.

" Very, very much." Involuntarily she squeezed his arm.

His face wore a wide, pleased smile.

" Your moustache gets larger and more wonderful every day," she said, gazing at him.

" I'm growing it to mark a big change in my life. I'm giving up all this." He flicked his fingers against his uniform.

" Oh, Louis, why? "

" Because I'm going to make a career—have a home—and children."

" Here in Bangkok? " she asked.

" Yes, but a lot of the time I shall be up North. Round about Chiengmai."

" Oh," she said. She sounded disappointed.

He looked at her. She seemed such a child.

" Come along," he said. " Let's see what's going on in the other pavilions."

Preecha asked Knox: " Have you talked to Mrs. Knox and Caroline about my invitation to Prachin? When do you think you'd like to come? "

" Later in the year, for we'd better wait till after the rains," Knox replied.

The Second King joined them.

" Tom," he said. " My sister Chandr has gone in there for the moment "—he waved a hand towards the *purdahed* pavilion —" she was looking for Mrs. Knox."

" I'll try and find Mamma and tell her," said Fanny. As she walked away the Second King said: " She is so very vivacious." Preecha agreed.

Alabaster walked by with the Regent's only son Vara, who was in his late forties, an amiable but undistinguished man, unlike his father in appearance and in manner. He stopped to talk, but Alabaster merely bowed to the Second King and to Preecha and went on.

The Regent, wandering among his guests, took Knox by the arm and led him aside. " Have you news for me? " he asked.

" No, not yet."

" Not yet," the Regent repeated. " Why? Do you think there is someone else? "

" No one that I know of," replied Knox.

" What about Louis Leonowens? " asked the Regent.
" They see a great deal of each other."

" She also sees a great deal of Nai Dee, Your Excellency."

" She sees a great deal of a lot of young men," grumbled the
Regent. " Prince Naret, I know he had an eye on her, but I
had a word with him and put a stop to it. Now, Tom, you
must be a little more active in this. I said I would wait, yes.
But it is a year now."

" Patience, Your Excellency, has always been your greatest
asset. In the end you somehow always manage to win."

" I know. But with marriage, if you want to see the children,
you cannot afford to wait too long." He gave an uneasy laugh
and moved on.

Knox noticed that the guests had begun to drift towards the
large pavilion which was used as a theatre. Seats had been
arranged in tiers under an awning, a bright yellow curtain,
richly embroidered, separated the small stage from the
extensive auditorium.

The Regent was already making for his seat beside the King
in the centre of the front row. He beckoned to his guests. It
took some time for them all to be seated. Across the aisle
Fanny saw her sister seated with Louis and Mrs. Knox.

The Minister of Foreign Affairs, Chow Phya Bhaunwong, a
half-brother of the Regent's, appeared on the stage in front of
the curtains and began a speech.

" It is my privilege, Your Majesties, Your Excellency, and
friends, to introduce the Royal Ballet. But before I do so I
should like to say just a few words. This delightful diversion
has been most generously provided for your entertainment by
that great leader and statesman, our Regent and Prime
Minister, from whose foresight and genius our country has
profited so greatly for so many years. He is . . ."

The Regent gesticulated wildly, but the Foreign Minister

went on: " He has built new roads, he has set up scientific and literary academies . . ."

At this the Regent rose. His voice was clear and authoritative. " I have not invited my friends here to listen to a eulogy about myself. Hunter "—his English secretary, standing at the end of the first row, stepped forward—" will you please go on to the stage and tell us in a very few words what we are going to see. Just that—nothing more."

The Foreign Minister, looking sheepish, bowed and withdrew. Hunter, addressing the audience in Siamese, introduced the first of the ballet scenes.

There was a look of astonishment on most faces, but whispered comments were reserved until later. The curtain rose at once and the splendour of the setting, the lovely costumes of the girls, their golden hats shaped like pagodas, the graceful movements of their arms held everyone spellbound.

Siamese ballet confines itself to depicting scenes from the Hindu classics, such as the *Ramayana*, which Siam shares with India, but they have evolved a style which is not seen anywhere except in Siam. In the Lakon, which was being performed, grace of movement attains perfection. The dancers are not masked and an unseen chorus sings a narrative to mark the postures and gestures of the players. The music is chiefly Indian, though it has a slightly Chinese flavour, supplied by the bamboo xylophones and the brass gongs.

When the performance ended, the Regent congratulated the dancers on their talent and thanked the King and his other guests for the pleasure their presence had given him. No reference was made to the Foreign Minister's ill-timed eulogy, though it was uppermost in the minds of the guests as they made their way to their boats. Many asserted that it was in keeping with their conviction that the Regent was a modest man, intent only on serving the country. It was clear, they said, that the boorish behaviour of the Foreign Minister had embarrassed and irritated him. Others felt differently. They thought the whole thing had been most carefully planned so that the Regent should appear before this large and representative gathering as a modest man who sought nothing for himself.

Preecha did not share this view. He said to Knox as he bade him good night: " The Regent has been greatly misunderstood and maligned. My family, an older family than his, has resented his authority—at any rate, some of them have; but he has shown us no ill-will. My father has been left undisturbed as head of the Mint and I, myself, owe my office of Governor to him."

" I thought the appointment was made by the King," remarked Mrs. Knox.

" By the King's influence perhaps, but the King was no more than fifteen years old at the time."

Knox, who liked the Regent, preferred not to believe the wicked stories told of him. They were not founded on verifiable evidence. The Regent had derived no pecuniary advantages from his position, on the contrary he had distributed vast sums out of his own private purse for the establishing of charitable foundations. He worked tirelessly for the public welfare. Knox believed that the cruel rumours circulated against him were based on jealousy, since no man can attain to such heights without making some enemies.

As they went to their boat, the Regent came up to bid them a second farewell. He also shook hands again with Preecha and his father. As the boats glided out into the night, Nai Dee called out: " Fanny, I haven't seen anything of you."

Knox saw the Regent place his arm around the shoulders of his grandson. That, he thought, was another quality which the great man possessed. He was affectionate, not only to his family, but also to his friends. Strangely soft and sentimental in some things, Knox reflected.

Mamma glanced at her husband, then at Fanny, and slowly shook her head.

When they got home Mrs. Knox followed her husband into his bedroom, and asked him anxiously if the Regent had spoken about Fanny.

" Yes."

" You see, I was right."

" He only asked me if I had any news."

" He is prepared to wait? "

" He has no alternative. Why are you so worried? "

" So long as we don't fall foul of that man. Fanny has a right to make up her own mind, of course, provided . . ."

She paused, for she could see that he was irritated.

" Provided—provided what? "

" Provided it isn't Preecha. I have nothing against him personally. He's an exceedingly nice man."

" I've told you again and again, my dear Prang, that there's not the slightest sign of a romance there."

" They've been seeing each other out riding—and now he has asked us to go and stay with him at Prachin."

" Is that a proposal of marriage—or even a sign that he's in love? If you'd like to know," Knox added, with a half laugh, " the Regent's far more worried about Louis. He said so. He made no mention at all of Preecha. It's only your over-active imagination."

" Are you thinking of going to Prachin? "

" I've told him to leave it until after the rains."

She breathed a sigh of relief. " Good! Meanwhile, it wouldn't be a bad idea if we asked Nai Dee to come to Paknam for part of the summer, or better still, let's go to Hua Hin. It will give them a chance to see more of each other. At any rate, it will show the Regent that we are doing all we can."

" I'm not going to Hua Hin. Paknam is nearer if I am wanted, and that's where I am going. You can go to Hua Hin if you like."

" I think I will—with the girls. Good night, Tom." She kissed him and went to her room.

Chapter Fifteen

PAKNAM WAS at the mouth of the river, a very few hours by boat from Bangkok. Knox rented a house there every summer, and cables from the Foreign Office or Singapore were brought to him by messenger and dealt with by the small staff he took with him.

Hua Hin, a fishing village about 120 miles farther out to sea and a great deal cooler, was the place to which the King and many of the nobles sometimes went for the hottest months. The Regent, because of his work, merely moved into his luxurious houseboat, moored a little way down the river to catch such breeze as there was.

At a hint from Mrs. Knox that they were going to Hua Hin, Nai Dee decided to spend the summer there too. Mrs. Knox was, of course, delighted and contrived that he should see a great deal of Fanny. She kept urging her to take Nai Dee out for a sail or go swimming with him.

Caroline preferred to lie on the soft white sands with her mother. Nai Dee would have preferred that. A little swimming, keeping reasonably close to the shore, was fun, but Fanny was far too energetic for him.

She looked on him rather as a brother until an incident occurred while they were out fishing which made her see him in a completely new light. It had been an unrewarding afternoon. After hours of waiting, Nai Dee got his first bite, but just as he was getting ready to haul in the prize, his little terrier, startled by a runaway horse, barked fiercely and darted after it. The fish was lost.

Nai Dee, enraged, called the dog to him, at first angrily, then coaxingly, and when the dog came, beat him unmercifully, in spite of Fanny's tearful pleading.

This brought back to her mind some vicious episodes of their childhood when Nai Dee's temper had been quite ungovernable and his craftiness in exacting revenge every bit as repellent. She recalled in particular the pretty little kingfisher he had tied to the end of a string and had tried to fly like a paper kite. The bird resisted and then, struggling to get away, pecked him hard. He had pressed his thumbs against the bird's throat until the life went out of it. Then she had cried and run away and would not be comforted.

A week or so later, just as their holiday at Hua Hin was ending, Nai Dee took her out for a walk alone and on reaching the farthest end of the beach, asked her to sit down.

She saw what was coming. But he was timid and hesitant and looked so boyish that she almost wished she could help him.

After further hesitation, with great gentleness and delicacy, he managed to say: " Will you marry me—please, Fanny? "

She did not want to hurt him. But she could only say: " I don't think we are suited to each other, Nai Dee, we wouldn't be happy."

" I would be very, very happy, Fanny."

" Thank you, Nai Dee. I am touched—and I appreciate the great compliment you are paying me, but——"

" Why do you think you wouldn't be happy? I promise I shall always be kind to you, Fanny. Most kind and gentle. I know I have a quick temper. I saw how upset you were the other day when I beat the dog. But I'm going to try hard to control my temper and with your help, Fanny, I am sure I shall be able to do so. I am trying already. Will you help me?"

" No, Nai Dee." She put her hand gently on his. " I can't."

He was taken aback. Staring at the sand, he asked in a quiet voice: " Is there anyone else? "

" No," she said.

He breathed with relief. " I thought it might be Louis."

" Louis? Not really. I'm not in love with him either."

" Then I shall wait," he said. " I shall wait as long as you like, Fanny. I have always loved you and I have always wanted to marry you. There shall never be anyone else. You will be my only wife, I swear it."

Before she could say anything more he added: " My Grandpa would like it too. He told me that he had talked to your father."

" I know," she said.

When she returned home, Mamma, after a quick glance at her face, asked: " Has something happened? "

" Oh, Nai Dee asked me to marry him. I told him I couldn't."

" How did he take it? "

" He didn't. He talked about waiting for ever—or almost for ever."

Mamma wondered what would happen now. As a Siamese she was a fatalist by instinct and upbringing. What had to be would be. But she could not help feeling uneasy.

Back in Bangkok, Nai Dee told his grandfather what had happened. The Regent comforted him, saying: " The door may be shut, but it is not locked. We must see that she does not lock it. Louis seems to be your only rival. We must get him out of the way. If he is not here, then she cannot fall in love with him. But there are so many, many girls. You could choose one—or more. Laotian girls, or Chinese girls, or one of our own Siamese girls—some of them are very pretty."

" They are not like Fanny. She is pretty, and so lively, so amusing, so gay. Her white, almost transparent skin, her flashing eyes with their long, sweeping lashes, her fiery spirit— that's what I like about her. There is nobody else like that."

The Regent smiled affectionately. " She is the untameable

kind. When she's roused she'll turn round and fight. Do you want that sort of a wife?"

"Yes, Grandpa. You've often said I'm like that myself."

"You'll be well matched," said the Regent indulgently.

The Regent rang for Hunter and told him he would like to see Mr. Louis Leonowens.

A meeting was arranged for the next morning. The Regent greeted Louis affably. "I understand from the King that you want some teak concessions in the North. I've been going into it. Many European firms have been after the same thing. So far, I have given them nothing. But for you—well, I shall see what I can do. Those teak forests belong to the local Chiefs, but they are not entirely independent and I may be able to arrange it. But tell me, what is your plan—to cut the teak and float it down and export it?"

"Yes, Your Excellency."

"I'll try and help you."

"Thank you, sir."

"You will need a steamboat to take you as far as the rapids. That will save a lot of time. I will give this to you as a present to start you off. How is that?"

Louis's face was flushed. He could hardly find words to express his pleasure.

"Your Excellency is most generous. Thank you very much, sir."

"All this will take a little time, of course," said the Regent. "You must be prepared to wait. Some months at least—it may even be a year."

"I have many arrangements to make too, Your Excellency. Elephants, coolies, and of course finance. I am in touch with the Borneo Company. They have promised to help."

"They are sound." The Regent smiled. "You know they were responsible for your coming here in the first place. They found your mother for King Mongkut, and so the chain is

taken one link farther. When it has all been arranged, I will
let you know."

" Thank you again, sir."

Louis went to the British Consulate that evening to tell the
Knoxes about it. Fanny congratulated him. " You are on the
road now," she said.

" You'll make a fortune, my boy," Knox observed. " With
the Regent behind you and the Borneo Company as an outlet,
nothing can stop you making a great success of it."

Caroline was excited, but a little crestfallen too, for it meant
Louis would be away for many months at a time.

Mrs. Knox reclined in her chair in reflective silence and,
after Louis had gone, said to her husband: " You see how that
old man's mind is working. He's done that to get Louis out
of the way."

" To leave the field clear for Nai Dee? "

" Of course. Louis has Fanny to thank for his good fortune.
Why else should the Regent, after refusing to grant the big
European firms any teak concessions, give some to Louis?
He has no experience, no money."

Knox laughed. " You may well be right."

It was the night of the November full moon and shortly after
Louis left, they went on to Phya Kesab's for the Loy Krathong
festival. It was a thanksgiving ceremony. The rains were over.
The strenuous months of ploughing and planting in the rice
fields were at an end. The harvest was at hand. In bowls made
of banana leaf, called Krathong, some shaped like birds, others
like boats, they placed their offerings of food and money and
clothing. The candles and the incense sticks in the bowls were
then lit and pushed out to float ("loy") along the canals and
the river—an offering, some said, to the water spirits, a floating
away of one's sins. It was a wonderful scene of flickering lights
as the boats drifted into the distance, joining thousands of
others.

Trakun had her own little boat, and Arun, whom Fanny met now for the first time, though only three, also had a boat of his own.

When they went in for refreshments, Preecha said: " Now the time has come for your visit to Prachin. When is it to be, Mrs. Knox? " She hesitated for a moment. " We could come in January perhaps, if that suits my husband. The girls, I am sure, will be delighted.

" My children will be there too. My sister-in-law, Thanom, Pet Pichai's wife, with whom they are now staying, will also be in Prachin, with her son Bhubarn. So we will be quite a large party."

" Yes," said Mrs. Knox—rather quietly, Fanny thought. Afterwards she said to Papa: " I hope Mamma is not going to back out."

" I'll try and get her to come," Knox replied. " But she doesn't care much for these long journeys. She likes her comforts, you know."

When the time came Caroline said that she would prefer to stay with Mamma. So, of the family, only Fanny accompanied Knox. He took with him Singh, his batman, Fanny took Oun.

Chapter Sixteen

Preecha called for them in his houseboat the *Sunbeam*. It was a large and luxurious boat, painted a sunlight yellow, with gleaming brasswork and a black funnel. It had an engine on the front deck, rather like a small railway engine, with pipes leading to the covered paddle-wheel at the back. At the mast flew his gubernatorial flag, a white elephant on a scarlet ground.

He came ashore in an open-necked shirt and loose cream trousers and talked to Mrs. Knox and Caroline while the luggage was being put on board. " I wish you were both coming too," he said. " Can't I induce you to change your minds even at this late hour? "

" I am sure it will be a delightful trip," Mrs. Knox replied. " Promise me you'll look after Fanny. She never does what she's told."

" Then she won't pay any heed to anything I say."

Fanny emerged from the house wearing a cream tussore suit, with a straw hat to match fastened under her chin with green ribbons.

" Mamma is trying to make you feel," she said, " that I'm going to be a terrible trial. I think she's trying to make you change your mind about taking me. Isn't that right, Mamma?"

" It's a bit late for that, I'm afraid. Children are a great responsibility, Phra Preecha—especially girls. You'll find that when your own daughter grows up."

" I should like to come to you for advice, then, if I may," he said with a smile.

Caroline and Mamma waved until the boat was out of sight.

Fanny's cabin, which was for'ard, was large and surprisingly spacious. Knox and Preecha had cabins at the back, by the paddle.

The boat turned southward and chugged noisily down the river.

"How long is it going to take?" Knox asked, making himself comfortable in a long, cane deck-chair.

"A little over a day. You've brought a lot of books, I see —and I've brought a lot more. In the evening perhaps we could play cards."

"Not me," said Knox. "I hate 'em."

"Then we shall have to think of something we can all do when Fanny runs out of talk."

"She'll never run out of talk," Knox assured him.

Preecha looked at her. They exchanged a smile.

Soon the houses on the outskirts of Bangkok were left behind. The palm trees and the mangrove swamps stretched for miles along both banks, with only a few houses here and there mounted on stilts above the marshy land. They passed many steamers and barges, sailing boats and sampans. At Paknam, near the mouth of the river, just past the beautiful white temple built on an island, they turned east into a canal. Here they saw naked children laughing and playing in the water, and women, in the water too, busy with their washing. Preecha dug into his pockets for sweets and threw them to the children, who, having already recognised his houseboat, had rushed forward with their hands outstretched.

The atmosphere was gay. "The Siamese," said Fanny, "remind me of the Irish. Not a care on their minds. To-morrow lies beyond the horizon. *Mai penerai*—it doesn't matter."

The trees were full of monkeys, smaller than those at the Consulate. One group in a tree were involved in a quarrel.

They kept up an enraged chattering and rushed at one another, biting, slapping, scratching. Many fell into the water injured and bleeding. The houseboat was stopped. Preecha brought out a gun and fired some shots into the air to distract and separate them.

Knox said: " We would have to shoot a few of them to stop the fighting, but since you would never agree to that, Preecha, we'd better go on and leave them to it. They'll fight to-morrow in any case and perhaps again a week later."

The houseboat moved on. After lunch they retired for the customary siesta, but Fanny found her cabin too stifling and came out and lay in a long cane easy-chair. When she awoke she saw Preecha with his back to the rails staring at her. He seemed embarrassed when she opened her eyes.

" I'm sorry," he said. " It was rude of me. But I could not help wondering what a pretty girl of your age dreams of."

" What made you think I was dreaming? "

" I saw the changing expressions on your face."

" Dreams are not as cheap as thoughts. A penny would not be enough," she said.

" I don't agree," he replied. " Dreams demand no effort."

" But they are revealing."

" Revealing of what? "

She laughed.

He came and sat in a chair beside her. " Tell me."

" Not even wild monkeys would make me."

" I promise not to laugh."

She considered the question for a moment. " No, I can't."

Knox emerged. His hair was ruffled, so was his beard. " You two quarrelling already."

" No—only pretending," said Preecha.

They passed some small villages with only two or three huts in each. Buffaloes were being goaded with long forks by little girls in enormous straw hats. Just ahead were a group of elephants, standing knee deep in the water, spraying their backs with their trunks.

They saw lots of brightly coloured parrots and many beautiful birds with long, magnificent tails.

" How can you go out and kill them, Tom? " Preecha asked. " That's something I could never do."

" I know," Knox replied. " And that's why I haven't brought my gun."

After dinner a piano was wheeled out on to the deck. " I got this especially for you, Fanny," Preecha said. " I hear that you play well."

He leaned over the piano while she played. She strummed some familiar music-hall numbers, till Preecha said: " Now let's have something serious."

" What? "

" Chopin—or the Moonlight Sonata."

" Listen! " Fanny exclaimed. " Listen to the *croak-croak* of the frogs and the chirping of the crickets and the wild noises of the night and the jungle—and the chugging of the boat— and you want me to play the Moonlight Sonata." She smiled. " All right." Her fingers moved gently over the keys.

Chapter Seventeen

As THE boat was recognised coming along the river towards Prachin, the wildest excitement developed. Women ran out of their homes, some even had infants at their breasts. Men rushed from the fields and from the small shops on the waterfront. Barbers came out with their razors still in their hands and men only half-shaved cheered with the lather on their faces. The children yelled with joy as they poured out of the school which Preecha had built for them. The priests came out of their scattered temples in their long saffron robes. At Government House faces appeared at the windows, then the officials and the servants dashed towards the landing-stage to await the arrival of the Governor. Running in front of them were Trakun and Arun and their Aunt Thanom.

The river is not as wide as the Menam is at Bangkok and one can call across it by raising one's voice. A wooden bridge spanned the stream.

The boat passed under the bridge to the landing-stage with its trim white wooden roof. Already it was crowded and more and more people kept on arriving. Disregarding protocol, Preecha waved both arms in greeting.

On landing, he introduced Knox and Fanny to the priests, to the officials and to the servants. She noticed that his manner towards them was as deferential as theirs was towards him.

Finally, he lifted his children on to his shoulders and, with the crowd following behind him, crossed the narrow, dusty road to Government House.

It was a handsome but unpretentious building, built of teak

and raised six feet above the garden. A stairway led up to a small veranda. The windows had green shutters, which were wide open. There were no guards.

The grounds were large. On one side Preecha had built the school, with a large playground behind it: many thought it was much too close to the house. On the other side, by the coach-house and stables, was the spirit house, mounted on a pole like a dovecot and painted pink. In this, it was believed that the guardian spirit of the place dwelt. There were a number of other buildings; offices for the officials, dwellings for the servants. In the grounds stood a large bird bath, the size of an English fountain.

There was a cluster of temples by the school, simple structures, not gold spired. Some were painted sky blue, others a light fawn, they were inviting rather than awe-inspiring. All had been built by Preecha. A small house beyond these was the home of the Abbot with a line of cells near to it for the other priests.

Preecha's office was in the house. In the front garden, just outside his window, stood a round metal chimney, rather like a ship's funnel; it was painted red. It belonged to the gold mine he worked at Kabin, forty miles farther up the river.

Fanny and her father were given large bedrooms, furnished comfortably and prettily. There was a vast central drawing-room, much larger than the one at the British Consulate, with English settees, marquetry tables and chandeliers. There were no women's quarters such as the Regent had in Bangkok. Preecha's wife had presumably had a room in the main building. Since her death there had been no women servants in the house, but now there were three, brought by his sister-in-law for herself and the children. Oun joined them.

There was the same easy informality in the house as on board. There were no settled arrangements and Fanny felt it must have been much like this even when Preecha's wife was there. The children went in and out of the rooms quite freely. The dogs wandered everywhere. Visitors came in unannounced and made themselves at home.

There was a charm about it all which appealed to Fanny. Knox responded less well. " It's a little like camping out," he observed.

" Oh, Papa, it isn't like that."

" Well, there's not much privacy. It was rather like this in the boat. But I expected it would be different here."

Preecha from time to time would go off without them and stay away for hours. When he came back he would say to Fanny: " I'm sorry I've been away so long, but I've been visiting the people in their homes—and if you go into one house, those living next door come out and invite you into theirs. They have no idea of time and I feel it would be lacking in courtesy for me to show any awareness of it."

His sincerity shone from his eyes.

Fanny got to know his children well. She found them affectionate and intelligent. They would come up and take her by the hand, often both at the same time, and ask her endless questions. She felt she had never seen a child so attractive as Trakun. Her skin was the colour of a stripped almond and above her round black eyes her eyebrows arched prettily. She had dignity and grace.

" The children have taken to you, Fanny. They will be very sad when you leave," Preecha told her.

" I shall have to take them with me."

" I wouldn't inflict that responsibility on you," he replied.

" They could come and stay with us from time to time."

" At the Consulate? "

" Why not? Mamma would love it, I'm sure—and Caroline would be in her element." Fanny changed the subject. " I meant to ask you about that chimney from your gold mine."

" You mean what it is doing here, outside my study window."

He smiled. " The workmen brought it to the wrong place and set it up here. They were very proud of what they had done and I had not the heart to tell them to remove it. So I ordered another like it, which has been put up at the mine."

" One can be too kind sometimes. Do you get a lot of gold out of that mine? "

" There's not much gold there. We get out all we can. But what you are really asking is ' Are you efficient—or too kind and complacent? ' " Fanny laughed, and he went on: " You get the same results in the end, whether you are harsh or gentle. Perhaps it takes a little longer with gentleness—though with harshness, it can take just as long, for the workers resent it, and where you have resentment you get delay. Isn't it better to get them to do it willingly? I suppose by European standards one might call me inefficient. But they are very simple people, Fanny—easy going. They have only a short span of life on this earth, and I don't think we have any right to torment and persecute them while they are trying to earn their daily bread. What purpose would it serve? To get a little more out of the mine for ourselves or in this case for the State? " He shook his head.

" I believe you are rather passive, rather complacent . . ."

" Not complacent, Fanny. I feel things too deeply to be complacent about them. When I served as a priest, as we all have to, I very much wanted to remain in the priesthood. I didn't stay because I felt I ought to resume the daily round—rejoin the herd if you like—and by my influence and example try and better the lives of others. One can't do much, though."

She felt a strange reverence growing in her as she listened. She was quiet for some time afterwards. Then he took her hand, saying: " Let us take the children for a walk."

Generally when the children went for a walk a number of people accompanied them, Preecha, Aunt Thanom, Oun and two maids, one for each child, for Arun had to be carried from time to time. They were often joined by Singh, Knox's Sikh batman, because he liked being with children. Sometimes the Chinese cook and a large group of villagers came along as well, and they were always followed by the dogs. Nobody, least of all Preecha, knew how many dogs he had. They drifted into the house, stayed for a day or more, then drifted away, returning whenever it suited them. Knox kept shooing them out of his bedroom, to the great amusement of all.

"Dogs all over the place. Birds settling in droves on the window-sill. Meals at irregular hours," he said to Fanny.

"The important thing," Fanny replied, "is that everybody is happy. Of course there are some loose ends. But Preecha's been alone since his wife died. He needs someone to tie them up for him."

Knox stared at her. He felt sure now that she was in love.

Chapter Eighteen

ONE EVENING, after a strenuous game of tennis, when Knox had gone in and Fanny lay in a long chair under the trees, Preecha, hugging his knees on the grass, said: " I believe that you like it here."

" Very much," she replied.

" So, if I asked you to come again, perhaps one day you might—return? " He said it slowly, hesitantly.

Without looking at him she nodded. His next question seemed to be hovering in the air. She waited for it, but it did not come.

They were silent for some time. She looked up. The sky was overcast. She could see no stars. She heard the faint noises of the night, the crickets, a roving owl, the distant barking of a dog.

" Fanny," he said at last, leaning towards her and taking her hand. " I think you know what I want to say. Would your answer be—yes? "

She nodded. " But ask it, Preecha. I'd like to hear you ask it."

" Will you marry me? "

" Yes." Then, after a long pause, she added: " I'm so happy. I've wanted this more than anything in the world."

" With all the world to choose from? "

He kissed her gently on the lips.

" Do you think your father will agree? "

" I hope so. I don't see why he shouldn't."

They kissed again. Then Preecha rose and helped Fanny to her feet. " We'd better go in," he said, " and tell him."

Knox had already bathed and changed and was seated in the dark veranda having a whisky and soda when they entered.

Preecha said: " I'm going to do this in the old-fashioned way. We've come to ask you if you will give us your blessing? "

Knox cleared his throat. " I've been expecting this." He stopped abruptly and appeared to be considering the position.

" Would you like a little time to consider your answer? " Preecha asked.

Before Knox could reply, Fanny said: " Papa, I want to marry Preecha. No one else will ever mean anything to me."

" Wait a minute, dear," Knox said gently. " One can't rush into marriage like this. It needs very careful thought. As your father, I'd be failing in my responsibilities if I didn't try to guide and help you. I've never denied you anything—now have I? "

" No," she said very quietly.

" But this is different. So much is involved. You're not old enough yet to know your own mind."

" I am." Her voice was a little defiant. " I'm twenty-one."

" Not old enough," he repeated.

" Fanny," Preecha said. " Your father is quite right. We must give him time to think about it. No doubt he would like also to speak to your mother."

" You've acted in a very proper way, Preecha," Knox said. " But we'll have to look at it from all points of view, and, of course, I want to consult her mother." He knew what his wife's answer would be. It was the one thing she dreaded. Now she would blame him for allowing them to see more of each other. He knew also that Fanny would not be easy to handle if their answer had to be " No." " Let's deal with this when we get back," he said. " You must try and understand that, darling."

Preecha's nodding head kept her from saying anything more.

At the end of the week they began their return journey to Bangkok. Trakun and Arun insisted on accompanying them. They were a little cramped in the boat. Trakun shared the cabin with Fanny, Arun was with Aunt Thanom in the cabin alongside. Shortly before lunch on the second day the houseboat pulled up at the landing-stage of the British Consulate. The Knoxes alighted, the others went on to the Amatyakun estate.

Preecha throughout the voyage was scrupulously correct in his behaviour. A warmth inevitably crept into the smiles he exchanged with Fanny. But only rarely did he so much as take her hand. They walked and talked and laughed, but always with the others around them. Once, finding themselves alone together for a few moments, they stood by the rails, looking at the dense jungle. The lights of the houseboat picked out the tortured shapes of the trees.

" I've been wondering," he said, " what thoughts you had, when you looked into the future. I'm sure it wasn't the sort of life I'm offering you."

" No," she said, " not quite. I imagined myself married of course. I've always seen myself as a wife and a mother."

" But in a different setting. In London perhaps, or Paris? Well, you've seen what it's like."

" I like it. Truly I do. Besides, it's the life we make together that matters. There—and in Bangkok. It's being together that's everything."

He nodded slowly.

" I've known that," she went on, " ever since I first saw you—that morning when you were out riding with the King."

" Then? But we hardly noticed each other, and there was Louis—and Lambton and Nai Dee. I heard that the Regent had set his heart on your marrying Nai Dee."

"He lost no time about that," she said.

"I wonder how he's going to take this. It's not going to be easy, Fanny."

"I don't see why it should make any difference. I'm free, so are you. Powerful though he is, the Regent can't compel us to do what he wants."

"The Regent is a law unto himself. He can't compel us— but he can be extremely disagreeable," he said.

"You seem uneasy."

"No. I'm prepared to face the consequences—so long as *you* won't have to. But I can't see how he can touch you."

"If you could peer into the future . . ." she began.

He shook his head. "No one can foretell the future with any certainty—and it can be most unsettling to base one's plans on fears and doubts."

"Others quite obviously wouldn't agree with you, look how busy the astrologers are."

"They are trying to find the most propitious moments in one's life. They say: 'Don't get married on Tuesday, wait till Friday—it's a more auspicious day!'"

"What about the birth of a child? You can't pick the most propitious day for that," she said.

"No."

"Then the child, by the mere accident of birth, could have a most appalling future."

"He could. That's why I'd rather not know. If you are told that something dreadful is going to happen to you, say in a year's time, the expectation of it will make you dread each day as the frightening moment approaches. It will destroy the entire year for you. Whereas, in your ignorance, you could be happy and gay and live quite normally."

He looked at her small, upturned face, clear in the ship's lights.

" Your horoscope must have been drawn up at your birth. What did it say? " she asked.

" I don't know. My parents never told me and I've never asked. Why? Do you want to know? "

" No. I just wondered. You sounded a little afraid of the future. I believe that the future is what we make of it ourselves."

BOOK TWO

The Houseboats

Chapter One

Mrs. Knox listened quietly while Knox told her of Preecha's proposal. There were no exclamations, no interruptions, no change of colour to betray the distress she was undoubtedly feeling. He ended: " Well, you feared it, and it has come."

Calmly, and without reproach, she said: " We could not have prevented them seeing each other—here in Bangkok. We must think now what it is best for us to do."

" You still feel they ought not to marry? "

At this all her pent-up feelings came surging to the surface. The words struggled to get out. She was almost incoherent. She shut her eyes and shook her head, then began again. " The Regent—we're turning down his grandson—his favourite grandson. He himself asked you. Fanny—you're giving her to someone the Regent hates."

" I've not turned down anyone. I'm not giving Fanny to anyone. She is making her own decision."

" But it is with your consent—ours if you like. We *must* prevent it, Tom."

" I think you are exaggerating. We have no evidence that the Regent dislikes Preecha or his family. They all have jobs of one sort or another in the Government."

" But people in the know say . . ."

" A lot of silly gossip. There has been rivalry, I know. But all that was long ago."

" It's too great a risk. The Regent could destroy her happiness. It could also affect our lives—yours and mine. We must stop it, Tom. We *must*."

" Fanny is in love with Preecha and he with her. Do you imagine she will listen to us? She can be very obstinate, you know," he said.

" I know. But I think Preecha will listen."

" He might. He's an honourable fellow. But what explanation could we give him? "

" I suppose we shall have to tell him the truth."

" Certainly. They have a right to know. They are not children."

She nodded slowly, then stared ahead without speaking. Knox sat on the settee beside her and took her hand. She clutched it saying: "I may be wrong—but I don't think I am."

" We need a little time," he said.

" It would be so much better if we said ' No ' now, Tom."

" And deprive her of what she believes is her only chance of happiness? That would not be right," he said.

" She's young. She'd get over it."

" All we want is her happiness," he said. " The Regent should not concern us."

Meanwhile Fanny was telling Caroline her story. She listened with lips parted and the colour drained from her face.

" Poor Louis! " she said.

" There was never anything between us, Caroline."

" He has always loved you. He talks of you all the time."

" The best thing, darling, would be for you to marry him."

Caroline turned quickly away.

" As soon as I've married Preecha," Fanny went on. " Well, Louis will have to find someone else, and I think it will be you."

" When's it to be—your marriage? "

" I haven't got Papa's answer yet." She pointed towards the study. " I wonder how they are getting on in there."

" Suppose they say ' No.' "

" I'll marry Preecha whatever they say."

" You *can't*, Fanny."

" *Can't* I? "

" That would be wicked," said Caroline.

" I *am* wicked."

They laughed and hugged each other. After a while
Caroline asked: " What're you going to say to Louis? "

" I'll tell him about it, of course. I must. I promised."

" When? "

" The first chance I get."

As it happened the chance occurred that evening. Louis
came in a boat along the canal and called to Fanny from under
her window.

" Are you in bed yet? "

" No. I'll come down. I want to talk to you," she said.

Caroline, undressing in her own room, heard his voice and
heard Fanny run down the stairs into the garden.

As Louis got out of the boat Fanny took his arm and led him
towards the post office, where the canal meets the river. They
sat together on a bench there.

He smiled. " Did you have a nice time? "

" Wonderful," she said.

" Oh! "

" Wonderful," she repeated.

" So it's Preecha—is it? " he asked.

She nodded. " He has talked to Papa. I said ' Yes ' and now
we're waiting."

He made a grimace.

" I'm sorry, Louis. I told you it wasn't much good waiting.
But you'll find somebody much, *much* better."

" Who? Caroline? "

" Why not? "

Louis left her with a thoughtful expression on his face.

Next morning, while they were out riding, Fanny asked her
father what they had decided.

"We'd better wait till we get back," he said.

They rode on in silence, her mind groping for a clue; his had already been made up.

After a time they saw Preecha riding ahead. He was alone. Knox, pointing towards him with his riding-crop, said: "I think it would be best if I talked to you together."

It was arranged that Preecha should come to the British Consulate at midday.

"It sounds a little ominous," said Preecha, with an uneasy smile. "It's not going to be just a simple 'Yes.'"

"It can't be answered as simply as all that," Knox replied.

"Will Mamma be there too?" asked Fanny.

"Yes. Mamma will be there," Knox said.

Preecha arrived just before twelve. Fanny was waiting for him in the veranda. Mrs. Knox was already in Papa's study. They exchanged a quick good-luck kiss and went in.

"I want first of all," Knox began, "to say, Preecha, that I have the highest regard and affection for you. I feel sure you will make Fanny very happy."

He paused and began to fill his pipe. Fanny and Preecha exchanged glances. Then she looked towards her mother, who sat with her hands folded in her lap and her eyes down.

"If that was all we had to consider," Knox went on, "the answer would be an unhesitating 'Yes.' We have our daughter's happiness at heart, but there are other considerations—extremely important considerations. They have to be faced."

He cleared his throat.

Before he could go on, Mrs. Knox, prompting him to get to the point, said: "The Regent."

"I'm coming to that," Knox said sharply. "But let's get our values in the right order. I have already indicated that I am not against the marriage. We must, however, examine its possible consequences. Unfortunately the Regent has chosen to take an interest in Fanny's future. I do not see what right he, or anyone else, has to come between you and your happiness. But there is more to it than that. The very close and pleasant relations that now exist between Great Britain and Siam could be seriously jeopardised if—and *if* is the operative word—the Regent finds this marriage not to his liking."

" I don't want to interrupt," Preecha said. " But I don't see why the Regent should object. Were you thinking of the supposed feud between his family and mine? "

" Partly," said Knox. " I don't myself attach any importance to that, though others do." He made a vague gesture towards his wife. " It is a thing of the past—isn't it, Preecha? "

" I would have said so, though no one can ever tell how the Regent's mind works."

" Exactly," interposed Mrs. Knox.

" But apart from that," Knox went on, " Fanny must have told you that the Regent has set his heart on her marrying his favourite grandson, Nai Dee—a nice young man, but Fanny prefers you. She has, of course, the right to do so. The question we have to consider is this. Would the Regent feel affronted if, after refusing Nai Dee, Fanny's choice falls on you? "

" Most definitely he will," muttered Mrs. Knox.

Preecha turned to her. " You are still thinking of the feud," he said. " I tell you, it doesn't exist any more."

" You can't be certain," she said. " You have yourself said nobody can be certain how the Regent's mind works. Once you are married, it will be too late. Anything could happen then."

" Oh, Mamma! " exclaimed Fanny in exasperation. " You want us not to marry—because of a *vague* fear that something might happen." There was sarcasm in her emphasis.

" All I am saying," Mamma replied, " is that we can't afford to take the risk. Something might happen. Suppose it did."

" Your mother and I have been going round and round this point," Knox said. " I don't entirely agree with her. At the same time, placed as I am, as the Political Agent and Consul General of Her Majesty's Government, it would not be right for me to expose the good relations between our two countries to such a risk. What I am going to suggest is this. Why not wait a little while? We must feel our way. If the Regent were affronted, my position here would be impossible. You do see that, don't you? "

Fanny got up and went and sat beside her mother. " Mamma, dear. There is no reason for you to be upset."

" No reason? " Mrs. Knox said. Her eyes were dilated, her face flushed. " All sorts of things can happen. They *have* happened." She turned to her husband. " I've remembered a lot of other things. Yu Fuang, a housemaid at the Regent's, was beaten to death because she broke a valuable Chinese vase. Then there was . . ."

" You are thinking of things that happened long ago," Fanny interrupted. " We are living in a different age, Mamma."

" A different age," Mrs. Knox echoed. " The Regent belongs to an age before mine even. Besides, anger is primitive in any generation."

" So is mine," said Fanny, rising.

" Just a minute, Fanny," Preecha said gently. " I respect your feelings, Mrs. Knox, even though I agree with Fanny when she says there is no real basis for your fears."

" Look here," Knox interrupted. " You are not planning to get married to-morrow, are you? All I am suggesting is that you wait a little longer—say a year . . ."

" A *year*! " exclaimed Fanny.

" We need a little time to sense the atmosphere—to see whether there is any foundation for your mother's fears. Not to wait would be folly. Surely, Fanny, you can see that."

"I can't," she replied abruptly. "A year is not a little while. It's a long time. I'm twenty-one and . . ."

"Fanny, dear," Preecha said, "your father's position has to be considered. While I do not think there is any foundation for your mother's uneasiness, perhaps "—he turned to Knox—"perhaps we could get engaged now and defer the wedding, let us say for six months. Would that give you enough time, Tom?"

"No. I am suggesting there should be no decision, no engagement until we know where we are. You are both young. You can both afford to wait a year."

"I have something to say too," said Fanny angrily. "Mamma's fears are sheer *nonsense*. She sees it all like a melodrama—the evil old Regent with a knife in his hand ready to plunge it into us the moment we marry. I don't intend to wait. I *won't* wait." She turned to Preecha. "And please don't say you will wait."

He put his arm round her waist. Then he turned to Knox. "I think we had better leave it for a while. You have given us your views. If Fanny and I had a chance of talking it over——"

"I shan't give in," she said defiantly. "We are both old enough and I can't see what harm there is in our getting engaged now and marrying in three months' time."

Mrs. Knox wagged a finger at her daughter. "Be careful, dear," she said. "That old devil is much more dangerous than you think."

Preecha led Fanny out of the room. They walked together across the lawn to the bench where she and Louis had sat the night before. A string of five barges, drawn by a tug, drifted by. There were calls from one boat to another and much laughter.

Fanny said: "I wonder where Mamma finds all these bogies?"

" I've always thought of her as being so calm, so composed," said Preecha.

" She is usually. But she's got worked up about this. All the same, I'm not giving in."

" Fanny "—he took her hand—" we have to be reasonable. Your father has a great deal at stake. If your mother happens to be right, our marriage would certainly affect the admirable relations that exist between your country and mine."

" And what do we do *if* she happens to be right? Say good-bye and part for ever? "

" It won't come to that."

" Can't we run away? " she asked suddenly. " It would solve everything. There'd be no waiting."

He smiled. " This is my home, Fanny. I have here my children, my father, my brothers. Besides, where could we go? What would I do in England or France? Let us wait," he said, " and *prove* that they are wrong. It will clear the air. There won't then be any doubts or regrets and the atmosphere will be what it should be for a happy wedding."

" Wait a year? " she gasped.

" The time will soon pass."

" Without even being engaged? " she said.

" Not officially engaged, but you and I know that we are engaged already. Your father's concern is that the Regent should not know, at any rate, not yet, which means that nobody must know."

" I want everyone to know," she said.

" So do I, my darling—and everyone will after we have disposed of your parents' doubts. And so in a little while," he went on, " go up and tell them we have decided to wait *because* we know their fears are groundless."

She was silent for a time, but when he rose to go she said quietly: " All right. I'll tell them—and let us pray the time will go quickly."

Her father was alone in his study when she went up. She entered the room smiling. He could see her answer in her face.

" Good girl," he said. " It will give me time to tap out the ground and prepare the Regent for what's coming. I think I'll have to do it by stages. Tell him first that perhaps you are not going to marry Nai Dee. We'll see how he takes that. Then, after a time, when he has got used to that, we can begin to prepare him for the next step, namely, that you are going to marry someone else—and later, much later, we'll tell him who that someone is. If all this came upon him at once—well, I'm afraid it would enrage him. You do see, dear, how important it is that we don't put a single foot wrong."

She nodded, almost in a trance.

He got up and put his arm affectionately about her shoulders. " I don't think there's anything in Mamma's fears. But it's my duty to find out."

" Don't you think the *fait accompli* would force him to accept it? " she said.

" No one can force the Regent about anything. But don't worry. I'm sure it will be all right." He kissed her on the forehead. " So we'll leave it as it is. No engagement for a year. No seeing him . . ."

" Not see him? " Fanny exploded.

" If you two are seen together all over the place you might just as well be engaged now. The Regent will hear of it in no time. He will get into a rage. He'll send for me. We'll have thrown away all our chances of preparing him."

" Not see him at all? " she repeated.

" You are bound to run into each other from time to time. What I'm saying is don't arrange to meet. Don't go about together, and when you do meet by chance, don't behave as though there is some secret understanding between you."

" You mean not even write to each other? "

" Write by all means, Fanny dear. There's no harm in that.

125

As soon as the air is cleared I'll let you know. Then we shall all be happy."

He lifted her face by the chin. It was a sad little face. As he kissed her again she burst into tears.

He held her against his breast and comforted her. " There, there. Don't distress yourself, darling. The time will pass much more quickly than you think."

Chapter Two

FANNY wrote to Preecha later that day and sent the letter round by hand to his father's house.

I don't know how we are going to live through the next twelve months. Papa now says that we must not even see each other for a year—apart from chance meetings. He wants the Regent to be told by stages, and by Papa personally, not by anyone else.

This is imposing a far greater hardship on us than we foresaw when we talked of it and decided to wait. Would you still have said " Yes " if you had known? When I think of the days ahead—empty—with only our letters to comfort us . . . I am going to write to you every day, darling, even if I have to keep the letters until I can get them off to you. I shall put down all my thoughts every day. Will you do the same—please? With all my love, Your ever devoted Fanny.

He replied at once. The messenger was asked to wait and take his answer back.

It is a great, great hardship. But I can see no other way. I too will write to you daily—and the chance meetings will bring us both some comfort, however guarded we have to be. I love you very much, my little Fanny. Yours, Preecha.

Inevitably, they saw each other out riding next morning. Preecha was with the King. Louis was also of the party. They bowed to each other but did not speak. Louis came over for a talk, but she hardly took in a word he said.

" What's the matter? " Louis said.

" I'll tell you later," she replied. The tears began to come into her eyes and she turned her head away.

The next morning Preecha was not out on his horse, but a letter arrived from him.

While it is enchanting to catch even a glimpse of you, it is torturing to be beside you and not be able to exchange more than a few formal words and even that we were not able to do to-day. I have in any case to go back to Prachin, but I am leaving earlier than I need to, so to-morrow morning while you are out on your horse, I shall be leaning against the rails of the *Sunbeam*, seeing again the scenes we so recently saw together and going over again and again in my mind the talks we had on that boat. All my love, Preecha.

Papa and Mamma felt it would be better, both from the point of view of appearances and for Fanny herself if they gave a few parties for her at the Consulate—"coming out parties," Knox called them.

The first of these parties was arranged for the Queen's birthday, the 24th May, 1877. The monsoon had already broken and the afternoon was warm and sticky, but the rain held off long enough for the party to be held in the garden. A *shamiana* was erected on the lawn and a new Union Jack was run up on the tall flagstaff.

Among the guests were the King and all the royal princes. The Second King, George Washington, was there too, and the Regent came with his son Vara and Nai Dee. All the foreign countries were represented by their Consuls. Among the British subjects were the chief traders from India and Burma and Malaya. A small local band played "God Save the Queen" and Her Majesty's health was drunk, as always, in tea.

When Fanny appeared among them, dressed in a wasp-waisted lemon-yellow gown of fine corded silk, with a tiny matching bonnet trimmed with feathers, tilted slightly forward, some of the men clapped their hands with delight. The women exclaimed and gathered round her. " You look very lovely," said Madame Garnier.

Louis raised his nose loftily. " Nice way to get yourself up," he said, " after turning me down." He looked across at Caroline. Her gown of pale-green taffeta was most becoming. He struggled through the throng to her side and they had a strawberry ice-cream together.

Some weeks later, while out riding, Fanny saw Preecha, who had returned to Bangkok a few days earlier. He was with Trakun, who pulled in her pony and waited for Fanny to come up.

" Hallo, Fanny," the child called, " we haven't seen you for such a long time. Why don't you come and see us now? "

For a moment Fanny found it difficult to swallow. " I will," she said.

" When? " asked Trakun and, as Fanny did not answer, she turned to her father: " You will make her come, won't you? Arun's been asking for you too, Fanny."

" I'll come, darling," Fanny said. " Soon. I promise."

She and Preecha exchanged a quick glance.

" Next week," he said. " Fanny will come next week and perhaps when I'm away she'll even take you out for a ride— if you're very good."

" I'll be very good," said Trakun solemnly.

In his letter brought by hand that afternoon, he said:

I have to go to Kabin on Friday morning. The children are so happy that you are coming to see them. Time seems to be moving much too slowly. When I'm away the days drag and when I am here the agony is worse. If only we could end it to-morrow and be together always. But we shall just have to wait—and wait—and wait.

When she arrived at Phya Kesab's the children rushed out

and hugged her. Kesab said: " Preecha has told me. Perhaps your father is right. Nobody can tell. It is best to wait. I hope I live to see you both happy."

She spent some hours with the children and the next morning she left home early to take Trakun for a ride along New Road. When she mentioned this to Mamma, Mrs. Knox was very upset.

" Fanny, dear," she said, " you must not think I am always saying ' No ' to everything you want to do. We must be careful, that's all."

" But, Mamma, Preecha was not there. We are both most careful to observe everything you and Papa have said. Am I not to speak to the children? Why? "

" Because, dear, the old fox has a very quick and suspicious mind. He puts two and two together and instantly finds the right answer. We are only doing this to help you, darling. It will ease things so very much if we keep to your father's plan of informing the old man by degrees, not all at once."

" It is so cruel," Fanny said sulkily. " It will hurt the children so much. What have they done? They are already wondering . . ."

" Your father has made a beginning. Do sit down, dear, and stop pacing about the room."

Fanny sat down reluctantly.

" He has told the Regent," Mrs. Knox went on, " that your delay in making up your mind may be due to the fact that, while you like Nai Dee very much, you look on the relationship more as that of brother and sister and apparently can't think of him as a husband. The Regent pooh-poohed the idea and said it was time you made up your mind."

She noticed her father standing in the doorway.

" He was not exactly angry," said Knox, " but testy. He said the boy could not be expected to wait for ever. Time was passing and he had refused to marry anyone else."

" Am I to be made a sacrifice," snapped Fanny, " to the future relations of England with this country? "

" Ssh! Sssh! " said Papa. " Nobody is asking you to do that. That is why I suggested you should wait."

" To-morrow I suppose I'll be told I must not leave the house at all, but must remain as a prisoner here in case I should run into Preecha's father—or one of his brothers—or his sister-in-law." She rose from her chair.

" Nothing like that," Knox snapped back. " So long as he feels there's no one definite in your mind. The Regent took comfort from one thing and one thing only," Knox went on. " He specifically mentioned that when Nai Dee proposed to you at Hua Hin you gave him reason to believe that there was no one else."

" There wasn't then," she said.

" Well, it's best left like that for a while," said Knox.

" But seeing the children . . ." she began, the words struggling for an outlet.

" It identifies you with the family," Knox said.

" We are a very small community here," added Mrs. Knox, " the Regent, the princes—a handful of people. Everyone knows everyone else's business. People will say: ' Ah, she's seeing a lot of his children.' And ' She doesn't see so much of Nai Dee now.' "

" But I do," she said. " He still keeps coming round."

" Please, darling. Try and be sensible," Knox said.

" I can't. I *can't*." Seeing the tears very near, Mamma came up and put her arm about her.

" It will all come right, darling."

Fanny brushed the tears from her eyes and smiled enigmatically.

" You can ask Nai Dee round as often as you like," she said. " I don't mind."

Knox and his wife looked at each other.

" And the Regent too. I quite like him, really," she added.

Soon after Fanny went to her room, Knox and his wife were surprised to hear the sound of laughter coming from it. They listened for a moment. Yes, it was Fanny laughing. What on earth was she up to?

Mrs. Knox rose from her easy-chair. " She must be hysterical."

She found Fanny lying in bed in her underclothes, kicking her bare legs and laughing. In her hand she held a letter.

" What's the matter, dear? " Mamma asked.

" I had a letter from Lambton as I was going out for my ride this morning. I stuffed it into my pocket and forgot all about it. I've been reading it now. He wants to marry me."

" Yes. It's funny." She left the room shaking her head. Fanny re-read the letter.

I have again and again turned over in my mind the thought of asking you to marry me, Fanny. But I suppose proposals of this kind come your way almost every day. I did not speak of it while I was with you because I was only too conscious that I had not much to offer. But as time has brought no announcement in *The Times*, for which, I confess, I have looked with some trepidation, I am prompted to write to you now about my own feelings.

I beg your forgiveness if this may seem over rash, but I assure you that I write, not because I feel I may be better than any of the others who have asked for your hand in marriage, but because you yourself seem not to have found these others acceptable.

Doubtless I shall fall into the same category, for I have indeed hardly anything to offer even now, save a life that I shall try to make as worthy of your beauty and your charm as I can.

It was this that had made her laugh, the circling, roundabout diffidence with which he made the approach. Papa would, of course, regard him as a very suitable son-in-law. But for her there could never be anyone but Preecha.

In the morning, as memories of her ride with Trakun, of the row with Mamma, of her tears, of the letter from Lambton, drifted back into her consciousness, Fanny, stretching herself luxuriously, saw Caroline come into her room. She noticed that her sister's face was tear-stained.

" Louis is downstairs."

" Have you been crying? " Fanny asked.

" No, I haven't," she said, stamping her foot and promptly burst into tears. " He's going to be away for five or six months," she sobbed.

" We're a nice pair! Me crying last night because I have to wait another ten months and you . . ."

" I'm sorry, Fanny. But at least you know that after ten months . . ."

Fanny, quickly drawing on her clothes, asked: " When is he leaving? "

" In a few minutes."

" Come on. Let us go down." She put her arm through Caroline's.

Louis was dressed for travelling.

" You are late this morning," he said. " No ride? "

" No ride," she replied. " But tell me about your journey, Louis."

" I'm going up to Chiengmai to look at the teak on my concessions. I've got three large concessions," he added proudly.

" The Regent has been generous," said Fanny.

" Very," he said. " I've seen the boat he's having built for me. It isn't ready. But it's most attractive, a paddle-steamer— black and white. It can take me as far as Paknam Po, a hundred and thirty miles upstream. After that the river's too shallow and we get the rapids. So we'll have to use native boats and pole our way up. There'll be a lot to see to when I get there. Girdling the teak—you have to wait two years before any of it can be felled . . ."

" Two years! " said Caroline.

" The Regent thought I might be lucky. Some of those concessions have been worked by contractors, so I may find trees that have already been girdled, or even ready to fell now. Besides, there's a lot to see to—elephants, coolies, arrangements for getting the logs down. Some usually get stuck and then the men, with the help of elephants, have to shift them. At Raheng they will be tied together in rafts and brought down here to the Borneo Company."

" What a lot of organising," Fanny said.

" And a lot of money too," said Louis. " But the Borneo Company is financing the whole thing."

" I dare say they'll make a lot out of it," said Fanny.

" So will the Regent," replied Louis, " or rather the Government. I have to pay a toll on each log that's brought down and that will help the finances of Siam."

" Wonderful how the Regent gets it both ways," said Fanny.

" What do you mean? " Louis asked.

Fanny hesitated for a moment. " He's not only helping you but helping himself too."

She was thinking of Nai Dee. " You're going to be away a long time, Louis?" Fanny asked.

" May I kiss you both? " he said.

Fanny held up her face. He kissed her on the cheek. Then he kissed Caroline.

After he had gone Fanny, seeing that Caroline was near to tears, said: " Let's go to church. We didn't go last Sunday or the Sunday before."

" We can pray for his success," said Caroline. " The church is just alongside the Borneo Company."

The church had been built twelve years earlier on a plot of

land given by King Mongkut through the intervention of his Prime Minister, now the Regent. The first service was conducted by the Rev. S. Mattoon, an American Presbyterian missionary, on the 2nd May, 1864, and was attended by Mrs. Anna Leonowens and her son Louis.

Now when Fanny and Caroline set out, the little bell was being rung to summon the small community of worshippers.

The church was almost full when they entered. The service was conducted by the Rev. Noah McDonald of the American Presbyterian Mission, who since the retirement of General Partridge, had been acting as American Consul.

Fanny noticed the earnestness with which Caroline got down on her knees and covered her face to pray and her repeated glances throughout the service at the Borneo Company building, which could just be seen through the small windows. The text of the sermon, which was " Seest thou a man diligent in his business? he shall stand before Kings," seemed to Caroline to have a particular application to Louis.

" I know he will succeed," she whispered to her sister.

Chapter Three

THE KNOXES went to Paknam in the first week of July. Nai Dee was asked to come and visit them as often as he could, and even to stay for a night or two if he wished.

This might help to keep up appearances and to allay doubts or suspicions. But Knox realised that he had not made much progress towards the goal he had set himself of revealing to the Regent by stages that Fanny was not going to marry Nai Dee.

Mrs. Knox still had grave forebodings. Soon after she learned of Lambton's proposal of marriage, she suggested to her husband that the best solution might be for him to take Fanny back to England and keep her there for some time.

" If only we could get her away from Preecha for a year or so," she said. " They may not talk, but they see each other, and it keeps the whole thing alive."

" We shall just have to wait and see. The Regent is being extraordinarily patient. Perhaps, given time, he may begin to realise he is not going to get his way."

Fanny's attitude towards Nai Dee was friendly, as it had always been. During their stay in Paknam he came twice for the day and he also spent a week in an uncle's house a few miles outside the town.

Only once did Nai Dee come near to making another proposal of marriage. He asked: " Have you thought about what I asked you at Hua Hin last year? "

Fanny nodded.

Encouraged by the nod, he said excitedly: " Is it going to be ' Yes,' Fanny? "

But she shook her head: " I'm afraid not, Nai Dee."

" How much longer do I have to wait? "

She wanted to tell him that her mind had already been made up. But this would have ruined Papa's plan.

" Just a few months more—that's all," she said.

Among others who came on a visit to Paknam were Prince Damrong, his brother Naret and Prince Bhanurangsri, a full brother of the King. His interest in Fanny had grown since the garden party at the Consulate on the Queen's birthday. He now informed her that he had been given a palace of his own to live in, at the side of the parade ground and quite near to the palace of the Second King.

" I want to furnish it. Will you help me? " he asked.

Fanny was delighted with the suggestion.

" That," said Mrs. Knox to her husband afterwards, " will add a fresh complication."

" Only a red herring, I fear," Knox said.

" I think Caroline will marry Louis," Mrs. Knox said suddenly.

Her husband looked at her through narrowed eyes. " One of your intuitions? " He laughed.

" No, just using my eyes. I've noticed the way he looked at her before he went away."

" I've always liked Louis," replied Knox, " but I couldn't stand his mother. She was always making a commotion about something."

They returned to Bangkok at the end of September. The rains were not quite over. But the very next morning Prince Bhanu called at the Consulate and asked Fanny to go over to his new palace with him.

They had a cup of tea together, then she set out in his boat. The palace was a large rococo building, its three floors were for the most part empty.

" I've cleared out all the things I didn't like," said Bhanu.

" An uncle of mine used to live here. He died three years ago and it's been empty ever since."

Fanny enjoyed planning the redecoration and the refurnishing. Cost imposed no restrictions. The King's overseers and contractors were called in. Firms in Singapore and Saigon were asked to send their representatives. She spent day after day working out colour schemes for the main reception rooms and choosing furniture from the lists brought to her. Many things were made by local carpenters and upholsterers to her design—settees, chairs, occasional tables. Even fireplaces, so rarely required in the tropics, were put in, because "they give a focal point to the room," said Fanny. Bhanu wanted more mirrors and much more gilt than she would allow him. Many eastern ornaments were brought in from the other palaces, but Fanny admitted them only sparingly.

When everything was ready, Fanny agreed to be hostess at a ball the Prince was giving.

The ball was held on the 7th January, 1878. The King's brothers, the Regent and Nai Dee were present. A cold prevented His Majesty from attending. All the nobles were invited, including Phra Preecha, his father, and his brothers.

Fanny looked arrestingly lovely in an evening-dress of turquoise satin, edged with lace. Her shoulders were bare, her short lace sleeves were caught up by tiny posies of rose buds and forget-me-nots. At her throat she wore a blue velvet ribbon, from which hung a small star of diamonds, a gift from Prince Bhanu.

She received the guests as they arrived and later opened the ball with the Prince. Preecha danced first with Madame Garnier. But when the lancers came on he and Fanny found themselves in the same set and had to clasp hands as they crossed and re-crossed, and even danced together at intervals.

" I can hardly bear it," she whispered to him. Her face was

flushed, her eyes afire. She noticed the Regent was looking at them.

" Only two months and seventeen more days," Preecha said when next they came together.

She danced with Nai Dee and later with the Regent, who appeared to be managing the waltz quite well.

" I think I know your secret," remarked the Regent.

She looked at him nervously. His thin moustache widened as he smiled, his teeth very white.

" Prince Bhanurangsri is in love with you."

Fanny breathed again.

At the end of the next week Louis returned from Chiengmai. He had been away nearly seven months.

He arrived at the Consulate in his new black-and-white paddle-steamer and pointed with pride to it from the veranda.

Caroline leaned excitedly over the rail. " Can you take me somewhere in it? "

" Come along," said Louis. " What about you, Fanny."

" I have a heap of letters to write."

" All right. Come on, Caroline. Let's go to Paknam."

" That's miles away."

" It will take us no time at all in a boat like this. I'll bring you back in two hours."

" Oh, Louis. Papa would have a fit."

The young Siamese mechanic started the engine and they set off, chugging past the sampans, the fishing boats, and the barges.

Louis, looking intently at Caroline's eager, excited face, asked after a while: " Do you think you would like it in the North? "

" I don't know. Do you? "

" Very much. But it would be nicer if you were there too."

" Oh, Louis! " Her face was flaming. " I'd—I'd love it— all those mountains . . ."

" Would you really, Caroline? "

She nodded. Her eyes were lowered. She was still blushing.
He took her hand. " Will you marry me, Caroline? "

She lowered her head still further. She could hardly speak.

" Caroline." He lifted her face gently. Her eyes were filled
with tears.

He put his arm about her and kissed her tenderly.

" Shall we go to Paknam now? "

" No, Louis. But we'll go to Chiengmai—one day, soon I
hope—unless Papa wants me to wait till I'm twenty-one."

When Caroline returned she found her mother still sitting
in the veranda. One glance at her daughter's face told her
what she had hoped to hear. She got up and kissed Caroline.
" I am very, very happy, dear."

Knox grunted from the doorway. " He has proposed, has
he? I must say these young people are getting much too casual
for my liking. He ought to have come up and had a word with
me."

Fanny rushed out of the drawing-room, where she had been
strumming on the piano, and hugged her sister.

" You might say you're pleased, Tom," observed Mrs.
Knox.

" Of course I'm pleased." He patted Caroline's shoulder
and planted a kiss on her forehead. " But I still think he ought
to have come up to see me."

Mrs. Knox noticed that Fanny was sitting quietly and
guessed what was going on in her mind. Perhaps they should
have curbed their enthusiasm a little. Poor Caroline! So little
ever seemed to come her way.

Caroline, twisting her hair nervously, said: " Louis talked
of our getting married fairly soon. He wants to take me with
him when he goes back to Chiengmai. You won't want me
to wait till I'm twenty-one, will you? That would be a long
time."

" No," said Knox. " But isn't Louis going to talk to me? "

"Of course," said Caroline. " It's just that he is a little shy."

The next morning, soon after Fanny and Knox had returned from their ride, Louis called. Knox was in his study and Louis went in at once to see him. Hesitantly he asked him for his consent.

Knox walked round the desk, his hand extended. " We were delighted when Caroline told us last night. I'm sure you'll both be very happy."

He went to the curtained door and called to his wife. She came from her bedroom in her curl papers.

"So you've come, Louis. I felt sure you would." She kissed him on the cheek. " That moustache of yours is coming along well. How much bigger are you going to grow it? "

She was always personal and blunt. Louis's mother had not liked that.

" Long enough," he answered, " to twirl on our wedding day —with the aid of a little pomade, of course."

" Oh," said Knox. " I didn't realise you were prepared to wait as long as that. Caroline said you wanted to get married soon. When are you planning to go North again? "

" In June—that gives us about four months."

" Not enough time to get a trousseau from Paris," said Mrs. Knox.

Caroline came in, her face beaming.

" Fanny and I were talking about that, Mamma. We thought we might go to Singapore."

" Go all by yourselves to Singapore! Your father wouldn't hear of it."

" Why don't you go with them," said Knox. " Then you could decide just what Caroline wants."

They laughed at this, but that was what they arranged to do. By the time they got back Fanny's year of waiting would be almost over.

Singh came in, salaamed and held out a silver salver. Knox took from it the large white envelope with a red seal. He read the letter quickly and, returning to his desk, said: " Well, children, I must do some work."

Knox scribbled a reply and handed it to Singh to give to the Regent's waiting messenger.

Chapter Four

" Tom," exclaimed the Regent, rising. " You're a good friend. I wrote—and within an hour here you are."

He led Knox to a large, comfortable chair beside the desk and held out a box of cheroots.

" The French, my friend," the Regent went on, " are up to their old tricks again. That is why I wanted to see you."

Knox was relieved that it was not about Fanny and Nai Dee. The French, he knew, had in the past caused considerable anxiety. It had begun a very long time ago with the expansionist ambitions of Louis the Fourteenth, but then the Siamese had acted swiftly. Suspecting French priests of being political agents, the Government had asked them to leave and thereafter all priests had been closely watched. In recent years the French had turned their attention to the smaller and less powerful countries on the eastern flank. In 1862 they had seized three of the richest provinces of Cochin-China, right up to the Gulf of Siam, and including Saigon. It was generally believed that the French were moving towards Bangkok and that in a few years all Siam would be under French rule. Knox remembered it all well, for he had been in the British Consulate at the time. Within a few months the French had thrust forward and moved into Cambodia, just beyond Preecha's province of Prachin, and declared it a French protectorate. This had greatly perturbed the Siamese, for Cambodia had for centuries been a tributary State of Siam and it had never been disputed that Siam had the right to decide who should be King of

Cambodia. Indeed, the Cambodian kings generally came to Bangkok for their coronation.

"When we were in danger sixteen years ago," said the Regent, "your quick brain, Tom, devised an admirable way round that French manœuvre. That treaty which you advised me to draw up and which King Norodom of Cambodia so readily signed, reaffirmed that his country was still under the control of Siam. It sent the French into a fine fury."

"Yes," said Knox, "and if you had stood firm it would have worked. What is it you want me to do now?" he asked. "I thought that the French had been behaving themselves lately."

"Only because of the disasters brought upon them by their insane Emperor. But they are now recovering from their defeat and they are striving to restore a part at least of their lost glory. All sorts of things are going on behind the scenes—underground, but none the less dangerous to our future."

"Here? In Bangkok?" Knox asked in some surprise.

"Yes, here in Bangkok. That is my information, though I have no actual proof—yet."

Knox scowled. "Do you suggest that the French Consul is a party to it?"

The Regent nodded.

"Not for a moment will I believe that. He is a damned nice fellow."

The Regent laughed. "Damned nice fellows can be up to all sorts of tricks. You remember his predecessor Aubaret? And how did he treat our Judge Mom Rachothai when he called at the French consulate on a mission of good will and peace? A man who was a cousin of our King and had been our ambassador to your Queen Victoria. The French Consul seized him by his hair and threw him down the stairs."

"Yes," said Knox impatiently. "But Garnier is not like Aubaret."

"I am not saying that Garnier would do anything like that.

He is more subtle. The French are very cunning. While they make their moves in Pnom Penh, their Consul here acts as cover and watches to see how we react to their manœuvres. They are interfering in every detail of Cambodia's administration. The country is being reduced to a colony. King Norodom is no more than a figurehead. In a year or two we shall have not Cambodia but France on our frontier. First Cochin-China and Annam, then Cambodia, next it will be Tonkin," the Regent went on. " Before we know where we are France will have all the countries in this peninsula."

" Are you suggesting that I should keep an eye on Garnier? " Knox asked.

" Yes. As a friend, you could find out what the French are really up to."

" Act as your spy? I'm sorry, Your Excellency, I cannot do that."

" You are too honourable, Tom, to engage in what you regard as an intrigue against a colleague. I know that. But this concerns you personally. If Siam is devoured, I cannot believe that you would be prepared to look on with complete detachment. You would not want to see Siam perish; and, much more important, the interests of your country would be most seriously affected. You would have France as your neighbour, your rival, your enemy, in Burma and in Malaya."

Knox was silent.

" Is it not one of your duties as Consul General," the Regent added, " to find out what is going on here? Very well then. This is part of your job. All I am saying is that, while you keep an eye on your own affairs, give some thought to our future too."

" I'll think about it," Knox replied. " I don't accept all you say. You're shrewd and you are often right, but not always. I hope that after my inquiries I shall be able to inform you that your fears are unfounded."

" If so I shall be happy. Meanwhile, I am strengthening our frontier at Prachin. We must not be taken by surprise if the French decide to strike suddenly."

After a pause, he smiled and said: " Tell me, Tom, is Fanny engaged to Preecha yet? Eh? " He laughed as though it were a joke. To Knox it came as a knife thrust, but somehow he managed to preserve his composure. So the old man knew. He wondered how.

" No," he said. " No, Fanny is not engaged to him. What made you think so? "

The Regent chuckled. " Preecha is attractive—Fanny is pretty."

" In fact," said Knox, " they hardly ever see each other. I am surprised at your question."

" It is true that they have been avoiding each other for about a year, ever since your visit to Preecha's home with Fanny. I have wondered why."

" I thought I saw them dancing together at Prince Bhanu's ball," Knox countered.

" Not together," the Regent corrected him.

Knox was about to rise, but the Regent held up his hand. He gazed at Knox through narrowed eyes for a moment, then said: " Think about France. Siam is a ripe plum. I don't suppose the English realise that or they would have tried to take it long ago. It's no good shaking your head. You have taken the best plums the world over. This country is rich in food. The mineral wealth is immense. The people are happy and contented and carefree—perhaps too carefree to resist. The fishermen returning home in their boats look up at the sky and feel the moon was lit for their benefit. The women shepherding their buffaloes back to the villages from the rice fields think the stars are theirs. How can I let France take all that away from them? While your country and mine remain friends, we shall not need to spend *our* substance on armaments.

It is because of this that I'm giving them roads and schools instead——"

" You are doing fine work, Your Excellency. Through all the years I've been here I've seen how you have gradually turned the gaze of your country westward."

" I am glad we have worked together. Your appointment was not popular with the late King Mongkut. He sent many letters to Queen Victoria asking that another man should be sent out."

" It was because of my connection with the Second King. That insane jealousy between the two brothers," said Knox, a little irritably.

" But," the Regent interrupted, raising a finger, " I only mention this now to point out that I at least was broad-minded. I had to handle the situation, and it was not always easy with King Mongkut. He was quick tempered, but in the end I think he even liked you."

" I'm afraid, quite apart from my association with the Second King, King Mongkut was also irritated by all those complaints Mrs. Leonowens kept bringing me. It was not at all pleasant."

" And now "—the Regent laughed—" her son is marrying your younger daughter. It is funny."

" I would myself have called it romantic."

He got up. The Regent saw that he was ruffled and slapped him on the back a little too heartily. " Thank you again for coming so promptly. I like the way you deal with things at once."

As they came out of the study, the girls could be seen peering through the curtains.

Knox returned home disgruntled. He called to his wife, who was with the girls in Caroline's bedroom, looking at lengths of material spread out on chairs and across the bed.

As she came into his study, he said: " That old fox—I'm beginning to think you are right about him."

He was walking agitatedly up and down the room.

" What did he say? "

" He asked point blank if Preecha was engaged to Fanny."
Mrs. Knox's face went white. " Do you think it was a shot in
the dark? Or—or has he put one of his spies on to their trail?"

" I told him they are *not* engaged. He sent for me to tell me
that the French were trying to push their way into Siam
through the eastern frontier. . . . My God, of course—I see it
now. He's going to get Preecha out of the way. He will keep
him in Prachin—away from Bangkok."

" This is frightening. Surely even you will believe me now."
He pursed his lips and said nothing.

" It's his way of warning us," she said. " I'm sure of it. We'll
have to tell Fanny." She nodded sadly. " It will be very cruel.
She has waited almost the full year. But we gave no promise.
We did not say ' After a year you can marry Preecha.' All we
said was ' Wait and see how things develop.' We shall have
to tell her of course—and Preecha too—that the Regent knows
and that the situation looks extremely difficult."

" Fanny won't give him up. Poor little Fanny! I'm damned
if I'm going to let the Regent mess up her life."

" How can you stop it? " she asked.

" There must be some way."

" If only we could push the marriage further and further into
the future," she said. " The old man might die. . . . Perhaps
if she went to England . . . Preecha could follow her . . ."

" We'd better have a word with her." Knox walked to the
door. They could hear the gay chatter of the girls upstairs.
Fanny was describing what she would wear at her own wedding.
Knox looked at his wife and shook his head.

" Fanny," he called. There was a burst of laughter.

She came down smiling. A strip of scarlet silk wound round
her head like a turban, and round her waist and shoulders she
had draped a plaid material. Behind her came Caroline and
Oun, both laughing.

Knox smiled gently. "All right, Oun," he said dismissing her. "You can come in, Caroline."

The smiles faded from the girls' faces as they sat down.

"I've just seen the Regent, Fanny," Papa began, "and I'm afraid that he's not going to take your marriage to Preecha well."

"What does that mean?" she asked.

"It means trouble," said Mamma.

Fanny looked defiantly at her parents. "We've waited because you asked us to and now, after a year . . ." Her lip trembled, but she fought back her tears. "We are going to get married whether the Regent likes it or not. We are not his slaves. I'm not a girl in his harem. It's my life and Preecha's. It's our happiness . . ."

"If he, my darling, interferes, you won't have any happiness," said Mrs. Knox sadly.

Fanny whipped off the turban and threw it fiercely across the floor. "Are we living in the Middle Ages? It's like the Montagues and the Capulets. The enmity has gone on for centuries—but I'm not a Montague or a Capulet. I'm neither a Bunnag nor an Amatyakun."

"The Regent has absolute power," said Mrs. Knox. "I've always feared this. Nai Dee is the cause of the trouble. I wish we'd never set eyes on him."

"We are *not* suggesting, Fanny, dear," said Knox in a mollifying tone, "that you should marry Nai Dee. We are only pointing out to you the dangers you may run into *if* you marry Preecha. We must not be blind to the consequences."

"Couldn't you wait a little longer, dear?" Mrs. Knox begged.

"No," said Fanny bluntly.

Caroline had been glancing miserably from one to the other. To think that Fanny, who had always seemed likely to marry the man of her choice, should be confronted with so many arguments and obstacles, while she herself was able to marry Louis. It clouded her own happiness.

" Oh, Fanny," she moaned and dissolved into tears. Mamma came up to comfort her.

" Where is Preecha? " Knox asked. " Is he in Bangkok? "

" No. He's at Kabin," said Fanny. " If you don't mind, I'd rather write to him myself about this."

Knox turned this suggestion over in his mind. He realised that she would use every argument she could muster to keep him from yielding any further; all the same, he said: " All right, darling. You write to him."

" Less than two weeks after we return from Singapore," said Fanny, " the year will be up. And after that nobody's going to stop us. Not the Regent, nor Mamma—*nobody*."

Knox drew his hand down over his face and sighed. Fanny flounced defiantly out of the room.

She went upstairs and wrote to Preecha at once.

My darling—while we have been counting the days, the hours and even the minutes, the Regent has been active behind the scenes. He knows about us. He sent for Papa this morning and he came back rather shaken, but he still appears to be on our side. Mamma, on the other hand, though her sympathies are with us, feels we ought to wait much longer—how much longer she did not say.

I told them I was *not* prepared to wait and I hope you will take the same firm stand. Please do—otherwise we shall fritter away our happiness for years on end without being allowed to see each other or talk to each other.

We leave for Singapore in three days, so I shall not get your answer before I go. But I think I know what it will be —at least I hope so. Write to me at the Royal Hotel, Singapore, as soon as you get this. Yours for ever and ever, Fanny.

Chapter Five

Knox, as he said farewell to them, thought her face looked small and shrunken. Her eyes were red-rimmed with crying. There was not the faintest trace of a smile. But she pressed her cheek against his affectionately, as though to say " I know you are on my side." From the deck, as the ship moved off, she blew him a kiss. Mamma had an arm about her waist to indicate that she, too, understood and sympathised.

As Knox turned away a great surge of bitterness against the Regent rose within him. He felt their relations could never be the same again.

Fanny went down to the cabin she was to share with her sister, but for the moment she was alone. Fumbling in her bag she brought out a letter from Lambton, which had been handed her on her way to the ship.

She had thanked him for his proposal and had told him that she was going to marry Preecha. In offering his congratulations Lambton was warm in his praise of Preecha. " He has a high code of ethics and probity and is a most entertaining companion, as I discovered during my time with him in the *Sunbeam*. He is also a man of culture and breeding. I am sure you will both be exceedingly happy. I cannot help adding that I say this with envy."

She saw Caroline come in.

"You will come down for my wedding, won't you, Caroline?" she asked.

" Of course, I will, darling."

The voyage to Singapore was uneventful. There the excitement of buying dresses helped to revive Fanny's spirits. Soon she was picking out dresses for herself as well as for Caroline, for she was determined to buy part at least of her own trousseau, in spite of Mrs. Knox's gentle discouragement. "We'll come back for yours, dear," she would say, adding: "Fashions change so quickly." Which was her way of telling Fanny to wait a little longer.

Singapore was a much larger and busier town than Bangkok. The streets were crowded with horses and carriages. Smart black-and-gold rickshaws, with designs of dragons on them, darted in and out of the traffic. To Caroline, who had only been there once as a child, it was a joy to see so many wheels. There were large, handsome shops with bags and trinkets, gloves and scarves and hats from London and Paris. The waterfront was lined with hotels. Enormous ships lay anchored off the coast, for this was a junction of the sea routes to the Far East and the South Seas.

Preecha's letter arrived on Fanny's last day in Singapore. It was brief. "I am so rushed, but I want to make sure you get even these few lines. I agree. It is wrong that we should be expected to wait any longer. We have complied with all the bans and restrictions. We will pay no attention to the Regent. He is keeping me here on the pretext that the French are about to attack us through Cambodia. I see no sign of any such activities. But he wants me to strengthen our eastern defences, which I am doing, though we are in no position to stop the French if they do decide to invade in force. He wishes me to remain here indefinitely. But I don't intend to stay. I shall certainly be in Bangkok on the seventeenth, the day on which our year of waiting ends. Your ever devoted Preecha."

On their return, Louis came out in a boat to meet their ship as it steamed up the river to Bangkok. This time he had come to meet Caroline and had neither Nai Dee nor Damrong with him. He waved eagerly. A flush spread across Caroline's face as she waved back.

Louis had planned a picnic to mark the seventeenth. They were to go, just the four of them, in his boat the *Magpie* up the river to Bang Pa In, where the King had his country seat. It lay forty miles to the north of Bangkok and was regarded as the Windsor of Siam.

Mrs. Knox considered that the plan amounted to an open declaration of war on the Regent. She had an anxious talk with her husband.

" She has waited her year," he said. " Put yourself in her place. Wouldn't we have seized the chance of celebrating together, wouldn't we? "

" Not if we had the Regent on our tail. If only you'd put your foot down . . ."

" That wouldn't be fair," he said. " It was kind of Louis to arrange it . . ."

" But it proclaims their resolve to marry. The two girls and their fiancés. Louis ought to have known better. His mother kept up a continuous fight with the old Regent all the years she was here."

" The Regent will have to accept it. I don't see what we can do about it now."

" We can, Tom. We *can*," she said desperately.

He scratched the back of his neck and frowned. " I can't see there's any harm in the picnic, dear. It's Louis's party. He has the right to invite Preecha or Nai Dee or anyone else. I don't see we have any right to interfere."

" Are you going to let them get married then? " she asked.

" I shall try at any rate to postpone it if I can. When did you say Preecha was expected back? "

" Not until the day of the picnic. And you know the Regent has expressly told him to stay in Prachin. He will be displeased that Preecha should come here in disobedience of his orders."

Knox shook his head. He was clearly uneasy, and that night he said to Fanny: " This picnic. I suppose it's all right—just the one outing. At any rate, you two are not going to be alone. But we'll have to be most careful, dear. The signs are not at all good. Preecha's had orders to stay in Prachin, I understand. You're both treading on very dangerous ground."

" We have done everything you asked us to. Now we are free to lead our own lives—and we're going to," she said bluntly.

Until a few minutes before they were due to start on the picnic there was no sign of Preecha. Both girls were dressed and waiting, and Louis with them. Hampers of food and champagne had been placed in the *Magpie*. Mrs. Knox sat unsmiling in the veranda, her hands folded in her lap. In her thoughts she saw the girls as little children again, Fanny with her hair in two short plaits, romping noisily round the house, Caroline with one long swinging plait, a red bow at the end of it, always doing what her sister did. Fanny was carefree, gay, and so very lovely. They used to say she herself was beautiful then. Sometimes now, when she looked into the mirror, save for the little lines about her eyes, she felt she was beautiful still. She glanced at her husband sipping his whisky, he was handsome and so dignified with his long dark beard. He was a fighter, but so fair, so just. How would it all end . . . ?

Suddenly Fanny ran to the rails and cried: " There he is." And they saw the *Sunbeam*. She raced down the stairs to the landing-stage and waited for the boat to swing in. Preecha leapt ashore and they stood clasped in each other's arms.

" At last! At last! " he said, kissing her eyes, her nose, her chin.

Caroline and Louis came down presently and the *Magpie* began her journey.

Bang Pa In was built on an island in the river by one of the earlier kings of Siam, but fell into neglect when the capital was moved from the sacked city of Ayuthya to Bangkok. But with the coming of the steamboat, its glories were revived. It was no longer inaccessible. King Mongkut built a house for himself amid the ancient palaces and temples and monasteries. His successor, while still in his teens, had another palace built for himself and a magnificent hall of audience, both completely Western in their architecture. The island glittered with lakes and golden temples.

The hampers were unpacked under some trees on the banks of the river. Beyond their small patch of shade the sun was blinding. They laughed and they talked and they sang while they ate, then Louis took Caroline by the hand and led her off towards the Palace.

" What shall I take you to see? " Preecha asked. He pointed to a bright yellow pavilion in the middle of one of the lakes.

" I'd rather sit here," Fanny said. She moved her hand towards his.

" We should have brought the children," she said.

" You talk as though we've been married a long time."

" I feel we have." She squeezed his hand, then raised his fingers to her lips.

" I do too, I feel we've been together for centuries—through many incarnations," he said.

" And still they want us to wait." She got up.

" Let's walk—somewhere—anywhere. Let's go to that temple by the lake."

They walked to the bridge and crossed it to the temple. The Buddha seemed to be smiling benignly.

" I wonder what he thinks of our future," Fanny said.

" You are not worried about it, are you? "

" No." She turned and smiled at him. He drew her towards him.

155

In the distance they could see Caroline and Louis returning.

It was quite late when they got home. Mrs. Knox had a
plate of roasted almonds in her lap. Knox was beside her in
the veranda puffing at his pipe.

The next day Preecha went back to Prachin.

Chapter Six

CAROLINE's wedding was arranged for the end of the following month, April, 1878. Preecha wrote to say that he would come. But the Regent sent him new orders; he insisted that more gold must be got out of the mine at Kabin. The Government was, he said, in urgent need of funds and it was Preecha's duty, as manager, to see that the mine was much more productive.

" I have been here for the past two weeks," Preecha wrote to Fanny. " Everyone is working as hard as they can. But evidently the Regent will not be satisfied unless I can perform an unending succession of miracles.

" What is behind it is quite clear now. There are no signs of the French on the frontier—that at least we know. But no one can check on the Government's need for more money. On that the Regent is the sole arbiter. Still, I shall be at Caroline's wedding whatever the consequences."

When the day came, the little church down the river was decorated with a mass of flowers and there was a congestion of boats at the landing-stage as the guests kept arriving. Three of the Royal princes were there, Bhanurangsri, Naret and Damrong. The Regent had been invited, but, even though he had accepted and had sent a small gift to Caroline, Mrs. Knox was surprised to see him in the congregation, seated beside Nai Dee. Preecha was not there.

Caroline looked lovely in her white satin dress and lace veil as she walked up the aisle with her father. Supporting Fanny as bridesmaids were the two daughters of the French Consul, and the elder daughter of the acting Dutch Consul, Mr. Muller, all in pink dresses with bustles, white lace collars and blue moire sashes. Two pages, sons of the Austro-Hungarian Consul, Mr. Masius, held up her long lace train.

Louis wore a frock coat of grey alpaca and piped trousers of white satin. His best man was Mr. F. S. Clarke, the manager of the Borneo Company.

The service was conducted by the Rev. Noah McDonald. The choir, composed chiefly of elderly men and women, sang vigorously. The address, happily brief, spoke of the hopes and dreams of youth finding fulfilment in matrimony.

There was a long wait while the register was being signed. Knox went in, but not his wife. Caroline looked radiant as she walked out on Louis's arm, her gaze straight ahead, too shy to turn and smile at the expectant congregation.

They left, as they had come, in boats. The reception was held in a large tent in the grounds of the British Consulate, the Union Jack fluttering from the towering flagstaff above. A small orchestra, partly Siamese, played Irish airs and some music-hall tunes. The King came to the reception.

Just as Louis was about to assist his bride in cutting the cake, Fanny, standing by the table, felt an arm about her waist and, turning, found herself gazing into Preecha's soft brown eyes.

" As you see, I have come. Hssh," he whispered.

She slipped her hand into his and shut her eyes.

Many eyes were turned on them, including those of the Regent. His lips smiled, but his eyes were stern and it was obvious to both Knox and his wife that he was far from pleased.

The toasts were given. Fanny heard hardly a word. Mrs. Knox could hear only the murmur of her own thoughts. Now Louis was replying. His graceful reference to the enchanted country to which his mother had brought him as a child, and to his desire to make this the setting of his future happiness, brought much applause.

Telegrams of good wishes from Anna, Louis's mother, and

his sister Avis, came from Canada, and from Caroline's brother Tom, who was still at Oxford. The presents were displayed in the veranda. Among them was a gold bracelet sprinkled with rubies from the King, a small diamond brooch from the Regent and a cheque for one hundred pounds from Anna.

The young couple left in the *Magpie* for their honeymoon. The water around was strewn with confetti. Mrs. Knox blinked back her tears as she waved her small handkerchief.

After the bride and the groom had gone, and the guests had left too, the family sat down to dinner. Knox and his wife ate quietly, without saying a word. Fanny and Preecha, their faces flushed, talked excitedly. Guests were referred to, the presents were discussed. Occasionally a question drew a grunt from Knox or a word or two from Mamma. It was over coffee and a brandy, after the servants had left, that the talk began to flow more freely, revealing that the parental silence was due to thoughts that had been held in check because they were greatly disturbing.

Mrs. Knox began on a maternal note. "This could have been such a happy day for you too, Fanny dear. It could so easily have been a double event. It seems to me quite wrong— and I am sure your father feels the same—that you, the elder of the two girls, should be prevented from marrying, when you are both so much in love with each other. But . . ." She completed the sentence with a shrug.

Fanny was about to say something, when Preecha raised his hand and stopped her. "It is natural for you to be concerned about your daughter, Mrs. Knox. But I cannot see what the Regent can do if she decides, as she has the right to decide, to marry the man of her choice."

"To her nothing," said Knox. "But what about you? Already you are virtually banished from Bangkok."

Preecha smiled. "Of course he is trying to keep us apart. No doubt he hopes that with me out of the way Fanny may find Nai Dee irresistible. But the moment we are married, he will necessarily recognise that it is too late to do anything."

"You expect him to accept defeat? I don't think he will," said Knox.

"What can he do?" asked Preecha. "The more we defer announcing our engagement, the higher his expectations will rise. By keeping him in a state of expectation and hope, we are actually inviting trouble. Indeed, by adopting such a course we may eventually rouse him to fury—and that may well be dangerous . . ."

Fanny looked at him with admiring eyes. She thought his arguments unanswerable.

"So you recognise that there is danger," said Knox.

"There is always danger, even in the most commonplace, everyday things," said Preecha. "Boats sink and fishermen get drowned. A large raw mango, the size of a coconut and hard as stone, fell on the head of a man working on my father's estate and killed him. That's the sort of risk . . ."

"And you are saying," Knox interrupted, "that you are prepared to take a chance."

"I am not a gambler," replied Preecha, "although so many of my people are gamblers. But I am prepared to take a chance, as we all have to."

"Call it what you like," said Knox, getting a little red in the face, "but you are in fact gambling not only with your own future, but with the future of my daughter."

"I am old enough to answer for myself," said Fanny. "I know you think it's a risk . . ."

"A very grave risk," said Mrs. Knox.

"I am prepared to face it," said Fanny. "Otherwise you'll be saying next we mustn't even write to each other. I don't call that living."

Preecha sipped his drink slowly. "You see how we feel," he said. "Although Fanny is old enough to make her own decisions, I would like to ask you for your permission to marry her."

" Soon," added Fanny.

" Yes, soon," he repeated.

Knox shot a glance at his wife. He saw the look in her eyes. " In the circumstances I have indicated," he said, " you can hardly expect me to give it."

" Very well," said Fanny. Her lips were pursed.

" You will no doubt take the law into your own hands," said Knox, and it was a statement rather than a question.

" What right has the Regent, or anyone else, to dictate to us? " said Preecha. He spoke with great emphasis, but added more quietly: " Provided, of course, that the man she has chosen is not one of whom you disapprove on personal grounds."

" I don't disapprove of you at all," said Knox. " But I still say that you are flying in the face of Providence."

They heard a strumming on a guitar and voices singing a Siamese love song. It sounded quite near—from a boat in the canal beside the Consulate.

" I think they are under Fanny's window," Mrs. Knox observed, adding: " I think I can guess who they are."

From an inner window Fanny saw the boat. In it were Nai Dee and Prince Damrong. Damrong was strumming the guitar, both were singing. They did not break off when they saw her, but merely waved a hand in greeting.

Mrs. Knox came to the window now. " Come along, come up," she called, " and have a cup of tea with us."

As they came up the stairs Nai Dee stopped suddenly on seeing Preecha. The pause was momentary. He made no comment, but gave the customary greeting with the palms of his hands joined together. Preecha returned it with equal ceremony.

Nai Dee accepted the cheroot which Knox offered him, lit it slowly and after a puff or two remarked: " I must confess to you that our purpose in coming to-night was to elope with Fanny. It seems wrong that she should be left like this."

There was an awkward silence, which nobody attempted to break. Nai Dee laughed a little as he sipped his brandy, then took the guitar from Damrong, his eyes shifting from one to the other.

" I see," remarked Nai Dee. " No elopement, no party. Let's go, Damrong."

" Have another drink," said Knox. " I think we are all a little tired. It's been a long and strenuous day."

Nai Dee rose. Preecha rose too. " Thank you," Preecha said, bowing to Mrs. Knox and then to Fanny. Her face looked strained, her eyes burned with anger.

But all she said was " Good night."

Nai Dee and Damrong kissed her extended hand. Then, together with Preecha, they left, Nai Dee strumming and singing as he went down the stairs.

Fanny watched anxiously from the veranda rails.

" You see," said Mamma. " They are not going to give in. They will fight to the bitter end."

Chapter Seven

PREECHA called in the morning and asked if he could see Fanny. She hurried down from her room on hearing his voice and clasped both his hands eagerly as they kissed. She loved his hands. They were so strong and yet they were so very gentle.

" I haven't thanked you enough," she said. " Will there be any trouble with the Regent? "

" I've just been to see him. I called on the King first, of course."

" You and the King get on well, don't you? "

" He has been kind enough to honour me with his friendship."

" He's an idealist too."

" Yes, he is—and one day perhaps "—there was a flush of hope in his face—" he may be able to carry out some of his plans."

" Tell me, how did the Regent take your unexpected return to town? Was he angry—or critical? "

" On the contrary, he was most kind. He said: ' I suppose being parted from your children makes things difficult for you in Prachin. You ought to get married, Preecha. Find a quiet, simple, motherly girl who will take them under her wing. It is not right that you should live alone.' He's very cunning."

" And what did you say? "

" I told him that was what I had in mind. He asked if I had anybody in view. I said it took two, sometimes even more than two, to make a decision." Preecha's eyes twinkled as he said that and Fanny said: " Good! "

" He then said," Preecha went on, " somewhat impatiently, I thought, that finding a bride should not be such a complicated matter. Siam was full of lovely girls."

" Why doesn't he say that to Nai Dee? "

" Exactly! I told him it was not only because of my children that I came, thoughtful and understanding though he was to allude to them. I came also to see my father and to report on the quantity of gold that, in my calculation, should be available for the Royal Mint during the next twelve months. He asked me what the figure was. I told him, and he smacked the table and said it should be more, much more. ' Try and double that figure,' he said. ' I'll give you a substantial bonus if you succeed—and I'll ask the King to raise you to the rank of Phya.' I said I would be glad to do it without any thought of reward, but I did not think it was humanly possible."

" Do you think they really need more gold? " she asked.

He shrugged his shoulders. " Of course they'd like as much gold as they can get. But it's significant that they should have started clamouring for it now."

She sat silent. He took her hand.

" Do you think we could rely on the King to help us? " she asked.

" In what way do you mean? "

" If we eloped . . . or . . ."

He laughed. " You mean lend us one of his golden ninety-foot barges and thirty royal oarsmen? "

" No. I mean if we decided to defy everybody and went to Prachin and got married there quietly. What do you think would happen? "

" If the Regent disapproved—*if*—I suppose I'd cease to be the Governor there. Not that that matters, though I like the place and the people like me."

" What I want to know is will the King assert himself if the Regent—well, if he tries to do anything awful? "

He considered it for a moment. " The King has been trying to assert himself ever since he came of age. But the old man is not easy to shift. He has gathered all the reins of power into his own hands. All the chief Ministers are his nominees. When he nods they act. This began years before King Mongkut died, and the Regent's position was greatly strengthened while the present King was a minor. The duel between them is being fought now. The King wants his full inheritance, the Regent is resolved not to surrender one iota of his influence and authority. Who will win we cannot tell yet."

A disturbed look came into Fanny's eyes.

" I am sorry, darling," he said. " I have caused a great deal of trouble. My mind advises caution, my heart says the opposite."

" Caution? Not get married? "

" I want you. I love you. I'll never give you up," he replied.

She breathed again. There was a smile in her frightened eyes.

" But I feel," he went on, " that perhaps if we wait just a little longer we may see the way ahead more clearly."

" Wait, when we've waited a whole year? . . ."

" At least the Regent knows now. A month or so may give us the answer. It won't be for long," he said, " and perhaps your father and mother could bring you to Prachin for a few days."

She looked at him sadly, then put her arms about his neck and held him close. Tenderly he kissed her again and again.

" When I get tired of waiting," she said, " I'll pack my things and come to you. All by myself—without Papa and Mamma. We'll get married then and the Regent will have to accept it." And so they left it.

The weeks passed. Letters were their only contact. Preecha had not been able to come back even on a brief visit. Fanny had been to see Trakun and Arun. One afternoon she took them out in a boat with Oun, and one morning she went riding with Trakun, but on both occasions she was chided by Papa and Mamma for her foolhardiness. " You are only inviting trouble," they said.

Parties were given for her at the Consulate. Nai Dee was a constant visitor, so were the three princes.

In June, Caroline's first letter from Chiengmai arrived and was brought round by a messenger from the Borneo Company.

Papa hurried out of his office, calling his wife and daughter to leave whatever they were doing and listen while he read it to them.

It was addressed to all three. After describing their long journey to the North, Caroline wrote of the joys of travelling through the rapids in a small country boat.

Chiengmai is much smaller than I imagined. I expected, as it is the capital of the North, to find a large, sprawling town, though not of course as big as Bangkok. But it is confined between high hills, with a narrow river flowing through it, and a bridge. There are roads, lots of roads, and no canals at all.

Louis's teak concessions are quite a distance out and he has to be away for weeks at a time. I can't say I like that. But we have made some friends here. The local Chief, whose ancestors were once independent Kings, has taken a fancy to Louis and has invited us to his Palace twice already. Unfortunately he is a great gambler. Cards are brought out after dinner. Louis plays, but I don't. I play billiards with the Chief's uncle. I don't think Louis really is going to be a gambler. I hope not.

The letter rambled on for pages. She described her house, a teak bungalow built by the river. Two rooms in it were set aside as offices for the Borneo Company. She went on:

Louis tells me that the Borneo Company, who were responsible for his mother coming here, used to import various things for King Mongkut from Europe—goods from Lancashire, and nails and knives from Sheffield, and brass cannon and cough mixture! It was in a letter asking for more cough lozenges, that the King arranged for the Company to get Louis's mother to come to Bangkok, as a teacher, not as a governess. Why Aunty Anna now calls herself a governess Louis can't understand. Louis is furious at her making him out to have been a cry baby and saying she had to carry him about in her arms. He was nine years old at the time.

Caroline went on to say that she wanted to have "lots of children," and perhaps the first one was already on the way. " Louis wants a boy and is going to name him after Papa, he says; but there are Thomases on his side too, so both families ought to be satisfied."

She ended with:

This bit is for Fanny. When will you be coming to stay with us? I have so much to tell you. The best thing you can do, Fanny dear, is to elope with Preecha and come and stay with us. Why not talk it over with him. I hope he will agree.

Papa, as he read this out, pulled a face and looked across at Mamma. " I am sure he will do no such thing," he commented.

" I hope not," said Mamma.

Fanny felt it was a strange twist of fate that Caroline, who had always been uncertain about her own future, should now be planning her life for her.

" What are you smiling at? " Mamma inquired anxiously.

" Working out your elopement? " Knox asked playfully. " I'd have to get you a boat, a ladder wouldn't be of much use here."

" You mustn't tease Fanny," said Mrs. Knox, seeing the look on her daughter's face.

Fanny rose and went up to her father, her hand extended. " May I have the letter? I'd like to read it again."

Just then Singh came up with the post. There were two for Fanny. One was from Lambton—" he is very faithful," Mrs. Knox commented; the other from Preecha.

Preecha wrote:

I have been trying to come and see you, but this has been made impossible by the Regent. He keeps making fresh arrangements to come and inspect the mines, but each time the plan has been cancelled at the last minute. This is his latest form of torture—to keep me here by saying he is coming, then deferring his visit until next week, and then again deferring it until the week after. He has now written to say that he is coming to Kabin before the week is out. How long he will stay he does not say. So I am unable to arrange a date for your coming here with your father and mother.

Fanny paused. Her disappointment was acute.

I have been involved in a great deal of reorganisation. But it has all been completed. What further work I will be required to embark on after the Regent's visit I cannot foresee. But it should not occupy more than a very short time. Then it will be possible to plan your coming here with your parents. I trust your mother will raise no objection. Please tell them that I have a comfortable log cabin near the mine and that I shall come to Prachin to meet you. We can spend a night or two at my house there, so that you may all get some rest after your long journey.

She had known ever since Preecha had first mentioned it that Mamma would make every possible endeavour to prevent the visit. Perhaps this then was the moment to act along the lines indicated by Caroline.

Fanny felt she had better deal with this at once. She thought it might be best to see Papa by himself.

When she told him of Preecha's invitation, he smiled and said that he had just received a note from him. " Your mother and I have already talked of it."

" Well? " she inquired, waiting impatiently for him to go on.

" Well, we thought we'd accept it. It would be a change for all of us."

" Good! " She leapt forward and flung her arms round him.

" We both want to help you," he said. " But we'll have to tread carefully. We thought, before we go, we ought to have a small party here and invite Nai Dee to it."

" I don't mind how often you invite Nai Dee before or after our visit to Kabin. Will you ask the Regent too? "

" He will be away. He left this morning for Kabin."

" Good! Preecha said he was expecting him. Thank you, Papa; thank you very, very much."

Later that same day, just as the sun was setting across the river, Nai Dee arrived unexpectedly.

" I have come for a purpose," he announced.

" As though you needed a purpose to come to see us," replied Mrs. Knox. It was her way of indicating that he was always welcome. Fanny's heart stood still. She wondered what his purpose was.

He held out a book he had brought with him.

Knox took it. " Why, it's Sheridan's *School for Scandal*." He looked at Nai Dee inquiringly.

" The King is building a temple at Bang Pa In. They are working on it now. It will be ready early next year. He plans to dedicate it in February, I think."

" I know, and it is to have a spire like an English church," Knox said.

" That's it. As it is the very first temple of his reign, many groups of people have been making token contributions. The Siamese of course. But the Chinese have also contributed, as well as the Indians and the Malays. And I thought that the European community might care to do something too."

" A very good idea," said Mrs. Knox. " And the play? "

" I thought the play would be enjoyable and raise money too."

Fanny took the book from her father.

" There's a fine part in it for you, Fanny," said Nai Dee. " Lady Teazle. Mrs. Knox could be . . ."

" What fun! " cried Mrs. Knox, clapping her tiny hands. " I haven't acted since I was a lady-in-waiting. The Second King used to have the most wonderful theatricals."

" Who else is going to be in it? " said Fanny, glancing through the lines.

" I've got a list here. But I haven't seen any of the others yet. I thought I would have a word with you first." He handed her the list.

" I see you're in it too, Nai Dee."

" What part are you playing? " said Mrs. Knox.

He looked across at Fanny shyly. " If Fanny wouldn't mind, I'd like to play Sir Peter Teazle."

" Why should Fanny mind? " said Mrs. Knox.

" No, of course not. When is it to be? "

" As soon as I've got the cast arranged we could start rehearsing."

" Quite soon? " Fanny said uneasily.

" In about a week's time. There's no reason why we should not be ready then."

There was, so far as she was concerned, a very good reason, for they were planning to go to Kabin in a week's time. Should she tell Nai Dee that? Papa and Mamma would certainly think it most unwise. They would be away for a fortnight, they could hardly be away for less. That would involve a delay of a month in Nai Dee's plans. She was not going to give in. She had no intention of abandoning her visit to Preecha.

" Why not wait until it's cooler? " she asked.

Knox glanced quickly at Fanny, then at his wife. " Where is it going to be performed? " he asked Nai Dee.

" In the large theatre in Grandpa's garden," said Nai Dee. " We've not had—not a European play—since Fanny got back. This should be fun. Don't you think so, sir? "

" Yes," Knox agreed. " I hope you have a part for me too." He reached for the cast list in Fanny's lap. " But I see you've left me out of it."

Fanny was simmering. She was irritated by the eagerness with which both her parents were entering into the project.

" Well, sir. You could play Sir Oliver Surface. You'll be far better than the French Consul. I wonder why I didn't think of you for the role in the first place."

" Let me see now," said Knox. " He's the . . ."

" The rich uncle from the East."

" Yes. The good, kind uncle," Knox said. " Obviously, Nai Dee, you couldn't see me as either good or kind."

All this laughter and small talk exasperated Fanny. Had they so soon forgotten what they had promised her only a few hours before? A month of rehearsals at least. . . . Preecha thought he could be here himself in a month's time— provided the Regent did not think of some new ruse to keep him away. Now her hopes of seeing him . . . She decided to speak.

" I'm afraid unless you put off the rehearsals I shan't be able to play," she said. " You see, I've arranged to be away —we all have in fact."

" You can't." Nai Dee was taken aback. Knox and his wife exchanged quick glances.

" When had you planned to go? " Nai Dee asked.

" We haven't actually fixed an exact day," said Knox hurriedly.

" I thought you had," Fanny intervened firmly. " We were going at the end of next week. Even if you want to change your mind, Papa, I shall not be able to take part in the play."

Knox was flabbergasted. He stared at her in harsh disapproval. Mrs. Knox gazed down at her fingers, revealing nothing of her feelings.

" Don't say that, Fanny," said Nai Dee. " We couldn't do it without you."

" Leave it for a day or two," said Knox, rising. " We'll see what we can do about it. It was only a tentative arrangement. I'll let you know, Nai Dee, within the next forty-eight hours."

Nai Dee rose too and looked about him with a puzzled air, first at Fanny, then at Knox, then at Mrs. Knox, who continued to stare at her fingers.

" All right," he said. " Then I shall say good night, sir— and wait till I hear from you."

He bowed to Mrs. Knox, then to Fanny, and left.

When they were alone, Knox said: " What's the meaning of all this? " It was obvious that he was angry. Obvious, too, was Fanny's determination not to yield an inch.

Her lips tightened, as though biting back words that were seeking to force their way out. In a quiet voice she spoke at last: " You said we were going."

" Yes. But we fixed no date."

" You said . . ."

" I said . . . I said . . . Can't you see what's at stake? The Regent personally involved. A play in his own theatre—and you expect me to brush this aside just for a romantic outing that can wait."

" Why should my plans always have to wait? Can't I for once have my own way? "

" And risk destroying all the goodwill I have built up here

through the years? This concerns me, your mother, our future here, the good relations between Britain and Siam . . .''

" Rubbish," said Fanny, turning away.

" Don't you dare say that," Papa roared at her.

" You might just as well say, ' Marry Nai Dee, because that will put the good relations between Britain and Siam on a far, far better footing.' I am not the daughter of Queen Victoria and I am not marrying the King. You and Mamma can do as you like, but from now on I am going to lead my own life."

"As a diplomat I have a duty, and my entire family," Knox said, slapping the table with vigour, " has a like duty, namely, to observe the conventions in relation to the country and the Government to which I am accredited."

Fanny rose.

" You'd better go to your room," her father said, " and we'll talk about it when we are all a little calmer."

" I have nothing more to say," Fanny declared. She walked to the tray of drinks on the table and did something they had never seen her do before. She poured herself out some whisky and, without diluting it with either water or soda, took it with her to her room.

Knox glanced at his wife with raised eyebrows. But they said nothing.

After a long time, Knox said: " There's no knowing what she'll do. You heard what she said. She seems to think she can go off by herself to Preecha."

" Of course she won't do anything so wrong and imprudent. She'll calm down. She's a child in many ways . . . and extraordinarily innocent . . .''

" She's unruly," Knox snapped.

She watched her husband for a while, seated there glowering, then she got up and went over to him.

" I am even more aware of the dangers than you are, Tom.

But we have done all we can. I don't see what more we can do now."

After a time they heard a soft, low voice singing. The tune was " The Girl I love sits up in the gallery." But the words they heard were " The Man I love is up in Kabin-buri."

" Drunk, I imagine," Knox growled. " That was almost half a glass of neat whisky she took up with her."

Chapter Eight

PREECHA arrived two days before the performance of the play. Rehearsals, especially in these final stages, kept them apart for most of the time. But they snatched some hours together and went to the shops in the bazaar. He wanted to buy her an engagement ring. Parental opposition was considered and brushed aside. It was a large and lovely princess ring, of zircons and rubies, rising in a tiny cone of precious stones. But Papa and Mamma were horrified when they saw the ring on Fanny's finger.

" I wouldn't wear it just yet," Mrs. Knox advised.

Fanny replied: " I've given way over the play and that is the last time I'm giving in. We are doing nothing we have to be ashamed of. One would think it was something criminal ..."

" Fanny, Fanny," Knox said in as calm a voice as he could muster, " try and look at your problem . . ."

She turned to leave the room.

" Fanny," her father called, but she walked on. He shrugged his shoulders. " If you won't listen, then things will have to take their course. At least don't tempt Providence," he added, raising his voice, " by wearing the ring on your engagement finger while you're still rehearsing with Nai Dee."

She heard him. She was resolved to wear it on the night itself, together with the wedding ring she would be required to wear as Lady Teazle. She smiled at the thought. Till then perhaps . . . and she transferred the ring on to her other hand.

But she put it back again on her engagement finger the next

morning when she went with Preecha to his house to spend an hour or two with his children.

As the guests arrived for the performance of the play, they were received by the Regent and conducted to their seats by his footmen. In the centre of the front row a place was reserved for the King, who came in as the curtain was about to rise.

All the seats were paid for. Indeed, in view of the cause for which the play had been organised, many were bought at two or three times their price.

The cast, save for Nai Dee, was drawn entirely from the European community, to which Mrs. Knox was now assumed to belong. In the role of Mrs. Candour, she had to appear with Henry Alabaster, who played Crabtree. This was at first a little embarrassing. Knox felt it would have been more appropriate to have cast Alabaster as Snake, who in the end confesses: " I live by the badness of my character."

Fanny looked very lovely in the beautiful dresses of the eighteenth century. The Regent, seated beside the King, chuckled over her lines and laughed uproariously when Knox appeared and strutted about the stage as Sir Oliver. He had a big part and played it exceedingly well.

Nai Dee, as Fanny's husband, was far more affectionate than the role required. Even in the quarrelsome scenes he worked in expressions of love and devotion that Sheridan had not provided. Preecha was greatly amused by this. He noticed that Fanny was wearing her engagement ring.

At the end the applause was tumultuous. Each artist was hailed with " Bravos." But for Fanny the most vociferous enthusiasm was reserved.

The Regent was in high spirits. He put an arm around Nai Dee's shoulders and, drawing Fanny to him, placed his other arm about her, holding them together, as though to indicate that it was how he always wanted them to be.

" You looked wonderful, you two," he said. " Not a very

nice husband, I'm afraid," he added slyly. " But you were well able to manage him. And now, Fanny—" he clapped his hands and a boy, of about twelve, knelt before him, holding up a casket—" I have got a small gift for you, something to mark the occasion."

He opened the casket and held it out to her. On the red velvet lay a brooch about four inches long. It represented a bunch of yellow roses, each made of a yellow diamond, with emeralds forming the stems and leaves.

With her eyes round and wide and her lips about to express her delight, she shook her head and held up her hand to decline it.

" I couldn't accept so fine a gift," she said. " It's too much for the little I have done."

" But you must." He lifted the brooch out of its case and turned it, now one way now another, so that the gems caught the light. " Here, let me pin it on for you."

She shook her head again, then she caught her mother's eye.

Mrs. Knox said: " Let me pin it on, or you'll poke the pin right into her. You've done many things, Your Excellency, and done them well. But I'm sure you've never pinned on a brooch in your life."

He laughed and handed the brooch to her.

Fanny gave in and smiled as she thanked him. " It is very, very lovely! " She saw that Preecha was watching her. He did not look as though he felt there were any reason why she should not accept the gift.

" And do I get nothing, Grandpa? " Nai Dee asked cheekily. " I played my part at least as well as she did."

" Yes, I have something for you too," said the Regent. " This." And he proceeded to twist one of the young man's ears.

The King came up and was effusive in his praise. He drew Preecha into the group and commented on his long absences from the capital. " The Regent says it's business that keeps you in your province. He says you are getting more and more gold for us. Won't you tell us what you are really doing. Have you fallen in love again, Preecha? "

He flushed, then bowed and, without a glance at Fanny, said simply: " Yes, Your Majesty."

" As I thought."

" He's doing good work there," said the Regent. " You see, Preecha, how we all miss you. Still, in a little while perhaps . . ." He chuckled.

Fanny noticed that the chuckle came as an afterthought, for the Regent's face was grave and unsmiling.

Turning to Preecha, the Regent placed a hand on his arm. " How long do you propose to stay in Bangkok? "

" A day or so," Preecha replied. " For I have one or two things I want to do before I go back."

" Good! Good! " said the Regent, but Fanny did not think that he sounded pleased.

The next day Fanny was able to spend most of the time with Preecha.

" My aunt has told me of a good astrologer," he said. " I think that we ought to see one."

Fanny hesitated a moment and then said: " After all, it is the usual thing, isn't it? Everyone does it. We might be told of a propitious date."

" Let's go," he said. " It's just across the river."

They made their way past the rows of floating houses and through the narrow, twisting alleys behind the Wat Arun.

The astrologer's house consisted of a group of tumble-down shacks perched one on top of the other at odd angles. It was in an upper room that they found him. They were ushered in by a toothless old woman.

He made Fanny and Preecha sit opposite him at a small table covered by an embroidered shawl that was frayed and dirty. He asked them for the dates of their birth. Then he consulted books and a chart of the heavens. Next he looked at their palms.

"I can see the signs quite clearly now," he said at last. "You want to know if you will marry. I see that you will."

"When?" Fanny asked eagerly.

"Fairly soon. Weeks—possibly months. But soon."

Fanny and Preecha exchanged delighted glances, but the astrologer's face was grave. "You will marry soon," he repeated. "But you will not be married for very long."

Fanny was startled. "Not for long?" she said.

"One year, two years. Perhaps a little more, or a little less."

"Why?" Preecha asked.

The astrologer took his hand and examined it closely. "It may perhaps be even less."

"Do you mean," Fanny asked, "that our love will not last, and we shall go our separate ways—all in one or two years?"

He scrutinised the lines on her small hand. "No," he said. "I do not see that. Your love will last for ever—there is devotion in his hand too." He took it again and traced the line. "Here—until the end."

"Then," said Preecha. "Why should we part? Will some-one part us?" He leaned forward and dropped his voice: "Do you see that one of us will die?"

"We will all die," said the astrologer. "That is written for all of us—some sooner, some later."

"But when?" Preecha persisted, thrusting his hand forward again. "What does it say?"

But the astrologer would not take his hand. "Who can tell? That is for the gods to decide."

"Are you saying," asked Fanny, "that we shall be parted—before the end—although we want to be together?"

The man nodded. "That is what I see—but I may be wrong."

" Then," said Preecha as he picked a volume off a stool and thrust it before the astrologer, " work out the dates again. Is my life short? Is hers? "

" No," said the man. " It seems you are both intended to have long lives."

Preecha rose. " Come, let us go." Then turning suddenly to the man, he asked: " You know who we are? "

" Yes, I know."

" Somebody has talked about us? "

" No. I have seen you about—many people have."

Preecha paid the fee and they left. When they got back into the alleyway he stopped and looked at her. Her face was pale and troubled, but she smiled bravely.

" We shall love each other for ever. For ever," she said. " But for some reason which he cannot give—or will not tell us—we are to be separated in a year or so. Not by death, thank God," she added. " But who will part us—the Regent? "

"I think he has been told to tell us that," said Preecha. "The Regent may have found out that he was the man we were most likely to consult, because my aunt comes here from time to time. Besides, that old devil is capable of getting in touch with every astrologer in Bangkok, to make sure. He is not going to deter me."

" Nor me," she said.

Chapter Nine

THE NEXT day Preecha was peremptorily ordered back to his province. The message, sent by the Regent himself, stated bluntly that harsher measures would have to be adopted at the mines. The men were clearly not working hard enough. " It is essential that you should be there to see to it."

When he came to bid Fanny farewell, he handed her the note. " This confirms it. The astrologer was put up to it, as we thought."

" I was thinking about that," she replied. " But there is one thing that puzzles me. If that man was put up to it, why did he say we would marry soon? He was quite definite about that. He said, ' Soon . . . months.' "

Preecha smiled. " That's the Regent's way of warning us, my darling. What he was really saying is this: ' You will marry and you will pay for it.' He meant ' if.' One could almost hear the *if* in his voice. And now it's good-bye for a while."

" Till when? "

" I'll come back for the dedication of the temple at Bang Pa In in February. It's the King's command. The Regent can't prevent me from coming."

" February is a long way off." Fanny began to count the months on her fingers. " I'll try and get Papa to bring me to Prachin."

He took her in his arms and kissed her. When they paused and gazed at each other, there were tears in their eyes.

" Try and come soon," he said.

" I will."

The next day Knox received a cordial note from the Regent asking if he would spare the time to come and see him. Knox set out in the late afternoon, after the Regent's siesta, wondering what could have prompted the unexpected summons.

The Regent was in his steam yacht, the *Rising Sun*, about three miles down the river. As his launch approached, Knox saw a number of priests in saffron robes leaving in their little boats. Alighting, he was received by Hunter, who, by expressively drawing down his chin, indicated that His Excellency was not in a good mood.

He was led through the large saloon to the office, where the Regent received him affably, but not with his customary exuberance.

"Sit down, Tom," he said. "I have to sign some letters and then we can talk." By the desk stood a Siamese youth, one of Hunter's many assistants. When he had dealt with the letters, the Regent rose, but he motioned Knox to remain seated.

" I wanted to see you about something that I hope you will regard as important. There's been a lot of talk about Fanny, who's an extremely beautiful girl. As you know, I love and admire her, but "—he came closer and leaned over Knox's chair—" do you think it right that she should be seen going out alone with Preecha? "

Knox, who had begun to feel, after Hunter's initial hint, that the interview might concern Fanny, had not expected the Regent to be so critical or so personal.

" It is her life," he replied bluntly. " I do not represent her. I represent the Queen of England. My duties are quite clearly defined. I can enter into the private life of neither the Queen nor my daughter. Each has a right to free and independent decision and action in so far as their own personal affairs are concerned."

The Regent was taken aback. He glowered at Knox and

then, quite suddenly, burst out laughing. " Well done, Tom. A speech like that should get you into the House of Lords and their lordships might not notice the flaw in your argument, as I have."

" There is none," he snapped.

" Oh yes, there is. If the Queen of England entered into a personal alliance—a romantic alliance—with an enemy of her country, her Ministers would be within their rights to intervene and to advise her to desist—and that is precisely what I am doing."

" An enemy? The Siamese and we are closely linked in friendship and have been for many years."

" I do not refer to our countries. I refer to Preecha. His is a proud and ancient family. But I have ruled this country for close on a quarter of a century, ever since Sir John Bowring's visit in 1855. I negotiated that treaty of friendship with Great Britain. Bowring, in his book, has been kind enough to pay me many tributes. He called me ' The most distinguished man of the greatest family in the empire. One of the noblest and most enlightened patriots the Oriental world has ever seen.' " The Regent began to pace up and down the room. " What has Preecha's family done for Siam? I have been too tolerant. I could have swept aside the entire brood. . . . *Bah*! " He paused and faced Knox. " I tell you this, I will not suffer the personal affront and the humiliation that your daughter chooses to inflict on me. To scorn and cast aside a member of my family and ally herself in marriage with Preecha—you cannot expect me to suffer that. Nor will I. I want to make this clear to you at this early stage, before things have gone too far."

Knox was angry at this intrusion into his private life and did not find it easy to control himself. At the same time he was able to understand the Regent's feelings. That he should regard Fanny's behaviour as a personal insult to him was understandable in an Oriental.

" Your Excellency," he said quietly, " is asking me to do something that is not easy. I have said so all along. Fanny is a girl with spirit and she is very much in love. We have tried to advise and guide her, not because we regard Preecha as unsuitable, but solely because of your feelings. It would be much easier for a Minister of the Crown to advise a sovereign on a thing of this kind. She would be more conscious of her duty to the State than I can expect Fanny to be. She is not conscious of any duty to you and, if I may be frank, nor am I."

The Regent's scowl was ominous. In a raised voice he said: " Then she must take the consequences and so must you. There is nothing I can add to that."

He rang the bell to indicate that the interview was at an end. As Hunter came to the door Knox rose and bowed stiffly. The Regent merely waved his hand in abrupt dismissal.

Knox walked in silence to the consular boat.

Briefly he informed his wife of what had happened. They felt that Fanny should be told at once.

Fanny stared at her father with startled eyes as he described the interview to her. He omitted no detail, but to drive the argument home stressed the Regent's tone of voice and manner.

Fanny's eyes, frightened and restless, darted from one to the other. She knew now that the Regent had prompted the astrologer.

Knox came and stood beside her chair, and put his hand affectionately on her head. " What he will do I don't know. We are English and he can do nothing to us. But what will he do to Preecha? "

" He can do nothing," Fanny said angrily. " Preecha's is a far greater and more powerful family . . ."

" Not more powerful," Knox said quietly.

" He is a friend of the King's. The Regent wouldn't dare . . ."

" I'm not sure," said Mrs. Knox.

" Don't you think the King would——? " Fanny asked, turning to her father.

" The King would not be able to prevent it. He has not been able to assert himself yet."

" Then this may be his chance. It's time he put the Regent in his proper place."

Knox shook his head. " A clash with the Regent might well endanger the King's position. I don't think he'd risk it. The fact that Preecha is a friend of the King's may even be a handicap. The Regent may be trying to strip the King of all his more powerful supporters."

Fanny shook her head in despair. She shut her eyes. " What can I do? Tell me, Papa, what can I do? "

" I wish I could tell you."

" Why don't you come away with us—or with me if Papa can't come. We could go away for a little while," suggested Mamma.

" A little while? Do you think the Regent is likely to change his mind? No. I'm not going to run away."

Mrs. Knox drew a deep breath.

" Do you think," Fanny asked, " it would do any good if I went to see the King? He has always been kind to me. Preecha is his friend and I feel sure he can help, and if I see him *before* the Regent does anything it might be easier for him to prevent it than to reverse an order already given by the Regent."

" I wish I felt he could," Knox sighed.

Mrs. Knox said: " I want you to think over what I am going to say, dear. Fortunately Preecha is away so you do not have to decide at once. But think—that's all."

" Think about what? " Fanny asked petulantly.

" What the Regent said was clear enough—and the consequences."

" What consequences? "

"They could be anything," said Mamma.

"They're not going to frighten me and I don't believe they will frighten Preecha either." She turned to her father. "If we marry—and we *will*—that'll make him your son-in-law. As British Consul General surely you can protect your son-in-law."

"Up to a point, I suppose, but it doesn't make him a British subject."

"Does it make me a Siamese subject?"

"No. If it were the other way round—a Siamese girl marrying a British subject becomes British automatically."

"It *must* work both ways, Papa. I am sure it could be argued successfully," she said.

Sadly he shook his head. "Arguments would be no good once the Regent has made up his mind. . . . You are very much in love now—and so is Preecha. But he's not the only man in the world."

"He is—for me."

"Of course you feel like that. But why take risks?"

"What is the worst the Regent can do?" Fanny asked. "Waylay us on a dark night and have us clubbed to death? Do you believe it could happen here, in this century . . .?"

"I don't think he'd go as far as murder," said Knox.

"I'm not sure he won't," said Mrs. Knox.

"No." Knox dismissed the thought. "But he'd strip Preecha of everything—every office certainly."

"So long as we are together," said Fanny.

"He might arrest him," Knox reflected.

"Arrest Preecha? On what charge?"

"Of course arrest would need justification," said Knox. "Specific charges would have to be made."

"The charge of falling in love?" Fanny laughed. "You see, all his threats are bluff." A great weight seemed to have been lifted from her.

But neither Knox nor his wife shared her sense of relief.

Chapter Ten

A LETTER inviting Knox, his wife and Fanny to be his guests for the dedication of the new temple at Bang Pa In, came from the Regent. "We could make the journey together in my houseboat and perhaps you could all stay with me for the three days of the celebrations," he wrote.

This proposal gave rise to a lively discussion. "Why can't we go in our own houseboat?" asked Fanny.

"You won't avoid meeting him," said Mamma, and added: "I hope you don't intend to cut him if he speaks to you, as he certainly will."

"Being civil to him because of Papa's position is one thing, travelling with him and living with him for three days is another. I'd rather not go than go with him."

"I've not been feeling quite myself lately and I am sure going to Paknam and getting the sea air will do me a lot more good than travelling to Bang Pa In. We are not obliged to go, you know," remarked Papa.

"I was looking forward to it so much," said Fanny sadly. Preecha had written to confirm that he was going to be at Bang Pa In and it was nearly four months since she had last seen him. Knox felt sorry for her.

"Let's see what the doctor has to say," he suggested.

Dr. Smith found nothing wrong with Knox apart from nervous strain and fatigue, but he advised a rest. Whereupon Mrs. Knox declared that he must go to Paknam and that she intended to go with him to see that he was properly looked after.

" If neither of you come I suppose I shan't be able to go to Bang Pa In," Fanny stated.

" Obviously you can't go alone," said Papa.

" Not in the consular houseboat? " Her only chance of seeing Preecha seemed to be slipping away.

" You can't spend three or four nights in a houseboat by yourself," he said.

" There will be servants," Fanny suggested hopefully.

" Yes," Mrs. Knox cut in, " but even so—a girl with just three or four servants—it is not done."

Fanny shut her eyes. There seemed to be no way out. She spent the afternoon writing to Preecha. She asked if it would be possible for him to stop at Paknam on the way.

The next morning a letter from the King, in reply to Knox's apology that for health reasons he would not be able to attend the ceremony of dedication, provided a way out.

His Majesty, after expressing his concern for Knox's health, added: " But if it should be possible for some members of your family to come to Bang Pa In, Fanny and her mother, perhaps, or even Fanny by herself, I shall be happy for a floating house, near the main Palace at Bang Pa In, to be specially prepared for them."

Knox read the letter out to Fanny.

" Mamma won't go," he said. " So you'll have to go by yourself."

" Will Mamma think it all right with just the servants . . .?"

" Yes," replied Knox. " You'll only be a few hours in the boat and then you'll be under the King's protection."

Fanny's eyes shone. " Please thank His Majesty very, very much."

So it was all settled, except that Knox had to write a letter to the Regent declining his invitation; he had some difficulty in phrasing it.

The King had said that the house would be ready by the

8th February so that the ladies might have a day in which
to settle down before the dedication ceremonies began; and
Knox suggested that Fanny should leave Bangkok during the
course of that morning.

Writing to Preecha of this unexpected change of plans,
Fanny asked if it would be possible for their boats to meet at
some point on the way to Bang Pa In, so that they might see
each other and talk, as obviously that would not be possible
during the ceremony.

The Knoxes left for Paknam on the 25th February, 1879.
That evening Fanny received a reply from Preecha. " I shall
be entering the river early on the morning of the twenty-
seventh," he wrote, " and shall be coming past the consular
landing-stage. Surely we could meet there and you could
come into my houseboat. My sisters and about a dozen women
servants will be on board, so it should lead to no talk. But I
see that is the day before you propose to go. Could you not
start a day earlier? "

Fanny replied: " As I am alone in the Consulate, I can
easily rearrange the date. But you had better not come here.
Can't we meet at some point north of Bangkok, and then
perhaps I could come on board your boat for lunch? My boat
could follow yours and I could get back to it later."

She then asked Gould, Knox's deputy, to have the launch
ready a day earlier and she arranged to take Oun and three
other women servants with her. Together she and Oun selected
the dresses she was to take.

On the morning of the twenty-seventh they set out shortly
after breakfast. A light breeze blew down the river, but the
sun was hot and blinding. Fanny stared ahead, looking for the
Sunbeam. At the appointed place it was waiting for her. She
saw that there were a number of women on board.

Preecha helped Fanny on board. Oun scrambled up after
her.

"Why don't you bring your luggage, then your launch could go back? There is no point in it following us."

"I'd rather have the launch with me," said Fanny. "I'm sure the captain and the other men will be glad to see something of the pageantry."

She was certain it would lead to a lot of talk if the consular boat wasn't there. She fell silent, wrapped in thought.

"What are you thinking about?" Preecha asked gently, as he slipped his arm round her waist. She smiled at him. It was comforting to feel him so near.

"I'll tell you later. I'd rather not talk about it now."

"All right." Then looking at her, he said: "Yellow suits you; I love that dress."

His sisters chorused their agreement, and then a flock of women servants came up and one by one felt the material, stroked the sleeves and exclaimed appreciatively.

After lunch, as they stood alone by the rails, Preecha took Fanny's hands in his and, looking tenderly at her, asked: "What is it that is troubling you?"

"Us," she whispered, "us and the consequences."

At that moment a small launch overtook them. In it, looking towards them, was Alabaster, his abundant side-whiskers blowing about his gaunt face. He blinked slightly as he went by, but did not greet them.

"He's racing on to inform the Regent that he has seen us together . . ." said Fanny.

"It's the sort of thing he would do."

"He doesn't frighten me—nor does the Regent. Mamma, of course, is terribly unhappy. Papa is trying to be understanding and helpful. But I feel that if anything went wrong, his whole career might be at stake."

"Yes," replied Preecha as he gazed down into the water. "I've been thinking a great deal about it, too, and I've been very unhappy about your parents." He passed his hand gently over

190

her arm and with a wry smile, added: " To them we must seem completely selfish and heartless. We want our happiness, to which we are entitled, of course, but have we any right to take it at the expense of other people's peace of mind? I'm talking now as though all this were happening to someone else, as though I were just an onlooker . . ."

" There are moments," said Fanny, " when I want to fight the whole world. I'm like that. It's your influence that has made me try to be a little understanding."

" And I was going to say that it's your influence that has made me want to fight. . . ."

They smiled wanly at each other.

" Well, which is it to be? " he asked.

" I'm not very good at making sacrifices," she said.

" Then we must defy the world, and take our future into our own hands."

" You mean go away from Siam and make a life somewhere else? " she asked.

" If we decided to do that then we would have to act swiftly, in case anyone tried to stop us—or rather, tried to stop me, for you are outside their control. But then, if the Regent were determined on revenge, he would vent his rage on my father— my brothers—my children, unless they, too, got away from the country."

They gazed silently across the river for some time. The stream narrowed. The undergrowth on the banks got thicker, the trees taller. As evening fell, lights came on in the scattered huts. Men were singing in their fishing boats. Ahead, at the fork of the island, they could see the spire of the new temple.

" It is just like an English church," Fanny remarked.

" Yes, and that should be a good omen for you."

They anchored short of the temple. The consular launch pulled up alongside. Preecha arranged for Fanny's luggage to be sent ahead to the floating house set aside for her by the King.

After a silent dinner, Fanny and Preecha went out on deck. By now it was dark.

" Is it to be good-bye? " he asked.

She buried her face in his shoulder and through her sobs she said: " These constant partings—they are dreadful."

He pressed her hand, opening and shutting her fingers. After a long silence, he said: " I know we are both thinking the same thing."

She looked into his eyes inquiringly. They were hardly visible in the darkness.

" We can't make human sacrifices of those we love—your parents, my children. Can we? "

The shake of her head was almost imperceptible. He sensed it rather than saw it.

" I never thought it would end like this." Her voice was no more than a faint whisper.

They heard the servants returning from the King's floating house. She took his face in her hands and kissed him. " Good-bye," she said.

He kissed her again and again. " I'm sure our decision is right," he whispered.

The servants' voices were louder now. From the bank they were shouting that the house was not yet ready. They were not expecting Fanny till the next day. No furniture had been moved in. There was nowhere for her to sleep.

" What shall I do now? " asked Fanny in a panic.

Preecha's sisters and the women servants, who had rushed on to the deck at the sound of the voices, suggested that she should spend the night on board.

" No, no," she stammered. " No. I can't."

" It will be all right," Preecha reassured her. " You can move into my cabin and I will sleep on deck. You've slept in it before—during our trip to Prachin."

" I know, but—it's different now."

" One of my sisters will sleep in the cabin with you," he suggested. " You can go to the house in the morning."

Fanny had tears in her eyes. Preecha's elder sister took her arm and led her to the cabin. She lowered herself into the bunk, but it was a long time before she fell asleep.

Very early the next morning, even before Fanny had left the *Sunbeam*, one of the Regent's messengers was on his way to Paknam. The message he bore was brief. It stated bluntly: " Very sorry Fanny could not come with us, but preferred to spend the night with Preecha in his houseboat."

Knox could hardly believe what he read. Mrs. Knox saw that his hands were trembling. She took the note from him. " Silly girl," she said. " Why did she do it? "

Knox ordered his boat at once.

" You are ill, dear," Mamma protested. " You should be in bed. And what good will it do now . . .? "

" Much rest I can get," he roared.

" I suppose it must be true? "

" I must go and find out," he said impatiently.

At Bang Pa In his boat went past Preecha's, but he kept his face averted. He called first on the King to pay his respects. The King said: " I am sorry the house was not ready when Fanny arrived yesterday. We weren't expecting her until to-day. But she is there now."

" Thank you, Your Majesty," Knox said. " You are most kind. I shouldn't be here, for I am supposed to be convalescing. But I came because "—luckily he had a passable explanation— " because Captain Hill of the Royal Engineers has arrived in Siam and has asked if he could have Your Majesty's permission to do some surveying between Bang Pa In and Tavoy. The district has not really been surveyed yet."

" Certainly he may have my permission, and I hope you will stay now that you are here and be with us for the dedication ceremony to-morrow."

" I hope Your Majesty will forgive me, but I fear I should find it too great a strain. With your permission I shall now supply His Excellency the Regent with the details of Captain Hill's tour."

The King shook hands, Knox bowed and took his leave. So the King had confirmed it—but without even a hint of criticism.

Knox was too angry to go and see his daughter. He wanted neither explanation nor excuse. What she had done could not be explained or excused.

The Regent kept him waiting for the best part of an hour and was far from friendly when Knox was ushered into his study.

" Captain Hill can make his tour," he said. " But what is Fanny up to? You can't say I didn't warn you, Tom."

" I know," he replied irritably.

The Regent went on: " This is another humiliation for me. She would not stay with us. We should have been delighted to have her, as she well knows. But instead "—he spread out his hands—" it is insufferable, unforgivable . . ."

" I'm sorry, Your Excellency. Had I been able to accompany her, as I had planned, this would never have happened. I offer you my apologies."

" And what does she say? " asked the Regent.

" I have not seen her yet," Knox replied. " Indeed, I had not proposed to do so, since no explanation can be acceptable to me."

" As her father, you should see her and point out her folly."

Knox rose. " Thank you, Your Excellency, for agreeing to make the arrangements for Captain Hill."

Without rising, the Regent dismissed him.

Against his intentions, Knox decided to call on his daughter. He found her dressed in a loose housecoat, looking sad and grave.

"Papa," she said very quietly as she came up to kiss him. But he held up his hand and stopped her. She saw that his face was white with anger.

"Why did you do it?" he asked, his voice shaking with emotion.

"You mean last night? The King's house wasn't ready and there was nowhere else to go."

"You could have gone to the Regent."

"That's the last place I'd want to go to."

"You could have stayed in the consular launch . . ."

"But there's nowhere to sleep in it."

"You could have slept on the deck. But you *preferred* to spend the night with Preecha. Didn't you realise how people would talk?"

"We weren't alone. His sisters were there. There were about twenty other women on board."

"That makes no difference."

"It does make a difference." She stamped her foot. "We weren't alone."

"Everyone is talking about it. It's all over Bang Pa In. It's become more important than the temple, the dedication—everything."

She shut her eyes as though to shut out his words.

"Papa," she said very softly, without looking at him. "Preecha and I have said good-bye. We have decided not to see each other again—ever. It is *awful*." Her eyes were full of tears.

"What's the good of saying good-bye after you've spent a night with him?" Knox bellowed.

"I *didn't* spend the night with him."

"Everyone believes you did. So it comes to the same thing." He strode up to her. "There's only one thing we can do now. Preecha will have to marry you. I'm going to write to him. I shall insist on his marrying you."

It was the last thing she expected. The colour returned to her face.

" I don't think he'll object," she said. " You forget that he wants to marry me—and I want to marry him."

" Well, you've got your way . . ." The words almost choked him.

He walked off. On reaching the veranda, he turned and shouted: " And let me tell you this. Don't come crying to me when there's trouble, as I'm sure there will be. You'll just have to find your own way out of it."

She was very angry too. " I won't come to you. I'll *never* come to you—no matter what happens. We are quite able to look after ourselves."

Chapter Eleven

INSTEAD OF going back to Paknam, Knox went to Bangkok. It was late in the evening. He startled the consular staff by striding into his study, ringing his bell and asking if Mr. Gould would be so kind as to come and see him.

Gould, who was at dinner in his own house, wondered what could have brought Knox back from sick leave at this late hour.

" Is the Sahib all right? " he asked Singh.

The Sikh salaamed again. " He has come in like the wind. Shall I tell the Consul Sahib that you are at dinner? "

" No. I shall be with him in a minute."

He hurried across to the Consulate. He saw at once that Knox, his hair ruffled as though he had been running his fingers through it, his beard in disarray, was distraught.

" I'm sorry to send for you, Gould," Knox said. " You weren't at dinner, were you? "

" That's quite all right, sir."

Knox motioned him to a chair and cleared his throat.

" This is a delicate matter," he began. " I'd like you to handle it—in your official capacity, of course."

Gould waited for him to go on.

Knox fumbled with the paperweight on his desk, moved it away, then brought it back again. " As a member of my family is involved, I feel it would be better if I kept out of it, for the time being, at any rate."

Gould nodded.

" You know that Phra Preecha has been anxious to marry

my elder daughter for some time. He proposed again about two or three months ago."

" Yes, sir."

" I have nothing against him. He is the eldest son of one of the most distinguished families in this country, and he is a very fine man indeed. An idealist—and practical as well. But Fanny is an extremely pretty girl—at any rate, a lot of young men seem to think so—and I have tried to delay a decision. But "—he cleared his throat again—" they have taken things into their own hands—Phra Preecha and my daughter—jumped the gun, one might say, though "—he raised his finger—" don't misunderstand me. She did spend the night in his boat, but there were at least twenty women there. They weren't alone."

" Yes, sir."

" Now people have begun to talk, so—since I have nothing against the young man—I feel it would be best if they got married. Now this is what I want you to do. Phra Preecha is in the *Sunbeam* at Bang Pa In. I had intended seeing him, but I decided not to. I'd like you to go to him and tell him this: ' Mr. Knox would like you to marry his daughter as soon as is conveniently possible.' I also require him to set aside the sum of £5,000 to provide for her future, should she survive him. I'd like you to act as one of the trustees of this sum. It should be sent home at once—before the marriage—and placed in the Bank of England. I hope you will agree to do this for me? "

" Of course, sir. When would you like me to go and see Phra Preecha? "

" I'd like you to go as soon as possible. It's too late to make a start to-night, but you could go first thing in the morning. And you must also tell him that he must not expect me to intervene at any time or in any way on his behalf. He must face the risks he has invited, even though he is marrying my daughter."

" Is it your plan, sir, to attend the wedding? "

" No. Neither Mrs. Knox nor I will be present. But if you would be so kind, Gould, I'd like you to be there, just to see that everything is legally and properly conducted."

" Will it be a Siamese wedding? "

" I suppose so. They could be married here at the British Consulate, but that might not be recognised by the Siamese, and I want this marriage to be recognised and accepted here, because this is where they are going to live. Oh, and another thing, I'd like you to see that my daughter is given the status of head wife. Of course, Phra Preecha has never had more than one wife before. She is dead, and Fanny will be his only wife now. But in this country, where men, especially among the nobility, are allowed several wives, we must make sure that my daughter has the rights and privileges of head wife."

" I will certainly see to it. Will you be staying on here, sir? "

" Only for to-night. I shall go to Paknam in the morning to fetch Mrs. Knox."

" And Miss Knox, if I should need to get in touch with her——? "

" There is no need for you to get in touch with my daughter. Your business is with Phra Preecha. When you've made the necessary arrangements, you will return here. He will inform you in due course of the wedding plans—where it is to be. Thank you, Gould."

" Good night, sir. I shall report to you on my return."

Knox nodded and returned to his desk. He passed his hand across his forehead. There were so many other things to see to. Fanny could not remain in the King's house at Bang Pa In with only the servants there. He wondered whether the Second King's sister, Princess Chandr, who had always been attached to his wife and to Fanny, would allow her to stay with her until the wedding. He knew she had not gone to the dedication.

He rang the bell and told Singh that he wanted a boat for

just a short journey, and went to call on the Princess. She was a tiny woman, not pretty, but with large attractive brown eyes. She was delighted to see Knox. " But you look so worried," she said.

When he began to tell his story she checked him, saying that she already knew what had happened. The news had travelled quickly. She thought it was the best solution that the two should get married at once and she gladly agreed to put Fanny up until the wedding.

When, a little later, Knox rose to leave, the Princess took both his hands in hers, saying: " It will be all right, Tom."

" I hope so," he said quietly.

It was very late when he returned to the Consulate. But he sat down and wrote a letter to Fanny, telling her to return at once to Bangkok as he had arranged for her to stay with the Princess Chandr until her marriage.

He told Singh that the letter was to be taken by special messenger in Mr. Gould's boat in the morning. He added that Miss Knox would be returning in the consular launch.

Fanny lost no time in complying with her father's wishes. Instructing Oun to see to the packing, she sat down to write to Preecha.

" My dearest love," she wrote, " soon it will be 'husband,' and then part of the astrologer's prophecy will have come true.

" Papa wants me to leave here at once and to go and stay with Princess Chandr in Bangkok. No doubt he has already written to you to say that he wishes us to be married without delay. My darling, I am so happy about this. I shall count the days as soon as I know how many I have to count to. Where shall we be married? In Bangkok? Or in Prachin?

" I am longing to reach your home—our home, I should say. I hope the people will like me as much as they like you—if they like me even half as much, it would satisfy me."

She went on writing until Oun came to say that all was

ready and her luggage had already been placed in the consular launch.

Winding its way out of the Royal Canal, the launch brought her in a few minutes to the main river. The scene here had changed completely in the two days since she had last seen it. The river was crowded with the large houseboats of the Siamese nobility and the gay royal barges, enormously long, with grinning figures on the prows, their gilded flanks glistening in the bright sunlight. There was a continuous din of gongs being struck and horns blown at the new temple. Saffron-clad priests kept arriving in small boats.

Fanny looked eagerly towards the *Sunbeam*, but could catch not even a fleeting glimpse of Preecha, though she noticed that there was great activity on the deck, as if the boat were getting ready to leave.

She wondered what effect his absence from the dedication ceremony would have on the King—and on the Regent.

Knox, meanwhile, had rejoined his wife. She was in a great state of agitation, for she was convinced that the most dire consequences would result from the marriage. Knox tried in vain to comfort her; he gave her brandy and patted her hands; finally he snapped at her:

" For God's sake, woman, if you have nothing but woe, woe, woe, to wail about, then shut up."

She stared at him, dumbfounded. Very rarely had he lost his temper with her.

" I have enough to attend to," he said apologetically. " I have to write to the King—I think he will understand. But the Regent won't. I had intended to write to both of them last night."

On the journey back to Bangkok he drew some scraps of paper from his pocket and began to examine his notes and compose his difficult letters. To the King he stated simply that he was arranging for Fanny to marry Preecha as soon as possible and hoped that His Majesty would agree that this was the best solution. His letter to the Regent he drafted again and again. Every phrase he set down seemed, when he re-read it, to be capable of a different interpretation and he was anxious not to be misunderstood. The letter was not finished by the time they reached Bangkok and he went at once to his study, where he struggled with it for a further two hours. He had to finish it, for he realised that any delay was also likely to be misinterpreted. His final draft read:

Your Excellency, I write only in the capacity of a friend to whom you have through the years shown many kindnesses which I can never hope to repay. As a father, you will, I pray, try to understand the singular difficulty in which I find myself placed. Unhappily, in the West, parental authority is neither heeded nor respected, as it is in this country. In consequence, we are, as you are not, in the hands of our children. That you should have honoured me by selecting my daughter Fanny to provide a link between our two families touched my wife and myself most deeply, and I am sure our daughter Fanny was also truly touched. But romantic feelings are often wayward and cannot be relied upon to coincide precisely with feelings of gratitude.

I appreciate your consideration in pointing out what might be at stake if my daughter answered the promptings of her heart. Both my wife and I were anxious to respect and, if possible, to comply with your advice—and, in the end (and I know that this will surprise you as indeed it surprised us) Fanny was herself prepared to comply too. Indeed, she had said good-bye to Preecha and they had agreed not to see each other again. In order to arrive at this decision, they had, of course, to meet. It was unfortunate that at the conclusion of this meeting, because the house kindly placed by His Majesty at Fanny's disposal was not ready, she was obliged to spend the night in Preecha's houseboat—not alone with him, for I would repeat with emphasis that she was in company with at least a score of women.

However, owing to the gossip to which this has given rise, I am the first to recognise that it is no longer possible that you should wish to further the marriage between my daughter and your grandson, Nai Dee. In the circumstances, I have taken the only course a father could take, namely, to insist that Preecha should marry Fanny without further delay.

I only hope that, after considering the facts, you will find it in your heart to understand and forgive what was no more than an act of thoughtless folly on the part of my daughter.

The two letters were despatched by special boat to Bang Pa In. He received a kind letter from the King. From the Regent there was no reply.

Knox was too angry with Fanny to wish to see her. But Mrs. Knox insisted on going to the Second King's palace where, in one of the houses in the women's enclosure, Princess Chandr lived very simply. Here everything reminded Mrs. Knox of her own youth.

The Princess greeted her affectionately. Fanny, her face flushed, hugged her mother, who said, with a wry smile: " You naughty girl! So you've contrived to get your own way."

" Contrived is not the right word, Mamma—unless we say Fate contrived it, for I didn't, truly."

" Well," replied Mamma, " it is settled now, and in spite of all we've said, your father and I hope you will be very happy."

Chapter Twelve

THE WEDDING took place in Preecha's house in Bangkok on the 10th March, 1879. Only members of the family and their closest friends were present.

Gould represented Knox, who refused to attend or to allow his wife to attend the ceremony. " It would not be politic for either of us to be there," he said.

As is the custom in Siam, the ceremony began the day before the marriage. Fourteen monks—the number must be an even one—arrived in the afternoon and sat facing an improvised altar, with an image of Buddha, surrounded by flowers, lighted candles and incense sticks, in the centre of it. A cord was bound round the pedestal on which the statue stood; it was then taken through a window and wound round the house. Everything within the orbit of this sacred cord was thus consecrated. The priests recited texts from the Buddhist scriptures and sprinkled holy water.

The next day Fanny, wearing an emerald silk *panung*, a richly-embroidered jacket, a chaplet of unspun threads on her hair and a garland of flowers about her neck, sat on the floor beside Preecha, their heads bowed, their palms joined. The guests entered the room in turn, women as well as men, according to seniority of rank and age, and poured water which had been blessed over the couple's extended hands. Preecha and Fanny were then pronounced man and wife.

Only when the ceremony was over and the feast began were Preecha's two children, Trakun and Arun, at last able to rush forward and take Fanny by the hand. " Our new Mamma! Our new Mamma! " they shouted.

Preecha, wearing his Governor's uniform and the orders of his rank, beamed with happiness. " No one can take you from me now," he said.

" No one," Fanny repeated.

Gould had already attended to all the business arrangements. He stayed on for the ceremony and for the reception, but he was one of the first to leave. He hurried back to report to Knox that the task with which he had been entrusted had been fulfilled.

Early the next morning the young couple and the children, together with their servants, among whom Oun now had a place, left in the *Sunbeam* for the seat of Preecha's government.

Prachin was *en fête*. The streets were hung with flags and banners of welcome. Small boats, laden with flowers, came out to meet them on the River Gang Paking, more than a mile from the town. The men, women and children in them sang as they pelted the bride and bridegroom with flowers.

On the river-bank a great feast was set out. The townspeople —close on four thousand of them—dragged Fanny and Preecha out of the houseboat and led them off as guests of honour. Buddhist priests joined with smiling faces in the laughter.

Meanwhile, Mrs. Knox, forbidden to attend the wedding, got two Buddhist priests to sit with her in the veranda of the Consulate and read the service. The tears coursed down her cheeks.

Alone in his study Knox sat smoking a cigar and thinking how it might have been—in London or in Ireland, the daughter he loved more than anyone else walking up the aisle on his arm and looking lovely.

After a time Mrs. Knox joined him. " Now there will be only the two of us," she said gently.

" Yes," he replied, and put out his hand to take hers.

The friendly attitude of the people made it easy for Fanny to settle down in her new home. The informality she had noticed during her earlier visit still prevailed. There were no guards at Government House. Visitors drifted in and out, bringing their children and their dogs with them; indeed, very often the children and the dogs drifted in on their own. This created an atmosphere which was new to her, for at the Consulate everything had been strictly ordered by Papa and Mamma.

Fanny, with something of her mother's temperament, fell in readily with Preecha's informal way of life, with the result that she was soon accorded the same affection that he received from the people of his province. Even the birds used to fly in from the sanctuary, sometimes in small droves. They would sit on the window ledge and look at her sideways, seeking to make friends, and, once they had got to know her, hopped on to her shoulder, pecking gently at her cheek.

A day after their arrival Preecha resumed his normal activities, one of which was administering justice. Often the court sat on his front steps, while he listened to the pleading and to the evidence. Sometimes he put his arm round the shoulders of the culprit while giving fatherly advice or a mild reprimand. Fanny, too, would be there, and Preecha would occasionally turn to her saying: " Well, what do you think? "

After a few weeks they set out for Kabin, where gold was being worked.

When their boat pulled up at the landing-stage Fanny saw a small steam train. She was surprised, for it was the first railway she had seen in Siam. They got into one of the trucks.

The journey took nearly an hour. When they arrived they saw men busy with pickaxes attacking the auriferous rocks. The ore was crushed and the gold extracted and weighed in a machine-house nearby. An English engineer named Pool was in charge of it. He had three engineers under him. There were also firemen, woodmen, carpenters, stone-breakers, blanket-washers and men feeding the batteries of the machines which went on throbbing night and day.

" To meet the Regent's demands," Preecha explained, " we have opened up fresh sections of rock."

In a series of offices clerks and accountants were busy working out the yield of gold from each ore and the cost per day of obtaining it.

Preecha knew nearly all of them by name and stopped to exchange a word with each of them. If he came upon a newcomer he would ask: " Where do you come from? Do you like it here? Do you find the work hard? Have you got your wife and family with you? No? Then you must send for them. It's not nice being parted. I'll advance you the money to bring them here and you can pay it back a little at a time."

As he moved among them, they stopped working to talk to him.

" You will have to keep away if you want to get more gold out of the mine," Fanny exclaimed.

" Our production is up," he retorted. " It's going up a little week by week. The Regent won't be able to find anything to complain of now."

" That'll upset him, for I'm sure he only keeps you here in order to find fault," Fanny replied.

After a few days at Kabin they went by elephant to Battambang and then to the Cambodian frontier along a dusty track, travelling through miles of jungle.

Along the frontier, at intervals of half a mile or so, there were lofty lookout posts, which Preecha had erected when the Regent had suggested that a French invasion was imminent.

When they returned to Government House at Prachin, Fanny began the daily round of visits to the homes of the people, and had long talks in the evening with the doctor, the school-master and the priests. Several times a week Preecha took her to the school, where they sat with the children and later joined in their games. In spite of all these activities, they also had time to themselves; then they rode and swam, played tennis and talked.

They were extremely happy until one morning a liveried boatman arrived from Bangkok with an urgent summons from the Regent requiring Preecha to return at once to the capital.

" I wonder what this means," said Fanny nervously.

" Nothing much, I expect."

" Anyhow, you're not going by yourself. I'm coming too."

On the 28th March they were back in Bangkok. As they made their way from the landing-stage to their house, Preecha's father hailed them from across the vast courtyard.

" What brings you back so soon? " he called.

" The Regent has sent for me. Do you know why? "

" Oh, has he? Not much news gets out from his palace. He's pretty foxy, that one. But I'm glad you've come. The royal ballet are performing the Khon this week, at the theatre by the Second King's palace, and they really are superb. I've never seen anything so beautiful."

After a talk with his father, Preecha arranged for him to take Fanny to the ballet. Meanwhile, he himself set out to pay his respects to the King and then to call on the Regent. He promised to join them at the theatre as soon as he could.

Later Phya Kesab and Fanny went off together. When they took their seats, Fanny kept glancing at the door hoping that Preecha would arrive before the curtain went up. But he didn't, and she sat wondering what on earth could have delayed him. Why had the Regent sent for him? She tried to concentrate on the play, but did not find it easy.

The Khon dancers wear masks, each of which indicates the personality of the wearer. These masked characters do not speak, a chorus supplies the dialogue, at times in song, at others in a sort of sing-song speech. In their movements and their postures, the dancers keep in precise accord with the chorus. The story of this musical play is the familiar one of Rama, the hero of the Hindu epic *Ramayana*, which tells of his war against the demon King who abducted Rama's wife Sita. An ocean has to be crossed for her rescue, siege has to be laid to the city of the demon, and a series of battles have to be fought.

On their heads the dancers wear crowns which rise like the gilded spires of the temples in the palace grounds. Jewels sparkle in their ears, on their necks, their bosoms and their fingers, flashing a thousand lights as their hands flutter.

As enchantment followed enchantment, Fanny glanced towards the entrance, longing for Preecha to come. After the pole dance, during the brief scene in which the demon tries to devour Rama and his brother Lakshman, Fanny's rising agitation turned to alarm. Why had he not come? What was detaining him? On the stage the colours changed as in a kaleidoscope, but she no longer took in what she saw. Finally, she rose and went out. Phya Kesab followed her slowly and a little breathlessly. They glanced to right and to left, but there was no sign of Preecha. In the distance his younger brother, Pet Pichai, could be seen running towards them. " Preecha has been arrested," he whispered.

" Arrested? " Fanny was bewildered and distraught.

" What has he done? " asked Phya Kesab.

" That I do not know. He was with the King. The Regent joined them and they talked for a long time. Then, as Preecha was coming out of the Palace, he was seized by the guards and led off."

" Where to? Where have they taken him? " Fanny, seized with panic, clutched Pet Pichai's shoulders with both hands. She was trembling.

Pet Pichai said: " The Second King, concerned for Mr. Knox, has set off by boat for Paknam."

"I am going to see the King," said Phya Kesab. "They cannot hold him without trial." And he strode towards the landing-stage, Fanny hurrying after him.

"This is the Regent's work," Kesab added grimly. "The King will have to deal with him."

The music, fainter now, still reached them as the boat pushed out. Kesab took Fanny's head in his hands and tried to comfort her, but she could not be comforted. Pet Pichai went on talking: "Something was said about the gold mines. They say Preecha was too harsh with the men."

"Harsh!" Fanny raised her head and shouted.

"It is lies—nothing but lies," said Phya Kesab. "The marriage is the cause of this."

"Oh-h-h!" She shut her eyes and clenched her fists, murmuring: "What have I done? What have I done to him?"

After a while, Fanny looked up.

"Where are we going? He's making for home. I thought we were going to the Palace," she exclaimed.

Phya Kesab replied: "I must go alone."

"No. No," Fanny insisted. "I must go to Preecha. I must go to him."

"We don't even know where he is," Kesab objected.

"In jail. We know he's in jail."

"He is not likely to be in the common jail. Probably he's in a room—in the Police Chief's house possibly—with a guard on the door. Let me find out."

When they got home she clung to Phya Kesab and would not let him go without her.

"Pet Pichai will stay with you—and his wife too. Let me go alone. Perhaps I can bring him back with me—they could guard him here. Then at least you would be together."

Fanny sank into a chair and sobbed.

Kesab took the boat for the Palace.

There nobody could tell him anything. Some had seen the arrest. " He was led off," they said. " He isn't here now."

" Where did they take him? " Kesab asked.

They did not know. He might be in one of the Regent's houses, or in the Foreign Minister's home. He could be anywhere. But certainly wherever he was, he was sure to be closely guarded.

Kesab decided to try and see the Regent, but when he had crossed the river he was told by the guards that it was late and the Regent had gone to bed. Nobody dared rouse him. The servants said: " Phra Preecha has not been brought here."

Phya Kesab tramped from one painted pavilion to another, the servants trailing behind him, repeating in whispers, so that their voices should not carry: " He's not here, we tell you. He is not here."

Eventually, Kesab returned to his boat and recrossed the dark and silent river to his home. It was not yet dawn.

He found Fanny still awake. Her eyes were red, but she was unable to cry any more. She raised her eyes as he entered.

He shook his head. " To-night I could not find out anything. I'll try again in the morning."

She stretched out her hand and took his. Pet Pichai's wife Thanom brought some tea. Together, in silence, they waited for the dawn.

Knox was already in bed when the Second King arrived. He was startled to see so exalted a caller at that late hour.

" I am sorry, my dear friend, that I bring bad news. Preecha has been arrested."

Knox's hand rose towards his head. He took a pace or two towards the cane chair in the veranda and sank into it.

" I feared something like this might happen. The Regent? "

The Second King nodded.

" Has he given his reasons? "

" He spoke of Preecha's insult to the King, contempt for the laws. . . . And there was some mention of misgovernment, cruelty to the men at the gold mines. . . ."

" As I feared. As I feared," Knox groaned.

" Nothing is clear yet," said the Second King. " I thought you ought to be informed at once and the Regent agreed that I should come. He said I should ask you if you would object to having Phra Preecha tried."

Knox leapt out of his chair. " These charges, if there were any truth in them, should have been brought *before* the marriage —not *after*."

The Second King shrugged his shoulders.

" It is a wicked plot! " Knox roared. " It's iniquitous. Preecha cannot have done any of these things during his honeymoon. All this has been cooked up because he has married my daughter—because Fanny refused to marry Nai Dee. What does the King say? "

" What can he say? "

" Preecha is his friend. The King knows that he is just, honest, gentle . . ."

" His Majesty is young—and helpless," said the Second King.

Suddenly Mrs. Knox, roused by their voices, appeared in the doorway, a wrap around her.

" Is there to be a trial, Your Majesty? " she asked.

The Second King turned again to Knox. " Would you object to a trial? "

" I would not object to a *fair* trial, held in open court, so that witnesses can be heard, examined and cross-examined. Nothing less will satisfy me."

The Second King rose. " I am sorry, my friend. I will do all that I can," he said.

Mrs. Knox's thoughts turned to Fanny. " I must go to her," she insisted.

Knox took her in his arms. " You always had forebodings."

" We must leave at once," she cried.

Knox roused the men, ordered his boat, and hurried to his room to get dressed.

They reached the Consulate a little before dawn. Life was already astir in the river, boatmen called to each other, women washed themselves at the edge of the water, children were splashing in it. But the town was not yet awake. The vast stretch of the Chinese bazaar was dark and silent. At the British Consulate only the guards stirred; two Indian soldiers, their rifles on their shoulders, stamped and turned in the way the Guards were at that moment stamping and turning outside Queen Victoria's Palace in London.

The servants were roused and told to prepare some tea.

" Go and see," Knox said to Singh, " if Mr. Gould can come at once."

When Gould arrived Knox told him to make all possible inquiries. When he left, dawn was breaking. The day was Saturday, the 29th March, 1879.

Chapter Thirteen

WHEN Gould returned he found Knox dozing in the long veranda chair. " Is there any news? " he asked.

" Nothing official has yet been given out. But such news as I have been able to pick up is not good."

" Out with it," snapped Knox irritably.

" It's just that . . ."

" Come to the point, Gould."

" Phra Preecha was tried last night by the Council of State; they ordered that he should be flogged."

" Flogged! " Knox's voice rose to a shout. He leapt out of his chair. " A nobleman in Preecha's position—and my son-in-law! Flogged! Have you learned what the charges are? "

" No."

" When was the trial held—before the return of the Second King, or after? "

" I'm sorry, sir," said Gould, " I don't know. I talked this morning to one of the clerks at the Palace . . ."

" That's no good," Knox interrupted. " He wouldn't know anything. Have you had a word with Hunter? "

" Not yet. I thought I ought to see you before I did that, in case you preferred to have a word with the Regent yourself."

" Yes, that's true. Without knowing the exact nature of the charges, how can I interfere? "

He reflected for a while. Then he said angrily: " The Regent certainly sought advice before he did this. No doubt he consulted Alabaster, who, being familiar with the regulations that govern our activities in the Consulate, must have told him

214

that I cannot possibly interfere. The first thing we have to do, Gould, is to try and find out what the charges are. Then we shall know where we stand and we shall be able to see what we can do."

" Yes, sir."

Knox rose at once and went to his desk. He decided to make a formal demand through the normal official channel, and accordingly addressed his note to the Foreign Minister, Chow Phya Bhaunwong. He realised that the Minister was completely under the domination of the Regent, who was also his half-brother. None the less, it was the only channel through which he could make his demand.

He wrote: " I understand that Phra Preecha has been arrested and, as he is married to my daughter, I shall be glad if you can furnish me with particulars of the charge or charges on which he is being held."

" Have this dispatched at once by hand, Gould," Knox said. " We shall have to wait in painful inactivity until we get a reply."

Most of the time Fanny sat numbed and stupefied. Suddenly she would jump up from her chair and rush out of the house; then she had to be seized and brought back.

" Let me go. Let me go to him," she would scream.

" Where will you go? " Phya Kesab asked gently. " As soon as we know where he is, we shall take you there."

By noon she had decided on a different plan. She would go at once to see the King. " Please let me go. Please." She turned from one to the other. " The King will surely tell us something."

" They will not let you see him," Phya Kesab explained.

" But," she cried in exasperation, " we cannot sit here doing nothing! "

" Nothing is happening to him," said Kesab, exercising great self-control, for he, too, had heard that his son had been flogged.

When afternoon came and still there was no news, Kesab and Pet Pichai decided to go to see the Regent—if he would receive them. Fanny insisted on going with them and ran ahead of them to the boat. Pet Pichai looked at his father.

" Let her come," said the old man. " We cannot hold her back any longer."

They were ushered into the Regent's main drawing-room, with its mirrors and Cupids and Sèvres vases and monstrous oriental figures, and asked to wait. After a time Hunter came in and told them that the Regent was not at home.

Phya Kesab looked him straight in the eyes. " That is not true," he said. " If it were, we would have been told when we arrived and not kept waiting for half an hour."

" His Excellency is not in," Hunter repeated.

" You mean he is not in to us," Fanny shouted.

" Sshh! " said Kesab.

" Can you tell us," Fanny went on, her voice still raised, " where my husband is? "

" I don't know," Hunter said softly.

" Do you mean by that that he is not in this house? "

" I can assure you, Miss Knox . . ."

" How dare you call me Miss Knox! Have you been instructed to do that by your master? "

" I beg your pardon, Baroness Preecha. I can assure you that Phra Preecha is not in this building. Where he is I cannot say."

" Cannot say? " she echoed. " What do you mean? "

" I understand how you feel . . ."

" Understand? " she repeated. " How can you understand? Your wife hasn't been arrested, has she? "

Hunter remained silent, and gazed at the ground.

Suddenly through a door at the far end of the room a figure emerged, gaunt, side-whiskered.

" Mr. Alabaster! " Fanny shouted. " What has Preecha

done to you? Could you think of no better way of punishing my father—or me? "

He looked at her and his face hardened. Then he walked on. After he had gone, she began to sob.

When her tears subsided, Hunter came up to her and whispered: " I would like to help you, Baroness, but what can I do? It would not help if I tried to intervene. Truly it wouldn't."

He paused. He looked at her large eyes, now so reddened with crying, and added: " I can tell you one thing. Phra Preecha is not here. And truly I don't know where he is, nor what the charges against him are. But I have heard that one of them—and I say one, because I fear there may be more— is that he contracted this marriage without first seeking the King's consent. His Majesty's consent is required for every marriage contracted by a nobleman, and it is especially necessary in the case of marriage with a foreigner."

As Hunter turned to go, he said: " Believe me, if I could help in any way, I would."

" Come," said Kesab, taking Fanny's arm. " Let us go. No purpose can be served by our remaining here."

She allowed herself to be led out.

For two days there was no news, then on the 31st March Knox received a reply to the note he had sent to the Foreign Minister. He was officially informed that " The Council of State and Privy Council assembled had heard the following charges:

While the King was residing at Bang Pa In, engaged in the consecration of the monastery Nivet Tham Pravate, attended by great numbers of noblemen of all ranks, His Majesty and the Senabodi observed that Phra Preecha Kolakan took the daughter of Her Britannic Majesty's Consul General to live with him there, without her father's consent, in his steam yacht, letting all men and all ranks see that he had neither fear nor respect for anyone, trusting to the British law that a woman over twenty-one years of age is her own mistress.

Her Britannic Majesty's Consul General, proceeding to Bang Pa In to have audience of His Majesty, became aware of this and was deeply shamed and grieved, and on his return was constrained to yield his daughter. Should no notice be taken of Phra Preecha's action, those who wish to guard their female relations may be much disquieted. The British Consul General is a person of rank appointed by Her Majesty Queen Victoria as representative of Her Government and his dignity is high, comparable to that of the high nobility of Siam. Is this contemptuous behaviour of Phra Preecha Kolakan censurable by the State? Is it an outrage of the high nobility or is it not?

Again Phra Preecha Kolakan, having by Royal favour been appointed to high official positions, now, acting on his own will, takes as his chief wife the daughter of a foreign official, without first submitting the matter to the King, or informing the great nobles and asking their consent. Is this presumptuous conduct an offence to the State?

Phra Preecha Kolakan, manager of the Kabin gold mines, has drawn from the Treasury more than 15,500 catties and has rendered only 111 catties, 8½ tamplungs and three cwt. of gold.

Now that he has behaved in this publicly vain and foolish manner, let the Council of State and Privy Council advise what shall be done.

The official statement added that the answers given were "that he has committed these offences, namely (1) of contemptuous and censurable behaviour in his yacht with the daughter of a foreign official; (2) contempt of Royal authority; (3) mismanagement of the gold mines at Kabin.

"Judges are to be appointed to audit his accounts and investigate whether the money was properly spent."

It was added that the verdict was "signed unanimously by the whole Council assembled, with the exception of some

members who were absent from Bangkok on account of illness."
There followed thirty signatures, eleven of these were of
members of the Royal family. Prince Damrong's was not
among them. Knox noticed that the Regent had not himself
signed the document.

The sentence was appended: " For such irregular, contemptuous and outrageous conduct, let Phra Perim Worathep
take Phra Preecha and cause him to receive thirty strokes, so
that other officials may not follow his example."

"Monstrous!" said Knox, looking at Gould seated opposite
him. " This is a foul slander on the good name and honour
of my daughter, which is an insult to me. To have flogged
Preecha is an assault on the dignity of my office as Political
Agent and Consul General, and therefore an insult to Her
Majesty. I must deal with this at once."

He rang the bell. Singh came salaaming to the door. " Send
in my secretary. I want him to take a letter." He turned to
Gould. " I suppose it is their intention to make this document
public, for it says "so that other officials may not follow his
example."

When his secretary came in Knox began to dictate a reply
to the Minister of Foreign Affairs:

" I am in receipt of the official report of the proceedings
against Phra Preecha, and note:

(1) That the charges brought against him were referred to a
court consisting of the Privy Council, who passed sentence
without even seeing the defendant or hearing what he had to
say, and that afterwards he was given a severe flogging which
was accorded the utmost publicity.

(2) That my daughter is assumed and publicly declared to have
been guilty of a great impropriety, without any inquiry having
been made as to the truth or otherwise of this allegation.

(3) That Phra Preecha has been tried and punished for an
offence alleged to have been committed against myself, Her

Majesty's Agent and Consul General, though I was not consulted in the matter and had not consented thereto.

To proceedings such as these it is impossible for me to submit. How far they were intended to be injurious to me is a matter with which I have not to deal, but in so far as they have taken place and that great publicity has been given them, I am obliged to call on His Majesty and the Royal Council for a written apology.

If what has occurred was done in haste and without consideration, I shall be glad to hear that such is the case, provided the apology is ample and sufficient.

If, on the other hand, I find that no apology is forthcoming, I shall proceed to take such measures as may secure the redress to which no impartial person can doubt that I am justly entitled.

I further trust that the Siamese Government will see the advisability of at once releasing Phra Preecha from his present confinement for any offence committed in respect of the charges contained in the document sent me."

He broke off and said to Gould: " Since they have already delivered judgment and inflicted punishment, there can be no reason for them to continue to keep him in confinement. Nevertheless," he turned again to his secretary, " add this:

" ' I shall thus be spared the necessity of demanding his release which I fully believe I am entitled to do on grounds which it is unnecessary to allude to at present.

" ' If Phra Preecha has been guilty of other offences, in respect of such offences all that I would ask is a fair trial, for I have no wish to screen him from any punishment to which he may be justly liable.' "

Turning to Gould, he asked: " How does that sound? "

" I suppose, sir, it is politic to add that last sentence? "

" I think so, for I must not appear to be interfering in any way with their laws."

Gould nodded.

Knox then instructed his secretary to make two extra copies of the letter, as well as of the Foreign Minister's official note. One copy was to go to the Foreign Secretary, Lord Salisbury, together with a covering letter setting out the background and facts. The other was to go to Fanny without any covering letter.

"I shall, of course, inform Lord Salisbury," Knox said to Gould, "that the Regent wanted my daughter to marry his favourite grandson and was furious at her choice of another suitor. I shall also mention that her many suitors included some of the Royal Princes, for Lord Salisbury must see this incident in its true light and must recognise that my daughter is not a person of a flighty or loose disposition. Far from it—very far from it."

Chapter Fourteen

To Fanny after two days of acute anxiety and scarcely any sleep, the papers sent by her father, while they brought information, brought no relief; indeed, the news that Preecha had been flogged caused her to become hysterical.

When she was able to think again, she told Kesab and the others: " Now they cannot keep him much longer. He has been punished. At least now they will let him come home."

Then slowly there seeped into her agonised imagination the thought that perhaps they would not let him come home yet. Other charges had been mentioned . . . the gold mines at Kabin.

Phya Kesab, able so far to restrain himself in Fanny's presence, could now contain himself no longer. He smote his head, wailing.

Then he rose briskly, and prepared to leave the room.

" Where are you going? " Fanny asked.

" To the Regent. I shall sit on his doorstep—for days if need be. Then he cannot avoid seeing me."

" I shall come too."

" No, Fanny. You can do nothing. Leave it to me." He hurried to his boat.

Fanny thought of Louis and of his close friendship with the King. Should she go to Chiengmai and see him? Writing would take too long. There was no one else she could think of. Not a line from Papa—just the documents, but at least he was fighting for Preecha's release. Not a word from Mamma either. Papa must have prevented her from coming or writing.

Darkness set in; Phya Kesab had not yet come back. Fanny went to see Pet Pichai.

"He knows what he is doing," Pet Pichai comforted her. "I am sure he has a plan. He is very shrewd."

Nevertheless, an hour later, Pet Pichai himself set out in his boat. He returned in the small hours, without having been able to find his father. "I only hope they have not arrested him too," he said.

Fanny decided to send a telegram to Caroline:

P. arrested. Must see Louis urgently. Please ask him return Bangkok quickly. Desperate—F.

She had just finished writing it when Kesab returned. He was weary and dishevelled and fell into a chair. Spreading out his hands, he said: "Nothing."

"Where did you go?"

"Many, many places. To your father——"

"Did you see him?"

"Yes. He knows nothing. He is awaiting an answer from the Foreign Minister. I then went to the Foreign Minister myself." He shut his eyes and shook his head.

"Did you see him?"

"In the office there were just the clerks, half of them asleep. They knew who I was, of course. They said the Minister was busy, but I brushed them aside and went in. He was alone in his room playing chess."

"What did he say?" Fanny leaned forward.

"He asked me to sit down and have a game. I swept the board off the table. I asked if he had received your father's letter. He said he had. I asked what he was going to do about it. He said he did not know. It was not for him to decide. The letter had been sent on to the Regent."

"Did you go to the Regent?"

"Yes. I have just come from there. I waited many hours—

but they kept saying: ' He is out. He is out.' I asked: ' Doesn't he come home to sleep? ' They did not answer."

She read out the telegram she intended to send Caroline. " If only Louis can see the King I think it may help."

The old man shook his head. " It won't help," he said sadly. " There's much more behind this plot than you imagine. Your marriage is only an excuse. There is the animosity against my family, which has been fostered for so long by the Regent and his supporters. And even that is not the root of the matter."

" I think I'll send the telegram, Phya Kesab. The King is now of age. If Louis talked to him it might give His Majesty the chance he has been waiting for—to assert himself and get rid of the Regent."

" You have put your finger right on the true seat of the trouble. The King wants to assert himself. He feels it is time he ruled. The Regent has been aware of this and it has suited him well to arrest my son, *because* he is the King's favourite. By this he hopes to frighten all those who are the King's friends and to warn them that each one of them will be dealt with in exactly the same way if they support the King in his struggle to be free of the Regent. This is a duel for power."

On the 3rd April Knox received the reply for which he had been waiting. The Foreign Minister wrote:

I beg you to understand that Phra Preecha's offence in having acted disrespectfully and contemptuously towards the King and towards great personages has already been punished. That matter is at an end.

But there are also other complaints entered which must be investigated. The common people have brought complaints against him, asserting that he had oppressed and harassed their relations—some even to death. Five different complaints have been made.

The letter continued:

Sir Thomas Knox,
Consul General in Bangkok

Fanny's sister,
Caroline, with her
son, Thomas George
Leonowens

Part of King Chulalongkorn's Summer Palace at Bang Pa In

The audience pavilion of the King's Palace in Bangkok,
where Fanny was received by the King

In regard to your inference that the matter was intended to be injurious to you, the King and the Royal Council are very sorry.

" My inference! " Knox roared. " They are sorry. . . . This is no apology." He turned to the Siamese version attached. " It's even worse in the original," he added. " I am not going to accept that."

He replied at once: " Merely to state that I have inferred that an injury has been done me is no apology. This is the last time I shall ask you for that which I fully believe I have a right to demand."

As Singh left with the letter, Knox turned to Gould. " You will observe how everything appears to be done in the King's name, whereas in fact His Majesty has had no hand in any of it. The whole of this monstrous manœuvre is part of the Regent's determination to curb the King's authority. If the King stands up to him, we shall win."

Then, the truth of what he had just said coming home to him, he wrote to the King. Ignoring protocol, ignoring the Regent, he asked urgently for an audience. " It will," he told Gould, " give His Majesty added strength if he feels he has the might of England on his side. I should like you to come with me, Gould. It will help to make the approach less personal."

Knox wrote again to Lord Salisbury. He stated:

After looking carefully into this matter, I cannot take any other view than that the Regent's motives are in part a desire to revenge himself upon Preecha and in part a determination to make an irreparable breach between myself and the King.

Phra Preecha's offence against the King was of a venial character. There is no law against marriage with foreigners, nor, as the document sent me states, is it customary for an official to ask the King's permission to marry one of his own people. Phra Preecha neglected to take leave of the King when he left Bang Pa In: this is his only offence, and considering his state of mind on this occasion, his neglect can hardly cause surprise.

I cannot desert Phra Preecha. Were I to do so no Siamese would ever dare to come near me in the future and my position would become intolerable—and indeed that of any other persons who might be appointed to succeed me would thereby be rendered extremely difficult.

Preecha is one of the King's favourites and probably among the most faithful of them. This being so, it is clear that in punishing him the King acted under compulsion, for he is certainly aware that one of the principal motives actuating the Regent is a wish to frighten all his faithful followers so that the King may fall wholly into his power.

Having got so far with his letter, Knox paused and sat trying to think of some way of strengthening the King's position. After a time a light came into his eyes.

" I've got it," he said to Gould. " I'll send for a gunboat, I'll telegraph to Singapore for one. Its sudden appearance will give them a shock. Can you imagine what they'll think when it comes up the Menam bristling with guns, and anchors just off the Grand Palace . . ."

" A brainwave, sir," Gould said. " It'll scare the hair off their heads."

" Now "—Knox turned again to his secretary—" to go on with the letter to Lord Salisbury ":

I am sending for one of H.M.'s gunboats and on her arrival here I will make a final demand for an apology and for the release of Phra Preecha.

If I find that there is a *prima facie* case against him on the new charges, I shall place no difficulties in the way of a fair trial. On the other hand, if he has committed no offence and

I find that the King wishes it, I shall have him sent out of the country.

I am convinced that on the arrival of the gunboat I shall at once obtain compliance with my demands.

Beaming, Knox turned to Gould. " I think that ought to settle it," he exclaimed.

Chapter Fifteen

CAROLINE sent Fanny's telegram by special messenger up to the teak forest where her husband was working. Four days later Fanny had a reply from Louis: " Setting out at once. Hope to be with you by the end of April." It was just like Louis, she thought, always kind and ready to help. He was leaving Caroline even though her child was almost due.

As the monsoon was not likely to break for some weeks, the journey through the low, shrunken rivers was bound to be slow. Louis's estimate appeared to Fanny to be over-optimistic. She must resign herself to a long wait.

She knew that new charges were to be brought against Preecha. Though her father neither wrote nor came, nor would allow Mamma to visit her, she realised that this was not due to anger or resentment, but to a strict sense of preserving his complete personal detachment from the affair, which he wanted to handle on an official basis. Mamma sent many messages. They were brought by Princess Chandr, who with commendable courage defied the Regent's disapproval and called on Fanny repeatedly. She could not provide information, she could not help in any way, but she was able to say: " I saw your mother. She is thinking of you and sends her love. She feels very deeply about all this, but thinks it better not to come herself for the time being."

Phya Kesab had called frequently at the Consulate and was able to tell Fanny that her father was actively pulling strings in order to obtain Preecha's release. He also told her that Knox had written to the King.

On the 10th April Fanny, who could bear inactivity no longer, decided to go and fetch the children. She set out in the *Sunbeam*, with only her servants to accompany her. When she arrived the people of Prachin gathered round her with sad faces and eager inquiries about their beloved Governor. Many asked if they might return with her to plead for his release.

" I shall need you all," she said. " I will let you know when the time comes."

After four days she returned to Bangkok with Trakun and Arun and Oun.

Knox, meanwhile, had received a further evasive letter from the Foreign Minister. He wrote:

I beg to explain that the reason why the Siamese Government considered that your feelings had been constrained was because—considering the great affection existing between a father and a daughter, and only desiring to encourage such relations in the future—they observed that Phra Preecha went and brought the lady to his own house and married her in pursuance of his will, without the presence of either father or mother or any of the other relatives, in a manner that has never been done before. Therefore it was thought that your feelings must have been constrained.

This letter greatly incensed Knox. In a sharp reply he pointed out that he himself had arranged this marriage, adding that certain conditions had to be complied with and an official from the Consulate, namely, Mr. E. B. Gould, the Vice-Consul, was present in person to see that these conditions were fulfilled.

On the following day a telegram came from Singapore which read: " No gunboat at present available. Will be despatched as soon as possible." It was signed Vice-Admiral Robert Coote, Commander-in-Chief, China Station.

This was exasperating; as soon as possible might mean days or even weeks. Knox instructed Gould to send a second telegram to the Admiral, asking that a gunboat should be despatched without further delay. " There must be at least one gunboat in Hong Kong or China that can be spared," he complained.

Completely frustrated and uneasy at receiving no reply from the King, who was usually so punctilious, Knox mounted his horse and rode off to the Palace, and on arriving there asked for an audience with the King. He was told that His Majesty was engaged.

Sensing this to be untrue, he tried to force his way in, but was restrained by the guards.

" Don't you dare lay your hands on me," he shouted. "Go in and tell the King I must see him. It's urgent."

At this moment the Lord Chamberlain appeared. Tripping rapidly down the stairs he came up to Knox and in an ingratiating voice said: " Please, please, Mr. Knox. The King will gladly see you. But he can't to-day."

" The matter I want to discuss with him is an urgent one."

" Yes, Mr. Knox, and His Majesty wants to see you—indeed, I have come especially to make an appointment. Would to-morrow afternoon——"

" This afternoon," Knox interrupted.

" This afternoon at four, then."

Knox looked at his watch. It was two o'clock. He glared at the Lord Chamberlain. " In two hours! "

" Only two hours, Mr. Knox. Please . . ."

" Four o'clock, then."

As Knox remounted and turned his horse, the Lord Chamberlain mopped his brow. " At four o'clock," he said to the guards, " you let the gentleman in."

Knox brought Gould with him when he returned at four. They were admitted at once and were escorted personally by the Lord Chamberlain to the Throne Hall. Knox was astonished to find representatives of the Regent and of the

Foreign Minister there. As the King entered with his A.D.C., Prince Kaphia, the Siamese officials grouped themselves beside the throne.

This meant that the King would not be allowed to talk freely; evidently he was still under the strict surveillance of the Regent. Knox asked the King if he could speak to him in private.

His Majesty demurred, but finally agreed that the others should be asked to sit a little farther away "at two fathoms distance," the King said, " from the Consul General."

This encouraged Knox, for it indicated that His Majesty was prepared to assert himself. The King insisted, however, that his A.D.C., who was acting as his secretary, should sit near enough to take notes of all that was said at the interview.

Knox began by saying: " I was a friend of Your Majesty's father. He loved and trusted me. . . . I have now come to ask his son who devised the new charges that have been brought against Phra Preecha ? "

The King replied cautiously: " The proceedings were drawn up by collective agreement."

Knox then said: " Her Britannic Majesty's Agent and Consul General has been slandered. It is my duty to point out that I regard this not only as an insult to myself but also to the country I represent, and thus I feel obliged to take the strongest measures to obtain satisfaction."

" What do you mean by the strongest measures? " the King asked.

Knox fumbled in his pocket. " Your Majesty may not realise the position, or the action which my Government may be obliged to take." In his hand he held a cutting from a newspaper, but instead of giving it to the King, he gave it to Gould and asked him to read it out.

The cutting was from the *Straits Times* of Singapore, dated Sunday, 13th April, 1879. It quoted a message from Madras, bearing the date, 3rd April. Gould read it aloud in English in a firm and steady voice.

" A Rangoon paper states that the ultimatum to be despatched to the King of Burma will contain the following conditions:

" A British garrison is to be cantoned at Mandalay, to be paid for by the Burmese Government.

" The British Residency is to be fortified.

" No decision of importance to be taken by the Burmese Government without the sanction, previously obtained, of the Resident, who is to have free admittance to interviews with the King in a manner becoming the dignity of Her Majesty's Representative.

" A proper and enlightened system of administration, fiscal and judicial "—Gould stressed the word judicial—" is to be introduced into Upper Burma, and faithfully carried out by the King's Government. All expenses attending the carrying out of these measures to be borne by the Burmese Government.

" All existing treaties with foreign courts to be cancelled, the King to be prohibited from entering into any further treaties without the sanction of the British Government, and to be prohibited from ennobling any foreigner in his service."

Knox was taking a gamble but, aware that he was in no position to deliver such an ultimatum himself, he had decided to hint at what might happen if the Siamese Government remained unresponsive to the reasonable demands he, as the Chief Representative of Her Britannic Majesty, had made. He watched the King's face closely as Gould read it. Not a muscle moved, His Majesty's expression remained rigid.

" These developments in Burma," Knox said, " occurred because the Burmese Government claimed that the question on which the English had intervened was an internal affair and did not concern them—it is a close parallel to the present case."

The King asked: " Did not this case arise because the King of Burma killed princes who were his relations? "

" Yes," replied Knox.

There was a pause. " Your Majesty was not the instigator of the present proceedings. Your Majesty could even now disassociate yourself from the arrangement."

" My name was at the head of the charges sent to the court," said the King.

" If," replied Knox with increasing emphasis, " Your Majesty does not disassociate yourself from the proceedings, Your Majesty will be responsible, and if I act the whole State will feel the consequences."

He had thrown down the gage.

The King was silent.

Knox went on: " There are many instances of kings disassociating themselves from the decisions of their advisers, upon whom the penalty then falls. Your Majesty can dismiss your advisers."

The King appeared to be considering this suggestion. Dare he take that step? He looked around him a little uneasily and said very quietly: " Phra Preecha committed an offence."

" Only the trifling offence of not taking leave of Your Majesty. His greatest offence was against myself. I did not exact vengeance, but gave him my daughter. Who else can have a right to punish him in my place? Using my name in these proceedings is a great insult to me."

" There was no intention," the King replied, " of insulting you. This is a misinterpretation for which the Minister of Foreign Affairs has already apologised. What more do you want? "

" A clear and unmistakable apology," Knox said, " and the release of Phra Preecha."

" You only ask these two things? And if they are granted

you will then withdraw from all other matters? " the King asked.

" Yes," replied Knox.

After some reflection, the King, glancing again across the room at the Regent's men, said: " The complaints against Phra Preecha are many and various. I ask you not to disturb yourself as yet. Wait and see the result of the examination. It is the general opinion that Phra Preecha has committed many grave offences. We must inquire into the truth."

" How can Your Majesty ask me to wait for the result of the trial? " said Knox. " The judges are evil men and dependants of the Regent. I urge Your Majesty at least to insist on the appointment of trustworthy judges; and I beg that the irons, which I have learned are fastened on to the ankles of Phra Preecha, be removed, though I still hope that, while awaiting his trial, he may be permitted through Your Majesty's intervention, to return home."

The King looked up at the ceiling, then still again at the Regent's men. " While the case is proceeding, how can he be released? " His Majesty asked.

" I did not know that it was the custom to put a man in irons pending trial," said Knox.

" It is customary," replied the King in a lowered voice.

At this point Gould interposed: " Your Majesty must recognise that if he is kept *incommunicado* this will prevent Phra Preecha from getting his witnesses."

Turning to Gould, His Majesty said: " Phra Preecha belongs to me. I have raised him up. I have treated him kindly. It is not my wish that evil should come upon him "—he paused and added: " *unless* he is guilty. If only he had first told me of this matter. But he told me nothing."

" Speak not of yourself only, Your Majesty," Knox said. " He did not even tell me. But his offence was small and the punishment is too heavy."

" There are also his offences as Governor of——" the King began, but Knox interrupted him.

" He was, *and is*, an adherent to Your Majesty. If Your Majesty is going to yield over this, you had better order a consignment of fetters from Birmingham, for Siam and all its people will become slaves of the Regent. He and the Foreign Minister intend to wrest the sovereignty from Your Majesty and destroy you."

To Knox's surprise, the King nodded. " I know," he murmured, " that there are some men who do not like me."

It was clear to Knox that the King did not feel he was strong enough to fight. At any rate, not yet. So he decided to make a statement which, he hoped, would make the King believe that he had the might of Britain behind him if he chose to act.

" I have sent for a man-of-war," he said slowly. " Unless I cancel my request, it will arrive within two or three days. In the circumstances I beg Your Majesty before it is too late to tell me clearly what action you intend to take in relation to my complaint and request."

The King appeared to be weighing the position. Then he asked: " What exactly do you desire? "

" I have three wishes," Knox replied. " An adequate apology. The immediate release of Phra Preecha; and should there be evidence which justifies a trial, then let the trial be conducted by fair judges, not slaves of the Regent."

After a long silence, the King said: " I must consult my ministers."

" Will you consult the Regent? " Knox demanded.

" He is a very great personage and must be consulted."

Knox rose, saying: " I am the representative of a very great country, and if I do not get satisfaction, its Government will certainly support me. And then Siam will suffer severely."

When they were outside, Gould said: " No one could have fought harder, sir."

His chief looked at him with gratitude mingled with embarrassment. " I went too far," he said, " I had no authority for some of the things I said. But let's face up to it, we are fighting now for my son-in-law's life."

Chapter Sixteen

IT WAS NOT until the end of April that Lord Salisbury received the first of Knox's letters, soon followed by the second.

He sent for Sir Julian Pauncefote, the Assistant Under-Secretary of State for Foreign Affairs. Sir Julian, just turned fifty, had been a barrister and had spent many years in the Far East. He had practised at the Hong Kong bar and had later been Attorney-General there, before returning home to be a Civil Servant.

Sir Julian had already read Knox's letters. " In my opinion, my lord, we cannot do much at this stage. We shall have to await developments, if there are any. If the apology is forthcoming, all may be well."

Lord Salisbury looked at the letters again. " I do not share your view, Pauncefote. Knox says quite specifically here, ' I cannot possibly desert Preecha.' I do not think Knox will be satisfied with an apology. He wants his son-in-law's release. But this man is a Siamese subject and there are other outstanding charges against him. What if the Siamese Government do not agree to release him? We cannot allow a gunboat to be used to get this fellow out of prison."

" If I may be allowed to point out, my lord," said Pauncefote, " his plea is not that his son-in-law should escape the law." He picked up the letter. " He writes, ' If I find that there is a *prima facie* case against him on the new charges, I shall put no difficulties in the way of a fair trial.' "

" All the same, we shall have to keep an eye on that gunboat," replied Lord Salisbury sourly. " We have enough problems on our hands—Afghanistan, South Africa and Burma, which has a common frontier with Siam. In the circumstances it would be disastrous to get involved in a war over the love affair of a consul's daughter."

Pauncefote felt that his chief's attitude was perhaps rather too prudent and unfeeling, so he ventured to argue with him. "We ought not to risk going to war, my lord," he said. "But the mere presence of a gunboat might have a great influence on the Siamese Government, since they would assume that we were prepared to act."

"If you wish to be prepared to act you may have to act," retorted Lord Salisbury.

"What would you like me to do about this, sir?" Pauncefote asked dutifully.

Lord Salisbury thought for a moment. "I can appreciate Knox's predicament. So do nothing for the time being. Let us see how things develop."

Pauncefote smiled. "The Siamese Consul General in London, David Mason, who is an Englishman, used to be in Hong Kong when I was there. I know him well and I'll keep in touch with him."

"Good, Pauncefote. But you understand clearly that whatever happens we shall not engage in war against Siam."

Louis arrived in Bangkok on the evening of the 5th May. As soon as his boat pulled up at Phya Kesab's landing-stage, he leapt out and dashed across the courtyard to Fanny's house. He was tired and unshaven, but looked bronzed and well. He took Fanny in his arms and kissed her.

"Oh, Louis," she cried. "I can't tell you how grateful I am to you for coming. How is Caroline? When does she expect the baby?"

"Any minute now, and she has not been very well. I'm worried about her."

Fanny's eyes began to fill with tears. "Then it was all the more kind of you to come. Do you think we can do anything, Louis?"

"I hope so. What are the charges? Why are they holding him? Why isn't he tried?"

Phya Kesab, who had hurried out of his house on seeing Louis, answered from the doorway. "They are bringing further charges. And when those are disposed of, they will bring still others."

"I must see the King," Louis said. "He alone can put a stop to this."

"Mr. Knox has already seen him," Phya Kesab said, his aged grey eyes soft and sad behind his gold-rimmed glasses. "It was unfortunately of no avail."

"I shall go to see your father now," Louis told Fanny, and strode briskly towards the door.

"Louis," Fanny called, "will you come straight back here, no matter how late it is? I'll be waiting up for you."

Louis thought Knox looked very haggard, and all Mrs. Knox's vivacity had deserted her.

They talked for a while about Caroline. "I wish you had brought her with you," said Mrs. Knox. "We can scarcely sleep for worrying.''

"Why don't you go and see Fanny?" Louis asked bluntly.

Mrs. Knox looked at her husband.

"Because," he said, "so far as I am concerned, this is an official matter. I can serve Fanny's case with much more authority by taking up this attitude. It must not become a personal matter, and I have been extremely careful that it should not be regarded in that light, either by the officials here or by the Foreign Office at home. I hope you appreciate my point of view, Louis."

"Yes, sir. But——"

" There is no ' but '. And surely Fanny knows that I am fighting for Preecha's release."

Louis was silent. Mrs. Knox stared at her husband. She could neither understand nor accept his attitude. He had insisted that, as the wife of Britain's representative, she would have to avoid doing anything that would compromise her husband or interfere with the execution of his duties. Officials had to control their personal feelings, he had told her—and their wives must do the same.

" What is the position now? " Louis asked.

" I have asked for a gunboat to be sent from Singapore. I think the King would like to intervene if he felt that he had sufficient support."

" When is the gunboat due? "

" It is overdue. But I heard to-day that it is on its way and should be here in a few days' time."

" Do you think the Regent will yield? "

Knox smiled. " Siam is in no position to fight Britain, as he well knows, and indeed I have heard that he has been trying to shift his position and is now putting it about that he had nothing to do with Preecha's arrest, which was, he says, the work of the Foreign Minister."

" I thought of going to see the King, sir," Louis said. " It's just possible he might be influenced by a personal appeal from me."

" I think he might," said Knox, " especially if the Regent is really climbing down. One of my demands has been satisfied since my interview, for yesterday I received a full apology from the Foreign Minister. But that was only one of three demands."

Louis rose to go.

" We can put you up," said Knox. " Or have you made other arrangements? "

" I've arranged to stay at the Oriental Hotel," Louis replied. " I thought it better not to stay at the Consulate."

The Governor's house at Prachin, in which Fanny and her
husband lived after their marriage

The view from Fanny's window in Prachin

Bangkok. April 6. 1879.

My Lord

I very much regret to have to lay before your Lordship a report of an occurrence in which I am to some extent personally concerned through another closely connected with me.

In order that your Lordship should clearly understand it, I have therefore to enter into matters of a personal nature very painful for me to have to relate.

My daughter since her return from

To The most noble
The Marquis of Salisbury. K. G.
H. his Principal Secretary of St &c
for Foreign Affairs.

The first page of Sir Thomas Knox's letter to Lord Salisbury, informing the Foreign Secretary of the diplomatic crisis caused by his daughter's marriage and reporting that he had called for the despatch of a gunboat to Bangkok. (Crown Copyright: reproduced by permission of the Controller of H. M. Stationery Office)

" Exactly," said Knox. " You see now how I am placed."

Louis returned to Fanny and told her of his talk with her father. They sat up until the small hours. " You look very tired," he said more than once. At last she let him go.

" Shall I see you to-morrow? " she asked.

" Yes, as soon as I have something to report."

Early the next day Louis set out for the Palace and asked if he could have an audience with the King.

The Lord Chamberlain, hearing his voice in the outer room, bustled in and, smiling, took both Louis's hands in his.

" Come in. Come in," he said. " How is the teak business? "

" Going remarkably well. Would it be possible——? " Louis pointed towards the audience chamber.

" I'll see if I can arrange for you to see His Majesty. What is it you want to discuss with him? "

" My brother-in-law's fate."

The Chamberlain, looking very embarrassed, remarked: " His Majesty is most unhappy. I am sure he will tell you that himself."

He clapped his hands for tea to be brought for Louis, and then went on: "I think His Majesty may be free, and I am sure he would like to see you."

The Chamberlain was away quite a time. Louis meanwhile sipped his tea. When he returned he beamed, and announced. " His Majesty will be delighted to see you."

The Chamberlain ushered Louis in, then withdrew. The King came forward and embraced him. " My dear friend. I did not expect you to be back in Bangkok for quite a time yet."

" I'd like to have a word with Your Majesty, if I may, about Phra Preecha."

The King's face clouded. The muscles round his lips began to work. Presently in a very low voice he said: " You know that I am very fond of Preecha. He has been close to me for many years—he is more than a friend." He looked down at his hands, then without raising his eyes went on: " I am King, I know, but "—he pointed to the table—" I am still the little boy they chased round that. My father appointed Suriwong Bunnag, who was Prime Minister, to be Regent as well. Now he has made his son Prime Minister, but he still holds everything in his own hands. When I came of age the Regency should have ended. But he has been the head of the Government for so long that it is not easy for anyone—not even me—to strip him of his authority. There is much that I want to do for my country and for my people. But I shall have to wait."

The King rose, walked to the window and gazed towards the elephant lines where the sacred white elephants were being tended.

" Many of those around me," he went on, " though they appear to be westernised, have only a thin coating—a veneer —of culture. I owe it to your mother that I learned so much. What she taught me has influenced my outlook greatly. But those I have to contend with still look at life in the old way. That is why I must go slowly."

Louis nodded. " I see how difficult Your Majesty's position is. But I am concerned for Preecha. Time is not on his side. Before you reach that goal anything might happen to him."

The King shook his head. " I am sure that his case will soon be settled."

" He has been punished. Why then is he not released? " Louis spoke firmly.

" He was punished on one count. There are other charges."

Louis's eyes narrowed. " I have read the list: misgovernment and misappropriation? "

The King looked embarrassed as he replied: " I confess I find these charges incredible."

" Are thirty strokes with a rattan cane not enough? "

" My advisers do not think so. They are collecting evidence on the other counts."

" And he will remain in prison—for weeks, possibly for months . . ."

" Believe me, I have sought some way of helping my friend. I have read books of law. I have considered whether a king can make a *coup d'etat* against his Chief Minister." He shook his head. " The Regent is too deeply entrenched. He has all the other ministers in the palm of his hand."

The King placed both his hands on Louis's shoulders. " There may have to be a further trial, but I hope it is just a matter of waiting, and then he will be free again. Please tell Fanny this, and also that I feel deeply for her."

" I am grateful to Your Majesty," Louis replied, then he asked: " Might it be possible for Fanny to see him? "

" I shall arrange it. Tell her that."

After she had heard Louis's account of his interview with the King, Fanny said: " Thank you for arranging for me to see Preecha. That at least is something."

Early next morning, a personal letter arrived from the King for Fanny. He said that the Lord Chamberlain would call for her on Thursday evening at six o'clock and escort her personally to a place where she would meet her husband.

Hearing this, Louis asked her permission to return to Caroline. His departure made her nervous, but he had been so good in coming the moment he had received her telegram, and Caroline would need him so badly if her baby were to arrive during the next few days, that Fanny felt obliged to agree, as willingly as she could, to his going.

The Lord Chamberlain arrived in one of the smaller royal barges with eight men at the oars. He greeted Fanny warmly, and then accompanied her from the house to the boat. They travelled down the river. By a small white house near the edge of the water they alighted.

The place was well guarded. Men with rifles stood round it and sprang to attention as the Lord Chamberlain approached.

" I shall not come any farther," he said. " But I'll wait for you in the boat. They have allowed you half an hour."

Eagerly, yet nervously, she entered the house alone. At the farther end of the small hall she saw Preecha seated at a table, his back to her. He was dressed in a *panaung* and a short unbuttoned jacket. At the sound of her footsteps, he turned. His face, drawn and pale, flushed as he rose and walked towards her. She rushed forward and they held each other in a long embrace.

There was no one else in the room. But the door was left wide open and she could see beyond it the long shadows of the two men on guard there with their rifles on their shoulders.

" Darling," she said, " how dreadful! "

" Sshh! " he replied. " It is nothing. I have a bed. My food is quite good. I am a guest, and the Regent has manners enough to see that his guests are well cared for." He said nothing of the irons on his ankles which, on the Regent's instructions, had been removed that morning.

She slipped her hands under his jacket. She could feel the weals under her fingers.

" Oh, what have they done to you? " She burst into tears.

" Don't let's talk about it," he said. " We have so much to say."

Clinging to him, she wept. Then he took her hands and led her to a chair.

" Sit here," he said, " and we'll pretend that we are alone— as soon we will be."

" But why are they keeping you here? "

He shrugged his shoulders. " There are further charges. They are collecting evidence, looking for witnesses. . . . I don't think it will be easy for them to find any, for I have not "— he shook his head slowly—" misappropriated any funds . . . or . . . misgoverned."

" What questions did they ask you at your trial? "

" I wasn't present."

" And they call this justice."

She sat in silence, looking up at him. " When is the next trial to be? Do you know? "

He shook his head. " Without evidence they cannot keep me here for long. . . ."

They clung to each other.

" I think I'm going to have a baby," Fanny said.

" How happy we are going to be."

She nodded. " I went to Prachin to fetch Trakun and Arun."

" I'm glad. They are always happy with you."

They could hear the guards outside. Suddenly one of them dropped his rifle with a startling clatter. Then he appeared in the doorway. " It is time," he said.

As Fanny was on her way home the monsoon broke. The rain fell in torrents. On the river the boats began to race for the shore and the people scurried for shelter. She thought that Louis would be having a quick journey home. To her surprise she saw him standing at the door.

" What's the matter? " she called to him.

" Our baby has died," he said.

Quickly she opened the letter he handed her. It was from Marion Cheek, an American mission doctor in Chiengmai. "Mrs. Leonowens has had a long and agonising time . . . her life was in danger . . . we had to assist the birth. . . . Most unfortunately the child did not survive."

" How terrible! " Fanny said.

" It was a girl," Louis murmured. " We were going to call her Anna after my mother. I went on to the Consulate to tell them. Your mother was terribly upset."

Fanny tried to comfort him. After a while he asked about her visit to Preecha. She told him: " He's in pain. He didn't say so, but I could see that he was, and there were marks on his ankles, though at least they have now taken off the irons."

Louis realised that they had been taken off only for her visit, and quickly changed the subject, saying, " I have a message for you from your father. The Regent, it seems, has sent a special envoy to London to see Lord Salisbury."

" That is bad news, isn't it? If the envoy is successful, they will have Preecha at their mercy. Oh, Louis, when will all this end? "

" Soon, Fanny, I hope. If at any time you feel there's anything more I can do, send me a telegram."

" You are kind, Louis—very kind. Thank you for all you've done."

Chapter Seventeen

Two DAYS later Fanny received a copy of still another letter which her father had sent to Lord Salisbury.

> I have learned from a reliable source that a special envoy is on his way to see your lordship, to lay the case of the Siamese Government before you. The special envoy is Phya Phat Karawong.
>
> It is important that your lordship should appreciate of what the Siamese Government consists. There are four men of weight in the Government: the King, the Regent, the Prime Minister and the Foreign Secretary. The Regent and the Foreign Minister are half-brothers, and the Prime Minister is the Regent's son. The Regent and the Foreign Minister can be regarded as one; on the other hand, I have recently learned that the Prime Minister is inclined secretly to side with the King against his father, and there is, I understand, a secret pact for mutual support between His Majesty and the Prime Minister.
>
> The special envoy, now on his way to London, is also a half-brother of the Regent, and a full brother of the Foreign Minister, both being sons of the same minor wife. The envoy was partly educated in England, and on his return was placed in charge of the Royal Bodyguard, but, having been found guilty of defrauding the men of part of their pay, he was discharged from this office two years ago. He has since ceased to be connected with the Royal household, but is in close alliance with his brother, the Foreign Minister.

I understand that he will be bringing to your lordship what is termed evidence against Phra Preecha. This evidence has been obtained in the following manner. First, all the thieves and robbers of the district of which Phra Preecha had charge, have been released and brought to Bangkok! Here they have been kept in isolation. Their evidence has been taken during the last two or three days. The witnesses have been heard separately behind closed doors.

The accused was not present during the proceedings, and remains in ignorance of the charges brought against him; he has never been asked nor allowed to bring evidence to rebut the charges. Those witnesses who are not prisoners and who have been spoken to since their examination, declare that they were threatened with punishment unless they gave false evidence against Phra Preecha, and that pressure was used to make them accuse him of the most atrocious crimes, although they never before even heard a whisper of them.

The evidence is not intended to be made public in Siam— where no one would accept it. It has been concocted for the purpose of being laid before your lordship, in order to prejudice you against Phra Preecha. The plotters' hope is that, if you are convinced by it, I shall not be allowed to interfere any further, and that in consequence they have Phra Preecha thereafter at their mercy.

Although he is my son-in-law, I hope that you will permit me to give you an unbiased description of him. He is the most civilised man in Siam, an essentially good man and incapable of cruelty. He has great energy and ability, and the province he governs is in far better order than any other I ever visited in Siam. Those of my colleagues who have visited it will bear me out on this.

They, the other Consuls here, have been anxious to give me every assistance, but I thought it best to decline any offers of help. Nevertheless, the French Consul, without informing me, wrote a private remonstrance to the Regent.

Phra Preecha's release, my lord, is essential, for a fair trial; if he is kept in prison those who wish to give evidence in his favour will be afraid to come forward. If his release is accepted, there will be no trial, of this I am convinced. If he is not freed, I believe the Regent is capable of executing him, though I do not think the King would willingly allow this. His Majesty might, however, be coerced, if he were to be deprived of my support.

I should like to add that the despatches borne by the envoy are mostly Mr. Alabaster's work.

Fanny had never imagined that Preecha's life might be in danger. She was appalled. She couldn't breathe, she thought she was going to suffocate. After a time she comforted herself with the thought that perhaps Papa had only put that passage in so as to influence Lord Salisbury. She prayed it might be so, but a new and terrible anxiety had now come into her life.

At nine o'clock on the morning of Monday, the 12th May, the gunboat, plunging through gusts of heavy wind and rain, steamed up the river. Its commander, W. H. G. Nowell, was unfamiliar with Bangkok; he saw the Union Jack flying from the flagstaff at the Consulate, but saw also that the many wharves, barges and houseboats made that section of the river too congested for him to anchor there. He went on and anchored opposite the golden pagodas of the Royal Palace. This caused consternation among the Palace guard.

Knox welcomed Nowell with a hearty handshake, and invited him to stay.

Nowell knew why *Foxhound* had been sent to Bangkok, for Singapore was full of gossip and paragraphs had appeared in the local press describing Fanny's romance and the arrest of the bridegroom, the Consul General's son-in-law. Neither Knox nor he referred to the matter that evening.

The next day Knox visited *Foxhound* with Nowell and lunched with the officers. Rumours had already reached him that there was dissension in the Government; that the King and the Prime Minister were in favour of a climb down, while the Regent and the Foreign Minister were against any concessions. He was also told that during the night Preecha had been removed under heavy guard to an unknown destination.

Nowell did not call on the King or the Foreign Minister; he received an envoy sent by the latter, but did not return his visit.

A few days later an invitation was sent to all the officers of *Foxhound* to attend a garden party given by the Foreign Minister. Three junior officers went along. But the next morning Nowell issued an order stating specifically that "no intercourse shall take place between officers of Her Majesty's warship *Foxhound* and Siamese nationals."

Lord Salisbury had deferred replying to Knox's first despatch informing him of the arrest of Phra Preecha. But on learning from Singapore that a gunboat had been despatched, he sent Knox a telegram in cypher, which stated: "The information in your despatch does not justify your official interference in regard to Phra Preecha. You must not use force, or threaten to use force."

The following morning Salisbury was handed a telegram addressed to David Mason, the Siamese Consul General in London, notifying him that the special envoy had sailed from Singapore by P. & O. mail steamer. The telegram added: "British gunboat at Bangkok at Consul Knox's request. Inform quickly Foreign Office and beg telegraphic orders that no hostile acts be done until arrival of mission. Wire reply."

Salisbury at once sent for Robert Bourke, the Parliamentary

Secretary of State for Foreign Affairs, and for Pauncefote, and tossed the telegram across the table to them.

" We had better telegraph Knox again," he remarked. " He must not go too far, or before we know where we are the fat will be in the fire. There'll be questions in the Commons for you to deal with, Bourke. The Liberals will be at your throat."

" I agree," said Bourke, " and I suggest we word the telegram forcefully."

Thereupon they drafted the text. It stated: " Siamese Consul General in London intimates you are contemplating warlike operations in Siam. Is it true? If so, why? Reply by wire."

To this Knox instantly replied: " There is no truth in the report that I am contemplating war on Siam. The report of war probably came from Siamese Consul in Singapore, very likely acting under instructions from here and was sent in order that H.M.'s gunboat might be recalled.

" Foreign Minister had been boasting that I would get no support from home and that he had taken means to prevent the gunboat coming up."

Salisbury grunted when he read this.

" If I may suggest, my lord," said Pauncefote, " I'd leave the gunboat there for a while, if your lordship agrees. It appears to me that the whole of this unhappy business has been brought about through jealousy and that a very admirable man may lose his life because the Regent has taken as a slight the rejection of his grandson by our Consul's daughter."

" All right," said Salisbury. " We can leave the gunboat there for the time being."

Encouraged by the presence of the gunboat, Knox called again on the King and asked if it would be possible for Preecha to be released on bail.

The King walked restlessly up and down the room. Through the window the gunboat was visible.

" I wish I could comply with your wishes, Mr. Knox," he said.

" Does that mean that Your Majesty cannot arrange for him to be released? "

" I'm deeply sorry that this is so."

Knox went on: " They are releasing prisoners to gather evidence against Preecha, but will not release Preecha to gather evidence for his own defence. Moreover, he is fettered without having been found guilty. Could not Your Majesty take steps to ensure that his sufferings are alleviated? "

The King's eyes were sad as he replied: " I can do nothing of myself, and any promises made by me at a private audience are valueless."

" Will Your Majesty not try to use your influence . . .? "

" I will *try*."

Knox returned to the Consulate distressed and angry. It was plain that, gunboat or no gunboat, the Regent was determined not to give in. He, too, was extremely active behind the scenes. He appeared to be actuated by the thought that, with the envoy on his way, it would help if Preecha was tried at once and all the evidence against him was forwarded to Lord Salisbury. " The evidence must be summarised and wired to Mason in London for him to pass on to Lord Salisbury," he ordered.

The telegrams were despatched almost daily, always, for some reason, from Singapore: " Case—murder. Two Chinese, seven Siamese witnesses. Statement follows present mail."

" Case—cruelty. Deposition sent by mail."

The Regent also wrote to Colonel Anson, the Lieutenant-Governor of the Straits Settlement, at Singapore, asking him to intervene on behalf of the Siamese Government. Further, every Englishman in the Regent's service was asked to write to the

Foreign Office in London in condemnation of Knox's behaviour. Some wrote anonymously. One of these, a man named Hicks, who had been master of a merchant ship and was now assistant-secretary to Hunter, declared that Preecha had sixty wives, many of whom he had murdered. The most fantastic stories were forwarded.

On the Regent's instructions the Foreign Minister sent a despatch to London, stating that Preecha, aware that he was about to be arrested, had decided to marry the English Consul's daughter as his only means of escape.

And, as a further means of currying favour with the British Government, the Regent expressed a wish to confer the Order of the White Elephant on Queen Victoria and wrote to London saying that the special envoy was empowered to ask if Her Majesty would be graciously pleased to accept it.

Knox too was busy. His active mind never ceased groping for some possible solution. One idea that came to him was that of inducing the Prime Minister openly to oppose his father. If he could be persuaded to do so, it would provide immense support to the King. He asked Gould if he would visit him privately and sound him out. Gould agreed to do this and went that same afternoon. He had not an appointment, he said, but assured the Prime Minister's secretary that he had come on purely private business and, if received, would not detain the Prime Minister long.

He was admitted. The Regent's son received him cordially. They talked of a number of things, including the gunboat, which the Prime Minister said he was surprised he had not been invited to visit.

" Why are the officers being kept in such seclusion? " he asked. " It would be pleasant to have the opportunity of entertaining them and of showing them something of our country."

Gould replied: " I will arrange that, Your Excellency. But

I think Your Excellency must be aware of the reason for the presence of the gunboat."

" Yes," said the Regent's son, " I know. But how long is this going on? "

" That, sir, depends on the answer to a question I should like to ask Your Excellency and which I hope you will not regard as an impertinence. Does Your Excellency approve of the course of action that is being taken in the matter which is at issue between your country and ours? "

" I do not," answered the Prime Minister without any hesitation. " I think the present course of action is crooked and only calculated to bring the Government of this country into discredit and trouble. If it were left to me I could settle this matter in two hours."

" Thank you, sir," said Gould. " I am certain Your Excellency could settle this matter, and perhaps it may still be done."

When Gould reported this to Knox he was jubilant. " Thank you, Gould. That takes us an important step forward. Meanwhile," he added with a smile, " I have just received from London the Order of St. Michael and St. George, which was, you will remember, at my suggestion awarded to the Regent. But I take it that I can hardly be expected to invest him with it at this juncture."

He rose and put the box containing the Order into a drawer, which he then locked.

Chapter Eighteen

THE INITIAL awe of the populace on the arrival of the gunboat was soon replaced by a friendly curiosity. They gathered in their boats around *Foxhound*, smiled and chattered and waved their hands in greeting. Many stood on their roofs to see the man-of-war.

Nevertheless, it was not long before Knox began to receive petitions signed by groups of Siamese and Chinese, begging him to send the gunboat away and not involve the country in war. These were followed by angry demonstrations in front of the Consulate, in which boys hurled firecrackers from their boats on to the lawn and shouted insults, while men carrying banners with the words " Knox—Go Home " paraded up and down the New Road between the Consulate and the Palace. After a few days the demonstrations ceased.

The second trial of Phra Preecha was held in the pavilion of Sata Bhitom, at Bangkok. Again the prisoner was not present. Nor was Knox, or any of Preecha's closest relations, who were not even informed that it was taking place. Indeed, many weeks passed before they learned of it.

The charge was murder—three murders, in fact.

The first witness, Nai Kak, stated that his brother Kurt had been flogged to death at Prachin, on the Governor's instructions. This had occurred, so he said, fifteen months before.

The next witness was the gaoler, Luang Prachan. He stated that Phra Preecha, on learning that Kurt had seduced a woman named Chip who was in his service, ordered that Kurt should be given twenty lashes and held in prison in irons. This, he alleged, had happened on the 5th April, 1878. On the 3rd May, Kurt escaped. Later he was recaptured, and then on Preecha's orders a chain was placed round his neck and he was thus tethered for twelve days in the open, in front of the Governor's house.

The gaoler handed to the judges a statement which he said was written by Kurt while in prison. The writer accused Preecha of embezzling the King's money. The statement, the gaoler asserted, had been given by Kurt to another convict who was about to be released. Knowledge of the existence of this letter came to the Governor, who ordered the witness to flog Kurt again. He gave him thirty lashes with a rattan cane, after which the prisoner was placed in a redwood cage under the gaoler's house. From this he contrived to escape; when recaptured he was beaten to death.

This was the only one of the three murders listed in the charges against Preecha for which any evidence was called. Other witnesses were brought in to supply evidence of Preecha's gross misgovernment of the province and others still, described as clerks at Kabin, to tell of the falsification of accounts in the working of the gold mines.

A charge of sorcery was next advanced. It accused Preecha of employing a woman named Plang to make a wax figure of the King, with which, by the aid of incantations, she guaranteed to produce a great love in His Majesty for Phra Preecha. It was as a result of this, it was said, that Preecha had enjoyed so many favours from the King and had obtained many honours and a great advancement in his position.

Only recently this same woman, the witnesses claimed, had made other wax images, one of the Regent and another of the Foreign Minister, with a view to bringing about their death. She recited spells, wrote their names on a piece of paper and placed this, together with the wax figures, in a coffin. As she was about to lower the coffin into the earth, she was discovered, and only thus was calamity averted.

One witness went so far as to say that Fanny had paid the sorceress's fee, since Preecha, being in prison, was in no position to remunerate her.

The hearing was over; the court postponed judgment. But a précis of each charge was telegraphed to the Siamese Consul General in London for submission to Lord Salisbury.

" All this is being done, my lord," said Pauncefote, " to blacken Phra Preecha and to prevent Knox from being backed up by us in his demand for his son-in-law's release."

" As a Siamese nobleman," said Salisbury sourly, " he is subject to the laws of his own country. I do not see how we can intervene. They must be allowed to manage their own affairs."

" Very true, sir," replied Pauncefote, " but it appears to me that we might be justified in demanding the release of Phra Preecha as an atonement on the part of the Siamese Government for the insult given to the British Consul. The course I would suggest for your lordship's consideration is the following: send for Mason, the Siamese Consul in London. He is a sensible and intelligent man and has great influence with his Government. It is not unlikely that if your lordship sent a message to the King through Mason to the effect that, with a view to terminating the dispute, Phra Preecha should now be released, he would acquiesce, in spite of these new charges of which we are so dramatically and constantly kept informed."

Salisbury did not agree. " In view of the fact," he said, " that Phra Preecha has already been tried on these fresh charges, how can we with any propriety require that the verdict of the court —which has probably been given by now and is based on evidence which we have not seen—should be quashed? " He reflected for a moment. " Perhaps we could ask for the prisoner to be re-tried in the presence of our Consul. But I have never heard of a precedent for such a demand. And if we demanded it we should be obliged to enforce it—or lose more prestige than we should lose by inaction now. I see no excuse," he went on, "for intervening simply because Phra Preecha has married the Consul's daughter. It would be best, I feel, that whatever we do should be done by way of persuasion. I suggest that you have a private talk with Mason and say that we——"

"May I mention your name, my lord?"

"You may say that Lord Salisbury would be pleased if Phra Preecha could be released, since the impression has undoubtedly been created, in view of the fact that no charges were brought until after the marriage, that the public humiliation of our Consul's son-in-law is degrading to the Consul and to his office."

Pauncefote was pleased. "Thank you, my lord. I feel that such action may well save the man's life."

The next day Pauncefote saw Mason, a short, square man with a thin moustache and a slight limp.

At first Mason demurred. "As the special envoy from Siam is now on his way to England," he said, "and is expected to arrive in London in a few days, I think his lordship ought first to allow him to state the case of the Siamese Government. It will convince his lordship of the need to remove Knox from his office of Consul General in Bangkok."

Pauncefote bridled. This was something new. Recall Knox? He had not realised that things had gone so far.

"Lord Salisbury," he said, "would decline absolutely to be dictated to on such a matter as that. He will see the envoy, of course. But if the message his lordship has sent is transmitted by telegram and acted upon by the King, the present tension will undoubtedly be eased."

Mason agreed, and the telegram was despatched.

Since learning of the special envoy's departure for London, Fanny had begun to feel that the wait would inevitably be a long one. He could not arrive much before the middle of June. Discussions with Lord Salisbury would take some time. If a decision were arrived at and telegraphed to Bangkok, then the earliest she could hope to learn of London's verdict would be in July. That meant more weeks of suspense and anxiety.

Through the window she caught sight of Kasim, one of the elderly Indian runners at the British Consulate. He was wearing the familiar livery as he walked from the landing-stage towards her house. She ran to the door, but the man's step betrayed no urgency. Seeing him stop and gaze about him in bewilderment, she hailed him. He smiled, salaamed, and walked on. She watched him go to Kesab's house at the end of the farthest courtyard. There he fumbled in his bag and brought out a letter. After some time she saw him come back through the blinding glare and leave. There was nothing for her.

Knox had written to ask Kesab if he could come to the Consulate, and a little later Kesab went to see Fanny. " There have been developments," he told her.

" Good news? " she asked anxiously.

" I don't know yet," he replied as he hurried on to the landing-stage.

Later that afternoon he returned sad and disconsolate.

" There are to be still further charges."

" Is there to be no end to this? " Fanny moaned.

" Here's a letter for you. It arrived at the Consulate while I was there." Kesab handed it to her.

She put the letter in her lap and covered her face with her hands. She was not going to cry. Her lips trembled, but she fought back her tears. After a while, she pulled herself together and tore open the envelope, which was addressed to " Miss Fanny " and written in Siamese. The letter said:

Our dear lady, We who love our great and saintly Governor are writing this to you and are despatching it to the British

Consulate by secret messenger so that it should not be known whence it has come.

When the sad news reached us in Prachin of the evil things that are being done to our beloved Governor, men and women gathered in great numbers at the gates of the Governor's house and waited there to learn if the news were true. Many were in tears, many protested angrily and shouted their wish to go to Bangkok to help our Governor in his hour of trouble.

But how can we act alone against the evil men in high places who possess all the power. We wait and pray that he will soon be restored to us. But our prayers have not yet been answered. If you should need us . . .

The letter was unsigned.

A great glow came into Fanny's eyes as she handed the letter to Phya Kesab.

" It is from Preecha's friends," she said. " They are ready to come here in their thousands to answer all the lies that are being told against him. They can help us, Phya Kesab. I must go to them. We can bring them here in boats."

" They are very kind," he said. " But nobody will heed them . . . nobody."

Fanny seemed to be possessed of a new vitality. " I am going to Prachin to see them," she said.

"They will be seized and put in prison . . ." Phya Kesab said.

" Not thousands of them," Fanny retorted. " They could not put thousands of people in prison."

" Fanny." The aged aristocrat rose. " Listen to me. They did not sign their names because they know that each one of them would be suspect."

" There is strength in numbers."

" I know. But what can they fight with? Their hands? "

" They have knives. They have sticks," she said.

" The Regent has guns. He will call out the troops." He shook his head. Then he said: " Fanny, do you know that I went to see the Regent again to-day? "

She looked up at him.

" I have gone there every day—far more often than you know."

" That proves nothing," she objected.

" It proves that *no one* can persuade the Regent. Without weapons we can do nothing." He paused. " To-day they said that they would arrest me if I came again."

" They wouldn't dare touch you, Phya Kesab," Fanny exclaimed.

" Wouldn't they? " he said gently. " I would have said that about my son—because of his friendship with the King. But they *did*. They are desperate men. They will stop at *nothing*."

" What do you mean? " Fanny felt that some new and unsuspected pit was opening.

Kesab remained silent.

" Do you mean that if it became necessary they would set aside—even the King? "

" Yes," Kesab said. " If he stands in their way, that is what they will do, and the King knows it. That is why he has to tread so warily." He came up to her and placed his hands on her shoulders. " When even the King can do nothing, how can these people help? "

Fanny's face was white.

That evening she received a letter from Caroline. After writing of her grief at the loss of her baby, she said that Louis was ready to come to Bangkok again if he could be of any help.

Some days later a letter came from Louis's mother. Anna wrote from New York:

I have read in the newspapers of the terrible things that are happening. I feel for you greatly, Fanny dear. I am certain that the young King, who was my pupil and who is actuated by such fine ideals, has nothing to do with these sad events. Nevertheless, I have written to him—begging him to intervene. I pray that this may achieve something.

But the villain in this, as during my own stay in Siam, is undoubtedly the Regent. I have always regarded him as a cold, callous brute, and have not hesitated to show this in my books. His few kindnesses to Louis were carefully calculated and undoubtedly done for a purpose, though what that purpose was I am unable to guess. He must have felt Louis was too close to the king. He does not wish the King to have a friend near him, which is why Louis is now four hundred miles away in Chiengmai, and I feel sure it is for the same reason that he has had your poor husband imprisoned—because he too was a friend of the King's. Preecha is such a good, kind man, as I have reason to know, for he helped me when I made my journey through his province when I was going to visit those awe-inspiring ruins at Angkor Wat.

I trust my letter to King Chulalongkorn may help. You are always in my prayers. I hope that all will come right in the end and that Preecha will soon be restored to you.—Your affectionate Aunt Anna.

Chapter Nineteen

THE SIAMESE envoy, His Excellency Phya Bhasha Karawong, half-brother of the Regent and full brother of the Foreign Minister, arrived in London in the middle of June. A suite of rooms had been engaged for him at the Alexandra Hotel in Knightsbridge. He had with him as interpreter Prisdang Choomai, a Siamese student who had spent some years in England.

The envoy was ill when he arrived, and took to his bed. The voyage had been long, the seas rough, and he had had to be carried ashore at Brindisi where Choomai went out to meet him.

The meeting with Lord Salisbury was therefore deferred, but Mason called at the Foreign Office to see Pauncefote and brought with him two great bundles of documents. They were verbatim reports of the case against Phra Preecha. One set was in Siamese, the other a translation.

" Has Mr. Knox seen these documents? " Pauncefote asked.

Mason hesitated, then he said: " The Siamese Government decided, Sir Julian, to refer this matter to Lord Salisbury. It did not therefore appear to them to be necessary to furnish Mr. Knox with copies of these documents."

" Mr. Knox will have to be kept fully informed of what is given to us," said Pauncefote. " I therefore would require that all these documents be copied in Siamese and in English, and sent out to him."

Mason scowled. " It would take up a great deal of time, Sir

Julian, to have them copied and sent out, and then to wait for his observations. Our envoy would have to remain here for many months."

" Your Government should have foreseen that, Mr. Mason. But it might perhaps be possible, if you telegraphed, for the documents to be copied out there. We shall certainly require to have Mr. Knox's observations. As an Englishman, Mr. Mason, do you think that the way in which these proceedings have been conducted is in accordance with our standards of justice? "

" Phra Preecha, sir, is a Siamese subject, and he is being tried under Siamese law."

" But there are people who will be affected by the court's decision who are *not* Siamese subjects but British subjects— namely, Phra Preecha's wife Fanny, and our Consul General, who is his father-in-law. Lord Salisbury did go so far as to discuss with me the advisability of having Mr. Knox in court to follow these proceedings. We have not yet raised this, Mr. Mason, but we are contemplating doing so."

" Very well, sir," Mason replied. " I will inform the Siamese Government of your views. But I foresee great difficulties."

After Mason had left, Pauncefote reported their conversation to Lord Salisbury. He seemed satisfied with the outcome, and commented: " It cannot do harm to keep the envoy waiting here. Nothing irrevocable can be done while these communications are taking place, and good may come of the waiting. Do you not agree, Pauncefote? "

" Yes, my lord, I only fear that Phra Preecha may die in prison and the verdict be anticipated."

" I do not think so," Lord Salisbury demurred. " They will not wish to anticipate the verdict while their special envoy waits here. But meanwhile since it is desirable to improve the atmosphere, I consider the gunboat should be withdrawn from

Bangkok and ordered to return to Singapore. You should send a telegram to that effect."

When the gunboat left, Fanny felt intensely depressed and disconsolate. Why had it gone? Was Lord Salisbury weakening? And what would happen to Preecha if that were the case?

Presently she saw the consular launch draw up at the landing-stage. Not wishing to be seen, she drew away from the window, but looked out from behind the curtain.

It was not a messenger she saw, but her father. What had brought him to visit Phya Kesab? It must be something important. Was it to do with the departure of the gunboat? She longed to rush out and speak to him, but she checked the impulse, for fear he should look past her and walk on. She drew back. She must wait till Phya Kesab told her why Papa had come.

With concentrated attention she watched the lean, bearded figure walking across the first courtyard. She noticed that her father's shoulders were a little bowed and that his pace was no longer brisk, but slow and halting. Then he seemed to be about to turn towards her house. She went quickly to the front door, which was open, but she held herself some paces from it, in the shadows. . . . Suddenly they were clasped in each other's arms and she was sobbing on his shoulder.

" Oh, Papa . . ." She could not say anything more. When, after a while, she looked up, she saw there were tears in his eyes too.

With her arm about his waist she led him in. They sat close together on the sofa, holding each other's hands.

" My poor little Fanny. I am not so cruel as you may think. I kept away *because* I decided to fight, and I had to fight as Consul General and not as your father. That was the only weapon I had. Poor Mamma . . . how this has made her suffer. You were never out of our thoughts."

" Thank you, dear Papa, for coming. Thank you for all you are doing."

" I'm afraid I have not been able to achieve anything much, but at any rate, we've stayed their hand—now we have to wait . . ."

" I am truly sorry, Papa, for bringing all this upon you. You were right. I see it now . . ." She knotted her fingers through his. " You are not angry with me now, Papa? "

" I was never angry with you—well, not for long."

" I had a letter from Prachin recently," she said. " It says thousands are ready to come and defend Preecha. They are angry and very sad."

Knox turned the idea over in his mind. " Banners . . . boats . . . crowds of people flocking into court. . . . I'm afraid it wouldn't do any good. They'd all be rounded up and put into gaol."

" That's what Phya Kesab said," replied Fanny dejectedly. " But I still believe that if I were to go to Prachin and talk to them, we might find a way."

" I had much the same idea myself," said her father. " I thought of starting a revolt—here in Bangkok—rousing the people and overthrowing the Government."

" You! " She was astounded. There was a glow of admiration in her eyes.

" Yes. It might work. Who can say? The King's supporters are deeply devoted to His Majesty. Their loyalty is beyond question. But with all these plots and conspiracies and fierce jealousies, they are afraid to come out into the open. They are scattered, unorganised, and no doubt wonder how far the King would be able to protect them. If they failed, some of them would undoubtedly be executed, others kept in prison—for years. One has to weigh all these factors. One can only do what is feasible."

" Is there any hope, Papa? "

" We must not despair, darling. They have passed no judgment as yet. Whatever they decide will have to be referred to the King. Nothing can be done until he endorses their verdict."

" One of the charges is murder, isn't it? " she asked.

He was silent for a time, then very quietly he said: " Yes."

" That may mean—the death sentence." Her voice was almost inaudible.

" I don't think the King would endorse that."

Fanny shook her head doubtfully. " Then it will be life imprisonment—a living death, and no hope of ever seeing each other again."

" Come home for a few days," Knox suggested.

" I will. Now." She rose.

Knox called to Oun: " Get the children ready. We are all going home."

Mrs. Knox was on the landing-stage waiting to receive them. She hugged her daughter. Then she asked her when her baby was due. Fanny told her that it was expected in November. Mrs. Knox suggested that she should be at the Consulate for her confinement, since then her child would be a British subject. Fanny replied that Preecha would like his son—for she was sure it would be a boy—to be Siamese.

In the evening a letter arrived from Lambton. Attached to it was a clipping from a newspaper. It was headed: " True Love in the Far East," and bore a Bangkok date line. It had been despatched by "An occasional correspondent of the *New York Tribune*," from which paper the *Daily Telegraph* had taken it. It gave a garbled account of Fanny's courtship, and stated that, as Knox refused his parental sanction, the daughter eloped with her lover. " This," the correspondent added, " has caused a scandal not only in Siam, but throughout the British colonies in the Far East." There was a reference to Preecha's arrest and to the arrival of the gunboat and the possibility of war breaking out between England and Siam as a result of this love affair.

Fanny wondered who could have written it. Was it some-body at the American Consulate? She turned to Lambton's letter. He wrote:

I had only just read *The Times* announcement of your marriage to Phra Preecha, who rendered me such great service when I was in Siam, and seemed to me to be such an exceedingly fine man, when the first of your father's despatches, telling of the sad proceedings against him, arrived at the Foreign Office and naturally it passed through my department, since Siam is within my competence.

I trust you will not think it impertinent of me to write to you. Officially I am unable to intervene, but I wanted you to know how greatly depressed I am at the thought of what you must be suffering.

Your father has set out the true position in his despatches. But—and this will sadden you, since you must be looking to us for help in this tragic situation—I do not believe that the British Government can intervene in a case which concerns a Siamese subject.

Please let me know if there is anything you feel I can reasonably do. I say 'reasonably,' because, as you are aware, I am merely a subordinate and have no control of policy. I can therefore only recommend; this, of course, I have already done. Salisbury is a warm-hearted and kindly man. I feel confident that if he can help you, he will do so. But the possibilities are, I fear, limited.

Chapter Twenty

WHILE THE Siamese special envoy was lying ill in his London hotel, and thereby prevented from presenting his credentials to Lord Salisbury, the Foreign Secretary was informed of a question that was to be asked in the House of Commons on the 26th June concerning " The Kingdom of Siam—Action of Mr. Knox, British Consul General," by Mr. Peter Rylands, the Liberal member for Burnley.

Salisbury sent for the Under-Secretary of State, the Hon. Robert Bourke, Conservative member for King's Lynn, who would have to reply in the Commons. Turning to Pauncefote, Salisbury said: " Do you not feel that some hand is behind this? The question surprises me, for there has been little about the incident in the Press."

Pauncefote read the question. " Mr. Rylands to ask the Under-Secretary of State for Foreign Affairs whether it is the case that Mr. Knox, the British Consul General in Siam, has ordered up a British gunboat from Singapore to Bangkok, in consequence of the punishment for treason of a Siamese minister, who is son-in-law to Mr. Knox? "

He passed the question to Bourke, saying: " The gunboat left some days ago."

" Had I better not say so? " Bourke said.

" No," answered Lord Salisbury. " The less said the better."

A reply was thereupon drafted, which ran:

Sir, a misunderstanding has arisen between Mr. Knox, Her Majesty's Agent and Consul General at Bangkok, and the

Siamese Government. I would rather not, at the present moment, enter into particulars respecting the causes of this misunderstanding. A gunboat has proceeded to Bangkok at Mr. Knox's request. Apology has since been tendered. It is hoped, therefore, that the difficulty is in course of satisfactory adjustment.

Mr. Bourke made this statement in the House on the 26th of June.

The following week His Excellency Phya Bhasha Karawong, short, plump, bespectacled, presented himself at the Foreign Office. He brought Mason with him, and an interpreter, although he spoke English quite well.

The meeting with Lord Salisbury was confined to an interchange of courtesies. On rising to leave, Phya Bhasha asked if it might be possible for him to see the fortifications at Dover, to visit army depots and barracks, and the stables of the Royal Horse Guards.

Smiling, Lord Salisbury replied: "I see that Your Excellency has in mind an interesting and also, let us hope, instructive, programme. I shall ask Sir Julian Pauncefote to make the arrangements. Your Excellency realises, I am sure, that such visits will take up a considerable time?"

"I propose to stay here for some months, after which I shall go to Germany . . ."

"I understood that Your Excellency's visit to London was in connection with the Phra Preecha case," Lord Salisbury interrupted.

"Yes, my lord." He laughed. "But during my stay here I may as well profit by seeing all I can."

"When has Your Excellency arranged to go to Osborne?" inquired Lord Salisbury.

"Her Majesty has graciously consented to receive me next week. I trust it will be possible for me to be accompanied by an interpreter and one or two Siamese gentlemen at present in London."

" Only the interpreter may accompany Your Excellency. No others." He held out his hand and bade the Siamese envoy good day.

" I notice," Lord Salisbury said later to Pauncefote, " that the envoy most scrupulously avoided discussing the dispute with me. He did not even inquire whether I had perused the documents they have sent us in such bulk."

Pauncefote smiled, his blue eyes glittering. " I am afraid, sir, the words he and I exchanged before I brought him in frightened him into silence."

" Oh, what did you talk about? " Lord Salisbury asked.

" We talked about the dispute, sir. His Excellency said that the only way to settle the difficulty would be by recalling our Consul General, Mr. Knox."

" Indeed! Has he come then to bargain with us and to instruct us whom we shall or shall not appoint as our representatives? "

" I warned him, my lord, that his reception by you would be far from pleasant if he made any such approach to you."

" I am glad you told him that, Pauncefote."

" In the circumstances, my lord, might we not consider whether the King of Siam could be persuaded to dispense with the services of the Regent? "

Lord Salisbury laughed heartily. " I should like to help Knox's son-in-law. We might consider this course of action. If as an earnest of their desire to dispose of the matter, they released Phra Preecha, and dropped all the charges against him, then—but quite independently of what they do—we might consider bringing Mr. Knox home on leave. If, on the other hand, the question of Mr. Knox's recall is pressed, our reply will be most emphatically in the negative."

" I will put that to them, sir," said Pauncefote.

" Deeply as I feel for Knox," Salisbury went on, " we are certainly in no position to take any risks. In the past a single gunboat has helped to untangle many grievous problems. But in this instance, although the gunboat was kept at Bangkok for a whole month, the matter has not been settled. This shows that the Regent does not intend to yield."

Meanwhile, Knox, unaware of these moves in London, was restless and anxious. He feared that the envoy might influence the British Government's attitude. He decided that his presence in London was essential, and telegraphed to Lord Salisbury applying for leave.

An hour after his cable had been despatched, he was startled to receive a telegram from the Foreign Secretary which appeared to anticipate his wish. It read:

Mr. Knox is instructed to come home in order to explain the grounds of his actions.

Knox thought the wording a little abrupt. He spent the next few days sorting out his papers and giving instructions to Gould.

Three days later he left in the *Bangkok*, and at Singapore picked up the French mail steamer from Saigon.

With his departure, Fanny began to feel the world darken, though why her hopes were fading she could not explain, even to herself. With Papa in London things might begin to change for the better, and yet she was disturbed and filled with foreboding.

This was justified when a few days later Pet Pichai arrived, breathless and distracted, to tell her that his father had been arrested. When she heard this she burst into tears, exclaiming: " And even this won't satisfy them—next they will arrest you and me and the children. There will be no end to their vengeance."

When her fit of sobbing had ended, she said: " I am going

to see the Regent—I *must*." Her eyes were fixed on the trees across the river. To their right rose the towering Wat Arun, at the base of which stretched the Regent's vast estate.

" You should not try to see him, Fanny," said Pet Pichai. " But there is a way of dealing with the most violent and fiercest beasts of the jungle, and that is the way I shall deal with him."

He strode up and down the veranda. He was like a wild animal himself. Suddenly he turned and bounded down the stairs into the Consulate garden.

" Pet Pichai! " She leaned over the veranda rails.

" I must see my father," he called to her.

Fanny went to find her mother.

Mrs. Knox was appalled to hear of Phya Kesab's arrest.

" They will get Pet Pichai too," she moaned.

She and Fanny discussed the possibility of a visit to the Regent. Mrs. Knox thought that some good might come of it, so Fanny wrote and asked for an interview.

For some days she got no reply. When it came, she saw that it was signed by Hunter. That was significant, for in the past the Regent had always written to her in his own hand.

The appointment, Hunter wrote, would have to be deferred because the Regent was leaving Bangkok on a tour of some of the provinces and expected to be away for two weeks or more. " He has instructed me to say," Hunter added, " that he will be glad to see you as soon as possible after his return."

During the days that followed Fanny became more and more restless. She went one morning to see Pet Pichai; he had not been able to discover where his father was.

Towards the end of that week Louis and Caroline arrived unexpectedly. This was a joyful surprise. Caroline explained it by saying that neither of them could bear to think of Mamma and Fanny alone in the Consulate while Papa was in London.

Fanny told Louis of her unsuccessful attempt to see the

Regent. He suggested that it might be as well for him to endeavour to talk to Nai Dee.

Fanny opposed this plan. She recollected the instances of
cruelty which he had shown on several occasions, and felt that
he was probably now gloating over her misery and Preecha's
sufferings. Louis disagreed with her. He believed that Nai Dee
was fundamentally kind-hearted and really devoted to Fanny,
and certainly he was the only person in the world who had any
influence over the Regent.

In the end he decided to write for an appointment.

His letter brought an immediate reply. Nai Dee expressed
his delight that Louis was back in Bangkok. " I'd like very
much to see you, and the sooner the better," he wrote, " for
we have so much to talk about."

Louis wrote and suggested that they might lunch together at
Falcks' Hotel. Nai Dee accepted the invitation.

Falcks' Hotel was dreary and uninviting. When Louis arrived
a noisy Danish sea captain was engaged in conversation with a
young American sailor who was seated on the other side of the
long dining-room table.

Presently an American missionary came in, accompanied by
an elderly woman. She was Scottish and also apparently a
missionary. They too conversed in loud voices.

Louis selected a table in the corner. Four places were laid,
so he asked the Chinese waiter to reserve it for himself and the
friend he was expecting.

" You want plivate talk? I have small loom. This side,
please," the man replied.

Just then Nai Dee walked in. He greeted Louis with what
appeared to be genuine pleasure. They followed the waiter into
the inner room.

When the first course had been served, Louis broached the
subject he had come to discuss.

" I've had nothing to do with what has happened," Nai Dee

protested. "It is truly distressing, especially for poor little Fanny. But you must agree that the way it all happened was most unfortunate."

"What way?"

"The night in the houseboat . . ."

"But she was not alone with him," Louis interrupted. "There were at least another twenty women there."

"So I've been told. But then—the hurried marriage, and Preecha's departure without a courtesy visit to the King, whose guest he was—Grandpa is very angry. It is an insult to our family." He was talking with mounting excitement. Louis interrupted him.

"We don't know why we love one person and not another. And that applies to you as much as to Fanny."

Nai Dee's expression changed to one of sadness as he replied: "I suppose I will get over it one day. . . ."

Louis seized the opportunity to press home the point that the happiness, perhaps the lives, of Fanny and Preecha lay in his hands. "Are you prepared to help them?" he asked.

Nai Dee was silent for a moment, then he said: "Grandpa will not be easy to handle."

"But tell me this, Nai Dee. Are you at least prepared to *try?*"

A tense silence lasted for several seconds, then Nai Dee said: "I'd better see Fanny. For her sake I'd like to do all I can."

"I'll tell her that, and I will add that you are well disposed."

"I've always been well disposed, and nothing that has happened has made any difference to my feelings. I'd like to help her. Tell her that."

To change the subject Louis asked: "What are you doing with yourself nowadays?"

"I work for my grandfather—I work in the Foreign Office with Mr. Alabaster," Nai Dee replied.

Louis was surprised, and said spontaneously: " I don't like that man."

" Neither do I," replied Nai Dee. " He's a hard man, with a twisted mind. He has a cruel streak in him."

When Louis told Fanny and suggested that she should see Nai Dee, she refused firmly and absolutely.

" He wants to help you, Fanny."

" He doesn't have to see me to do that. No, Louis. It's because of him that all this has happened. I can't see him."

Chapter Twenty-one

THE REGENT's tour did not take him to Prachin. He circled the adjacent provinces, where his agents had already been active, assembling what they proposed to present as fresh evidence against Preecha.

Two Chinese carpenters who, it was stated, had been in Preecha's employ, were said to have been involved in a noisy brawl outside Government House. Preecha, it was alleged, strode out, sliced off their pigtails with his sword, and then ordered the men to be put into a boat and taken down the river, and finally thrown with their hands tied, into the crocodile-infested waters. This incident was said to have taken place four and a half years earlier.

The next charge bore no indication of date or place; the relevant spaces were left blank, to be filled in later. But the time was set down as "4 p.m." It, too, described a murder alleged to have been instigated by Preecha.

A third accusation charged him with having placed a man named Nai Sai in a boat with heavy chains round his neck. He had, so it was stated, tried to escape by jumping into the water and had been drowned.

The charges were not made public in Bangkok, but were forwarded to London.

The blanks left in the second charge for date and place did not make a favourable impression on Lord Salisbury. But he was concerned that another question was to be asked in the House. Bourke had had an interview with Mr. Rylands, who had tabled the question. He had come away with the impression that Rylands himself was not animated by ill-will but that he was being manipulated by someone who was extremely hostile either to Knox or to Phra Preecha.

The interview bore fruit, for at question time in the House of Commons on the 1st August, Mr. Rylands said: " After the explanation which has been given the other night in regard to this matter, I will not trouble the Honourable Gentleman, the Under-Secretary of State for Foreign Affairs, with the question on the subject which stands upon the Paper in my name as follows:

To ask the Under-Secretary of State for Foreign Affairs whether he will explain to the House the circumstances under which the British Consul General in Siam ordered up the gunboat *Foxhound* from Singapore to Bangkok, and for what purpose the vessel has been detained there until the present time; whether it is the fact that, under the orders of the Consul General, the Commander and Officers of the British gunboat have been prevented from paying visits to the Siamese, or giving them invitations to the vessel; and, whether these proceedings on the part of the Consul General have the sanction of Her Majesty's Government?

But, he added: " I should like to know if, when the Consular Report is received, the Government would be prepared to come to any decision on the subject, and lay Papers on the table? "

Mr. Bourke, in reply, said: " I must express my obligations to the Hon. Member for putting the question in this form. An inquiry is still going on at Bangkok, and the Foreign Office will, no doubt, before long arrive at a conclusion upon it; but I am afraid I cannot say that the Papers will be laid upon the table of the House until that conclusion has been reached. However, the Hon. Member will not be able to see the Papers until next session, and therefore the Question had better be postponed until that time, seeing that he will be in no worse position by then."

Some days later the Siamese envoy wrote to the Secretary of State for Foreign Affairs stating that he had been instructed by telegram to demand that Mr. Knox should not be allowed to return to Bangkok, since his interference in the internal affairs of Siam were detrimental to the maintenance of law and order.

He also asked to see Lord Salisbury.

When he arrived, he informed Lord Salisbury that Phra Preecha had been found guilty on all charges, copies of which had recently been sent to London. Sentence had not yet been passed, but he was instructed to state that his Government was not prepared to brook any interference in their internal affairs, and moreover that they were insistent in their demand for the removal of Mr. Knox, whose presence in Bangkok might result in the country falling into a state of anarchy.

Lord Salisbury expressed surprise and displeasure, and dismissed the envoy without making any commitment. He was, however, disturbed, and asked Pauncefote anxiously when Knox was expected to arrive.

" Not for some weeks," said Pauncefote.

" A pity ! We cannot keep the envoy waiting too long for an answer."

They spent some days drafting it. In due course the following reply was sent:

Your Excellency—Your Government must use its own judgment as to the further steps which they may think proper to take in regard to the case of Phra Preecha, and Her Majesty's Government have no reason to apprehend that Mr. Knox will improperly interfere with the course of justice, nor do Her Majesty's Government consider that the circumstances of the case justify the demand of the Siamese Government for the recall of that officer.

As, however, Mr. Knox is about to arrive in this country on leave of absence, Her Majesty's Government will suspend their judgment with reference to his proceedings until they have had an opportunity of hearing his explanations on the subject.

As he signed it, Lord Salisbury turned to Pauncefote, saying: "I think this is as far as we dare go. I trust the consequence will not be a death sentence."

Early in September, a liveried messenger arrived from across the river with a letter for Fanny. The boat was waiting, Singh told her, in case she wished to send an answer.

The note was written by the Regent himself. It was brief. "I shall be glad to see you, Fanny. I'm sorry I have been away so long. Would Friday afternoon at three suit you?"

Her hopes rose. Perhaps, seeing her again . . . She would not cry, please God, but she could plead.

When she told Louis of the Regent's letter, he suggested that, in spite of her refusal to see him, Nai Dee had perhaps exerted his influence over his grandfather.

The next day Louis and Caroline left for Chiengmai.

The rains had been heavy during the past month. The floating houses rode high. The waters of the river topped the banks and swept under the raised houses. The lawn at the Consulate was awash and the boats came past the landing-stage up to the garden stairs.

The veranda was kept shuttered all day and all night. The window-panes were spotted and streaked by rain. Indoors the twilight darkened as each thunderclap brought a fresh whirling downpour.

On Friday the rain stopped, but the sky was overcast. Fanny dressed herself with care, hoping that no traces of her grief would be noticeable. Inside she was in a turmoil of doubt and uncertainty. How was she to handle the Regent? Would he be understanding? Or would he bluster and reproach her?

Hunter was waiting on the landing-stage for her. He escorted her along the damp paved walk, skirting the pavilions. They went past the theatre in which she had played in *The School for Scandal* not so long ago. The lovely gardens on either side, though awash, were still full of colour; hibiscus and oleander bloomed above the waters.

They entered the main building and walked through the salons with their large mirrors, marble sculptures and Louis Quinze chairs. Hunter announced her as " Miss Fanny Knox." She turned to him and said: " The Baroness Preecha." He merely bowed and withdrew. It was clear to her that he had been instructed to announce her in this way.

The Regent rose from his desk and extended his hand in an apparently friendly greeting.

" Well, Fanny. I *am* glad to see you again, in spite of all that has happened. Sit here, near me, so that we can talk."

She sat down, and folded her hands in her lap.

" Your brother-in-law Louis, was here recently, I am told," he went on. " He is doing well in the North and will one day be a very rich man. I am glad I was able to help him."

" Thank you," she said softly. He was reminding her of what he had done for the family; soon, no doubt, he would say, " I helped your father too . . ." And then he would end up by saying: "And look how you have repaid me." She decided to anticipate him.

" Your Excellency has always been very kind—to my father, to our family generally, and to me especially."

" I always looked on you as my granddaughter," he said, smiling. So there it was. Danger. She was resolved not to be roused. She had been wondering how to begin; this gave her an opening.

" You have rendered very great service to Siam and to its people," she said. " You have been striving to lift this country out of its primitive way of life. Bit by bit you have been bringing Siam into line with England and France. You have built roads and canals, and encouraged trade. You have invited Europeans to come in and build factories. You have done so very much."

She paused, and he remarked:

" A good little speech, Fanny. You've got something of your father in you. Your remarks are a subtle approach to telling me that I am *now* allowing the country to slip back."

" Yes," she said.

He shook his head slowly. " No. The arrest of a man who has charges against him is not the act of a barbarian. Preecha, who has received many favours from us . . ."

" And has rendered good service to the country, within the limitations of his office," she interrupted.

" True, but he has also rendered bad service, and it was because of his evil deeds that he was charged and brought to trial . . ."

" It was not a fair trial! " Fanny exclaimed.

" It was a just trial, conducted by the most honoured judges in the kingdom. Witnesses were heard; I have read their evidence."

" Was my husband heard too? "

" Certainly."

" In the court?"

" He was tried in strict accordance with the laws of this country."

" I understand there were two or three separate trials."

" There were, in fact, two trials, because there were two sets of charges, apart from the initial trial for insulting the King. We now await the verdict of the court."

Catching at a straw, Fanny pleaded: " Until the verdict is

given, can my husband not be allowed to return to his home? And is it too much to ask that the verdict be delayed until after our child is born? "

The Regent was silent for a moment. " I will see that they withhold their verdict until your child is born. That much I promise you. But Phra Preecha cannot be allowed to go home."

Having gained one point, Fanny felt encouraged, and continued:

" He is a man of honour and integrity. He will not abscond."

" The evidence brought before the court does not wholly support you in that view."

" If he has insulted you and your family—as you feel he has by marrying me—then the fault is as much mine as his. Why not punish me? I am at least equally guilty."

The Regent smiled. " Your lapses, as a British subject, do not concern me. Besides, *you* have not committed such crimes as those with which Phra Preecha has been charged. For them he will, of course, have to be punished."

" What sort of punishment? " she asked in a voice that was scarcely audible.

" The crimes include murder. You know what the penalty for murder is, even in your own country."

Fanny felt cold all over. " You . . . mean . . ." She could not go on.

He nodded slowly.

Suddenly her anger began to rise. But she held herself in check and said in a controlled voice: " Does Your Excellency really imagine that Preecha is capable of committing such crimes?"

" It is not for me to imagine. It is for the judges to examine, weigh up, and decide." The Regent's thin lips tightened. Into his narrow eyes came a hardness. " I make allowance for your state of mind and for your present condition. So all I will say is this. You cannot expect the judges to look on Phra Preecha with the eyes of a bride. Justice could not be administered in that way."

Tears of anger began to well up in Fanny's eyes, but she blinked them back. " I am not going to cry," she told herself. " Oh, God, help me to say the right thing."

" Can you," she began after a long pause, " can you do nothing for me then? And if you cannot, tell me, please, Your Excellency, what can I do? "

" You can do nothing but wait."

Panic seized her. She wanted to go down on her knees and implore him to be merciful, but around his tightened lips the cynical smile of his power over her and her happiness seemed to flicker. She recognised that no imploring would help. Pressed back, her tears began to hurt. She felt suffocated.

Then suddenly the words poured out of her. " For years," she said, " I have looked on you as a kind man. But now I see that you have in you the good and the bad, and the bad is— *evil*."

The Regent rose from his desk. His face was flushed and angry. " You had better go," he said curtly.

She saw him return to the desk and ring his little golden bell. At its sound the world around her seemed to darken. She thought that she was going to faint.

Hunter appeared in the doorway.

" Miss Knox is not very well, Hunter," she heard the Regent say. " Will you assist her to her boat."

Hunter came forward to take her arm, but she jerked herself away from him and stumbled forward. Somehow she got through the door and blundered across the large ornate drawing-room.

Out in the grounds she saw that the sky had turned black. A storm was blowing up. The wind whistled in the trees. The river was choppy.

The uniformed attendant in the consular boat helped her on board and the oarsmen set out at once with brisk strokes to complete the crossing before the storm overtook them.

Fanny sat dazed, her hands moving restlessly in her lap. The one word that kept ringing in her brain was " Murder." He had been charged with murder. The verdict of the judges had been deferred, but in the present relentless mood of the Regent, she already knew what the verdict would be.

Now she could afford to cry, but the tears would not come; they seemed to have hardened into knots behind her eyes.

As the boat neared the Consulate she saw Aphilla, Preecha's younger brother. She tried to call to him, but before she could make a sound, he turned and saw her.

He waited and helped her to alight. She noticed that he was very much upset.

" What is the matter? " she asked in a frightened voice.

" They have taken Pet Pichai."

" Oh, God! " Fanny gave a low moan, and fainted.

The servants rushed forward. Mrs. Knox came running down the stairs. Aphilla took her up in his arms and carried her to her bed. Just then the rain began to fall in a great clatter.

Singh dashed out under an umbrella to fetch Dr. Stevenson Smith, the consular doctor.

With Oun beside them, the two children stood pale and frightened in the doorway of Fanny's room.

The doctor took a grave view of her condition. He feared a miscarriage.

Mrs. Knox went deathly white. " Again," she wailed. " Caroline lost her baby. Can't anything be done? "

Singh dashed out to the apothecary with a prescription, and waited while it was made up.

" If she gets restless in the night, send someone along to fetch me," the doctor said. " On no account must she be left alone."

Mrs. Knox had her mattress brought into the room and laid on the floor beside her daughter's bed.

For some days Fanny showed little sign of improvement. She vomited constantly, and the doctor thought that this was likely to bring about a premature birth.

Day after day he watched by her bedside. On the 5th October the child, a small and sickly boy, was born.

Three weeks later, when Fanny was up and about again, she had him blessed at home by Dr. Noah McDonald, the American missionary who had officiated at the marriage of her sister. He was given the names of Henry Spencer Knox Preecha. Louis and Caroline were his godparents by proxy, and apart from Mrs. Knox and Gould, and Preecha's two children, there were no others present.

Chapter Twenty-two

APHILLA sent a message through to Preecha to inform him of the birth of his son, but no one could tell whether it reached him.

Fanny wrote many times. Some envelopes she addressed care of the King, with a covering note begging His Majesty to arrange for them to be forwarded. But to not one of them did she receive a reply.

They were unable to discover where Pet Pichai or his father were imprisoned. At the end of the week Aphilla too was arrested.

Now that her child had been born, Fanny expected daily to hear the dreaded verdict. As she held the child in her arms and gazed at his frail body, her eyes would fill as she wondered whether Preecha would ever see him.

No congratulatory messages came from the family of the Second King, who had always been so friendly, or even from the members of other foreign consulates. Ever since Fanny had come to live in the house the consuls had kept away, apparently fearing that they might incur the displeasure of the Regent.

On the 14th November, the Siamese envoy returned from London. He called the next day on the Regent and the Foreign Minister, and by the end of the week the rumour spread that Preecha had been removed from his place of confinement near Bangkok and had been taken under armed escort to his own capital of Prachin, where he was lodged in the common gaol.

There could, many realised, be only one reason for that: the verdict had been delivered by the judges and had been confirmed by the Council of State. If the death sentence had been passed, it would have to be submitted to the King for his endorsement. Without it no action could be taken.

Fanny could learn no definite news and indeed knew not where to seek it. She sat for hours on end on a chair in her bedroom, staring into space. She tried to think what she should do, but in her distracted state she could not collect her mind.

In her despair, she thought of Louis. If only he were here. He had told her to get in touch with Nai Dee. She felt that now she would have to see him. Hurriedly she scribbled a few lines. "Can you help me, Nai Dee? Can you give me news of Preecha? I hear he has been taken to Prachin? Is it true? And if so, what does it mean? Your grandfather *must* know."

She sent Singh with the note and stood at the veranda shutters, watching his boat put out. She waited there, anxious and dazed, searching the distance for a sign of the boat's return. She waited a long time.

When lunch was announced, her mother called to her to come to the table. She could not bring herself to eat. Her gaze strayed to the shutters, and beyond them to the river, which she could just see through the slats. From time to time she left the table because she thought she saw the familiar scarlet boat returning.

"Why are you so jumpy?" her mother asked at last.

"I have sent Singh with a letter to Nai Dee because he seems to be my only hope. But Singh has been gone a long time . . ."

"He may be out."

Fanny looked at her with frightened eyes.

"I am glad you wrote, though. He *is* our one hope."

When she heard her mother's words, Fanny felt that in some measure she had already succeeded. Glancing again at the river, she saw the consular boat in the distance. Overtaking it was a small launch, which sped downstream and seemed to be making for the British Consulate. It was a handsome new paddle-boat, bright green, with red awnings. Her heart leapt at the sight. She flung the shutters open. Mrs. Knox came pattering up to her. Although it was some months since either of them had seen Nai Dee, they knew that he had bought a new launch; they also knew that it was green and was called the *Parakeet*.

Mrs. Knox smiled at Fanny. It was as though by a miracle their problems were about to be solved. Nai Dee seemed to them like a young knight coming at great speed to their rescue.

Swiftly the boat pulled in. They could see him now, and he waved to them in a friendly fashion.

Fanny went down to meet him. He had put on weight. His face was fuller, his shoulders a little heavier. He smiled as he held out his hand.

" How are you, Fanny? I heard that you had a bad time when the baby was born."

" That was nearly two months ago. I'm well now."

He looked at her face for some moments, then he moved forward to greet Mrs. Knox. When he had done so, he turned again to Fanny, and said:

" I was expecting to hear from you. Didn't Louis tell you? "

" Yes."

" Grandpa left for Prachin this morning . . ." A cold shiver ran through Fanny, and Mrs. Knox grew pale. ". . . If we are to do anything we'll have to hurry. That's why I came at once."

" You mean we had better go to Prachin? "

" Yes. And we'd better start now."

Fanny hurried across the lawn to the boat. Trakun and Arun came running after her. " Where are you going? Are you going to see Papa? " they asked.

" Let me pack a few things for you," said Mrs. Knox. She

ran back into the house, and beckoned to Oun to bring the children in.

Fanny stared at the boat while she waited.

"Handsome, isn't she?" said Nai Dee. "I got her for the Bang Pa In dedication. I had thought you and I might have gone out in her."

Fanny was silent.

Mrs. Knox returned with Oun, each of them carrying a small bag.

As Nai Dee's boat pulled out Fanny said: "What are they going to say about *this*—you and I alone together in your houseboat?"

"It is no time to worry about that," he answered. "If I had thought of it you might have brought one of your women with you. But I have three or four on board and I am sure they will be able to look after you well. Anyway, it's only for one night."

The cabin was large, and well furnished. "I shall be occupying a cabin on the lower deck," said Nai Dee, "so, in fact, we shall be observing the proprieties."

"Thank you," she said. "I think I shall lie down. I'm very tired."

"Try and sleep." He gave her a friendly smile and withdrew, shutting the door gently behind him.

A Siamese girl tiptoed in and drew the coverlet off the large bed. Fanny lay down, still fully dressed, and stared at the painted ceiling, on which were reflected thin bars of sunlight let in by the venetian blinds.

For some hours she lay there, unable to sleep, turning over in her mind the frightening possibilities. Why had Preecha been taken to Prachin? Why had the Regent gone there? This couldn't be a coincidence. And Nai Dee seemed to be conscious of a need for the utmost urgency.

But there must still be time, she told herself, to avert what had been planned. The death sentence could not be carried out without the Royal sanction. Would the King consent to the murder of his friend? The ultimate decision would have to be *his*. Had he given it?

Panic seized her. She sat up. Would the Regent have undertaken the long journey in person if the decision had not been made? He wouldn't, she told herself, he wouldn't . . .

She was lying on her bed, fully dressed save for her shoes, when she heard a knock at the cabin door. She had not been conscious of the passing of time and saw with surprise that the sun had set and the brief tropical twilight had given place to night.

The knock came again, followed by Nai Dee's voice: " Are you asleep? "

" No," she said.

He opened the door and held it slightly ajar. Behind him stood the Siamese girl with a light. He stepped aside to let her pass. He could now see Fanny's frightened face.

Looking fixedly at him, she began to cry.

He sat down on the edge of the bed and put his hand lightly on her shoulder.

" Don't, Fanny—please don't. I'm going to help you. I swear I am. We'll get there in time."

Everything in the cabin was throbbing. The glass on the carafe tinkled ceaselessly.

Fanny drew up her knees and buried her face against them as she sobbed.

" Please, Fanny," he repeated. " I shall talk to Grandpa in the morning. I shall *beg* him . . ."

She looked up at him, her eyes swimming.

" Do you know the verdict? "

He nodded.

" Guilty? "

He looked away.

" It isn't true! " she screamed. " He didn't do any of those things. It's all because I didn't marry you. If it would save his life . . ." She dissolved in a paroxysm of sobs.

Again he tried to comfort her. " I will help you, Fanny. You did hurt me. You were—and are—everything in the world to me. But I had nothing to do with this. I swear I've had nothing to do with it."

Fanny went on sobbing. She could not be comforted. He tried to soothe her. " Come, Fanny. You have cried enough." He fumbled in his pocket for a handkerchief. " I *swear* I'll help you," he said yet again and with even more emphasis.

He lifted her head and began to dry her eyes.

" Come out on to the deck; it will do you good."

She allowed herself to be helped down from the bed and in a daze walked out of the cabin and on to the deck. A stiff breeze whipped strands of her hair about her face. He led her to a long cane chair and made her lie on it.

He stood beside her for a while, then brought up another chair for himself. A servant came up to announce dinner, but he waved the man away.

" Tell me, Nai Dee. You must tell me. What are they going to do to him? "

" I don't have to tell you of my shortcomings, Fanny. But I'm trying to restore to you the man you love. My rival. Not at all like me. But in love one does strange things."

They had turned off the river some hours before and were travelling along canals. She gazed out at the jungle which bordered the banks, the attap palms by the water's edge, the tall bamboos, the wild orchids, each in turn lit up by the boat's lanterns. She was trying to calculate how far they were from Prachin and when they would get there.

" Do you believe me? " he asked.

" Yes, Nai Dee. Or you wouldn't be doing this. I have always liked you. Apparently, quite unwittingly, I misled you, or you would not have continued to hope that one day perhaps . . ." She did not finish the sentence.

After a pause he said: " I have tried to hate you. When all this happened—when you went off with him and "—he made a gesture with his hand—" all my worst feelings surged up. If you had been near enough I would gladly have plunged a knife into you—into both of you. But deep down—my feeling for you was still the same."

After a while she asked for a glass of water, and he went down and fetched it himself. He stood beside her while she drained the glass.

" Thank you," she said. " I think I'll go and lie down again now."

He took her hand and led her towards the cabin door, saying: " I don't want thanks. My one thought now is your happiness." He raised her fingers to his lips. " May I come and sit with you for a while? " he asked. " I cannot bear to think of you brooding, crying perhaps, frightening yourself quite un- necessarily. You will not be able to think of other things—I know that. . . . But perhaps if I am with you . . ."

She walked on blindly, and he followed her into the cabin. " When you want to sleep I shall leave you. I promise that."

Covering her eyes with her hand, she flung herself face down- wards on the bed. While she sobbed noiselessly, with only her shoulders heaving, as if she had not enough energy left to weep, Nai Dee bent over her and tried to soothe her with words of comfort. He stroked her neck, toyed with her hair, and brought his hand down along her spine.

Suddenly she turned and half-sitting up, said: " What are you doing? Don't touch me. Leave me alone, Nai Dee. You said you wanted to help me." Slowly her face hardened and her eyes narrowed. " Will you please go? " she said.

" Why, what have I done? "

" Go—please."

" Fanny, whatever happened wasn't intended. And what's all this fuss about modesty? At a moment like this . . . Have you nothing better to think of? "

He swallowed. His throat was working. " You don't imagine, do you, that I brought you along in this boat in order to have you at my mercy? We are alone, yes. The servants are mine, you could not expect them to help you. But don't let your imagination run away with you. I'm not going to rape you."

" I'm sorry," she said softly.

" Come on." His voice was quieter now. " Try and be reasonable. Have some soup—or some tea; sit at the table—it will be a change."

" I'll join you in a few minutes," she replied.

She washed the tear stains off her face, changed into a looser and more comfortable dress and went out on deck. There she found him awaiting her. He took her arm to guide her to the narrow companionway.

Two places had been laid at the small dining-table and a servant waited behind each chair. She wanted only soup and some toast, but sat with him while he finished his meal.

For a while they hardly spoke. Then Nai Dee asked her if she felt better.

" A little," she said.

" I am not asking anything in return for what I may be able to do," he said. " But you would do well to remember that we are fighting for the life of your husband . . ."

" His *life*? "

" He was charged with murder."

" What do you expect of me? "

" Well—nothing." He let this sink in, then said: " You women seem to regard your virtue as far more important than human life. You, for instance, seem to look on yours as more precious than even the life of Preecha."

" How dare you put it like that? "

" Well, you *do*. If I were to say you can have Preecha home with you for the rest of your life, provided you were prepared to sacrifice one night—or part of a night . . ."

" My reply," she said angrily, " would be this." She raised her hand to slap him across the face, but he gripped her by the wrist, saying with an uneasy laugh:

" Don't let us come to blows, Fanny. It is only because I regard you as a close and dear friend that I am undertaking this journey. I was merely posing the question of values in order that you should see them in a proper perspective."

In her anger she had risen, now slowly she sank back into her chair.

" Are you sure you can save him? " she asked without looking up.

" Of course I am sure," he replied.

She fell silent again. Suddenly she clapped her hands over her ears as though to shut out the murmur of her own thoughts.

" What is the matter? " he asked. But she did not answer.

After a while she said: " What is the guarantee, if I paid the price, that you will pay yours? "

" I don't understand what you mean."

" I mean this. What proof is there that you will, or can, keep your part of the bargain? "

" Since Grandpapa is there, this matter can, and *will*, be settled in a matter of minutes."

" It has not been so simple up to now," she said.

" That is because I have not so far taken a hand in it."

He took a cheroot from the box on the table. The servant came and lit it.

" In not many hours from now we shall be there," Nai Dee said between puffs. " That is the measure of my friendship and of my regard for you. But I am a human being and not a machine."

Fanny shut her eyes. Then looking down at the table, she said: " I cannot fight any longer." Slowly she rose and walked to the door.

For some time after she had gone Nai Dee sat there, puffing at his cheroot. Then he too rose and walked up to the deck. The night was calm. The launch chugged along the canal, flanked on both sides by the tangled jungle.

He tossed his cheroot into the water and crossed the deck to her cabin door. It was open and he walked in.

Chapter Twenty-three

EARLY next morning, long before Nai Dee's launch had reached Prachin, the town was astir. But it was not a normal awakening to a new day. In the open space in front of the temple by the Governor's house and not far from the drab little prison, a posse of soldiers who had been brought from Bangkok by the Regent were busy taking up their positions. A dozen priests, lingering for a while by the temple, after a time trooped out on to the ground. From various directions groups of people could be seen approaching slowly; it seemed that they came reluctantly, for the police were urging them on from all sides. As they neared the open space, they stopped. A few turned and tried to run away, but the police drove them back. Eventually, with their heads lowered, they squatted on the ground in solemn, silent, sullen lines—men and women, a sprinkling of children and packs of dogs which dashed about between them.

The priests, standing together in their saffron robes, started a mournful chant, and some moments later a small procession, headed by the Regent and the Foreign Minister, came on to the ground and took their places near the centre of the wide circle. At the striking of a gong, four policemen led out the prisoner. Preecha, chained at the ankles and with his hands pinioned behind him, bore himself well; his head was erect and he had the air of an aristocrat, neither defiant, nor inviting pity, but calm and seemingly at peace. He looked thin and frail, but his deeply sunken eyes blazed with fire. Behind them walked the executioner carrying a long sword and accompanied by an assistant bearing another.

At a small block near where the Regent stood, Preecha was made to kneel. For a moment, before he dropped on to his knees, their eyes met. Preecha's lips tightened. The Regent's expression remained unchanged. The executioner, dressed in scarlet, waited for the sign to be given.

A herald stepped forward and, motioning to the priests to stop their chanting, recited the charges against Preecha and announced that, in accordance with the law of the country, having been adjudged guilty, Preecha had been brought here to the scene of his crimes in order that his punishment should be witnessed by the people over whom he had ruled.

Many covered their eyes and turned away their heads. But the sign was not yet given to the executioner. Instead the Regent went up to the prisoner and said: " I had looked upon you as a friend for many years. You had the trust of His Majesty the King as well as of all the Ministers of State. This trust you betrayed. Nevertheless, before the verdict is carried out, I ask you, because of the high rank you held and the many favours you received, if there is anything you would like me personally to do for you—as a friend."

Raising his head, Preecha gave a brief nod.

" Speak then," said the Regent, " and if it is within my power to confer it, you may rely upon me to do so."

Preecha's lips moved, but his voice was low and inaudible. The Regent stooped. Again the prisoner murmured some words which the Regent was unable to hear. Stooping lower still, the Regent said: " Try to speak a little louder, man."

Then, looking defiantly into the Regent's eyes, Preecha spat full into his face. " For your soul I have pity, for you nothing but contempt," he said.

298

As the Regent angrily wiped his face, many in the crowd rushed forward to free Preecha. But the police made good use of their sticks and their knives. As soon as one group was driven back, another broke loose to aid the rescue. But their unco-ordinated efforts were fruitless; soon they were forced back and the Regent himself gave the signal to the executioner.

The squat, heavy-shouldered man in scarlet bowed to the Regent, then, swinging his sword above his head, circled round the prisoner in a ceremonial dance.

The priests, averting their faces, began to chant again, but their voices were broken by emotion and down their cheeks tears coursed. Slowly, like a flock of saffron moths, they made their way back to the temple.

The spectators prostrated themselves before Preecha and broke into a loud lamentation. They neither saw nor heard the executioner's sword descend. It was done swiftly, but for some time they kept their heads lowered to the earth, reciting a litany in praise of the man they had looked upon as their benefactor, their friend and their saint.

After the Regent and his party had left, four priests, together with the servants from Government House, who had known and loved Preecha, covered his body with a large saffron sheet, and then removed it reverently to the grounds of the temple for burial.

An hour later Nai Dee's handsome green launch with its red awnings came down the river and edged slowly up to the landing-stage.

Fanny, awed by the hushed silence and the deserted river-side, sensed that what she had most feared had come to pass. As soon as the launch was tied to the landing-stage, she leapt ashore and ran to the house that had been her home.

She found the servants weeping. They came up to her, knelt at her feet, kissed the hem of her dress and her hands. There were anguished lamentations all round her.

She was too stunned to cry. Her tears seemed all to have been spent.

As she entered the bedroom which had been theirs, she fainted.

When consciousness returned to her, she saw the Abbot and the priests from the temple around her. She could feel them trying to lift her up. She opened her eyes and burying her face against the Abbot's arm, she gave vent to her grief.

The Abbot helped her to a chair, and patiently he and the priests and Preecha's chief executive officer, Luang Sawang—who surprisingly had not been involved in any of the charges of maladministration—stood beside her waiting until she was able to hear what they had to say to her.

The first words she heard were those of the Abbot, who said:

" Luang Sawang and I have made all the necessary arrangements for your safety. Our kind lord's possessions are to be seized. His wealth has been confiscated. They will take this house very soon. But we have made arrangements for your safety."

" I am British," she replied. " Neither the Regent nor the King can touch me . . ."

" We know that this is so, but there are the children. His children by his first wife, and your little son. They plan to take them away too."

She went pale, and panic seized her.

" But—but they are in the British Consulate. Surely they are safe there . . ."

" They are safe only while they are there. And we do not know what ruse," the Abbot went on, " they may adopt to get them out of the Consulate. You must take them away."

" We have got a boat ready for you, my lady," Luang Sawang said. " It is only a small boat and it will take some time to reach Bangkok. From there you must leave for England as quickly as you can—taking the children with you."

" Yes," she said in a dead voice. " Yes."

" Two of us," the Abbot said, " will accompany you to Bangkok. I have brought these robes." He held out the saffron robes of his order. " If you wear them and travel with us . . . you should be safe. We can set out this evening at dusk."

" Where is my husband? What have you done with him? "

" He lies in our temple garden. The service will be continued by his graveside by night and by day for a week."

" I want to go there," she said, rising from her chair.

" Come, my child. I will take you."

As they came out into the veranda one of the servants pointed to a note that had been left on the veranda rail.

" For you, my lady." The servant made no effort to pick it up.

" Where does it come from? " Fanny asked.

The servant pointed to the green-and-red houseboat at the landing-stage.

Fanny struck the note off the rail and walked on with the Abbot to the temple grounds. There, amid the abundant offerings of flowers and fruit, stacked in pyramids around the freshly-dug grave, she knelt and prayed; the priests knelt beside her.

When she returned to Government House she saw Nai Dee's boat pulling out. His note lay on the damp earth below the veranda; with a feeling of revulsion she turned away from it.

As she entered her bedroom she saw some birds alight on the window-ledge where she and Preecha had so often fed them. One she recognised as Sam, who used to hop on to Preecha's shoulder.

Before long a great weariness overcame her. She felt a weight pressing on her head, and went to lie on the bed.

She must have been asleep for some hours. The Abbot was standing beside her when she awoke. " It is time," he said. In his hands he held the saffron robe.

She put it on and went with him to the boat, where another priest was already seated. Two men worked the oars and they set out through the night.

Very early on the morning of the 27th November, three days after the execution, the boat brought her to the British Consulate in Bangkok. Trakun and Arun greeted her with cries of joy. Next she had a talk with her mother, who had already heard the tragic news, then she was informed that Gould was waiting to see her.

He told her that the King had five times refused to endorse the verdict, but that the Regent, calling personally at the Palace, had exerted the greatest pressure on His Majesty and, in the end, had induced him to append his signature to the warrant. He added: " The King wept as he signed it. The Lord Chamberlain told me this."

Fanny said: " I have been advised to leave the country as soon as possible, taking the three children with me. Is there any possibility of my being able to do this? "

" Yes," replied Gould. " Fortunately there is a British steamer in Bangkok. She leaves in two hours. I have sent Singh to reserve accommodation for you. I imagine you will want to take a servant with you."

" I'd like to take Oun," she said.

" Yes. Take Oun," Mrs. Knox said.

" The five thousand pounds that was yours by the marriage settlement," said Gould, " I have already transferred to the Bank of England. It will be there awaiting your arrival. So you will have something for yourself and the children to live on. After you are safely on your way, I shall send a telegram to your father to tell him by what ship you are arriving."

Mrs. Knox clung to Fanny, crying: " When shall I see you again, my darling? My whole world is crumbling about me."

" I'll come back. It may not be soon, but I'll come back.

302

I have a score to settle here. I owe it to Preecha that such a thing should never happen again."

As the ship sailed, Fanny took a last look at the river. All around her the passengers were laughing and joking.

When she reached Singapore she felt that she could breathe again, for here at least she felt safer. Yet she wondered whether the Siamese might still be able to do something about the children. She had to wait four days for a British steamer and chafed at the delay.

She would have worried still more had she known that the Siamese Consul in Singapore had already telegraphed to London, informing Mason that the Siamese Foreign Minister wanted him to take up the question of Fanny's nationality with Lord Salisbury without delay. " Please establish her nationality urgently. Point out Fanny married Siamese official and is therefore herself now a Siamese subject and under our jurisdiction. She must be handed over to us, together with the children."

On receiving it, Mason hurried to the Foreign Office. Pauncefote took the telegram to Lord Salisbury, who studied it for a long time in silence before he said:

" So it appears that they intend to get her too."

" And the children, my lord," said Pauncefote.

Lord Salisbury looked grave. " This question of nationality. Can you see any way round it, Pauncefote? "

" I've been trying, my lord, but the Act governing the marriage of women to aliens states that the wife, in such an eventuality, automatically assumes her husband's nationality. I do not see how we can get round that."

" Let us look at the Act," said Lord Salisbury.

He ran his finger down the page, then after a moment looked up at Pauncefote and smiled.

" I do not see it stated anywhere in this document that the provision which relates to English women marrying aliens is

303

applicable to heathen countries. Will you therefore," Lord Salisbury continued, " inform the Siamese Government that Her Majesty's Government deem that the lady is entitled to be counted a British subject and consequently will enjoy our protection."

BOOK THREE

The Return

Chapter One

KNOX ARRIVED in London on the 11th November, 1879, and went to stay at 93 Jermyn Street. A few days later his favourite sister Fanny, after whom he had named his elder daughter, came over from Roslea Manor, in Northern Ireland, to see him; almost at once she contracted a severe chill and died. Her funeral brought together a large number of the family and afforded Knox an opportunity of seeing most of his relations; but the tragic event delayed his meeting with Lord Salisbury.

When he saw him, the Foreign Secretary expressed his deepest regret at not having been able to support him effectively in his fight for his son-in-law's life, and paid a tribute to his years of devoted service in Siam. " I should like to thank you, Mr. Knox," he said, " for the service you have rendered. During the course of many years you have discharged your duties with diligence and fidelity to the satisfaction of the Foreign Office."

Knox was taken aback. " Does that mean——? " he began.

Lord Salisbury nodded. " Your great experience will doubt-less have led you to the inevitable conclusion. We cannot send you back to Siam. In any case, it is just forty years since you first set out for the East, and you have, I feel, had more than your full share of the tropics. The course I would suggest to you is that you send in your resignation. The pension I have in mind is £1,026, about two-thirds of your present salary. I propose to recommend to Her Majesty that she may be graciously pleased to confer on you the honour of Knight Commander of the Order of St. Michael and St. George. The pension and the honour will serve to show you and the world in general that we are well pleased with your long and excellent service."

On his return to Jermyn Street, Knox wrote his letter of resignation; his handwriting was almost illegible.

When Bangkok learned the news many tributes were sent him. The Chinese merchants, the Burmese British subjects living in Siam, the Malays, the Indians, both Moslem and Hindu traders, drew up illuminated addresses expressing their deep regret, and paid respectful tribute to his understanding of their problems and the just and determined manner in which he had always upheld their rights.

A day or so after sending in his resignation, a telegram from Gould informed Knox of Preecha's execution and of Fanny's departure from Bangkok. It stated that a reward of five hundred pounds had been offered for Fanny's infant son. Gould added that Fanny did not know this and that she had taken all three children with her.

Early in the New Year, Knox set out for Marseilles to meet her. She and the children arrived on the 13th January, 1880. He found her looking drawn and strained, but resolute.

Knox decided that it would be better for them not to go straight on to England. The extreme cold of winter would be too sharp a change after the heat of the tropics, especially for Spencer, who was still delicate. So he took them to Biarritz, where he rented the Villa des Lauriers at 11 rue Leroy, near the Port Vieux. They decided to spend some months there until the weather at home was more temperate.

Many distinguished visitors had rented houses for the season. Lord Salisbury was there, the Duke of Abercorn, Lord Aylesbury, Lord Hamilton and Sir Victor Brooke. Quite a number of them knew Knox already.

" This is where I should like to settle," he told Fanny, " if only I could persuade your mother to come here. But "—he spread out his hands—" you know what she's like. I don't suppose I shall ever persuade her to leave Siam."

" And you'll never go back? " she said.

" How can I? "

Fanny went up and pressed her face against his. "I'm sorry, Papa. But for me you'd have been able to settle in Chiengmai —near Caroline and Louis."

" Never mind. I may prevail on your Mamma to come here one day."

The children loved Biarritz and so did Oun. It was so different from anything they had ever seen before—the cliffs, the hilly streets, the railway trains puffing along by the sea, the ramparts, the omnibuses, the magnificent villas, the enormous hotels, the large shops where one could buy things undreamed of in Siam.

One day Fanny said to her father: " The children are certainly enjoying themselves. I am reluctant to take them away. Perhaps I can leave them here with you when I go to London? "

" Why must you go to London? " he asked.

" There are things I want to do."

" Restless? "

" I suppose so."

She met Lord Salisbury once at the English Club. Knox introduced her to him.

" I was grievously distressed, my dear," he said to her. " I feel most deeply for you."

Fanny mustered a faint " Thank you," and moved away.

It was not until February, when Lord Salisbury had already left, that Fanny felt she ought to have discussed what she had in mind with him. She must do so when she got to England.

Politically, a great deal happened soon after her meeting with Lord Salisbury, for at the end of March the General Election brought about the fall of Disraeli's Government and the

Liberals came in with a surprisingly large majority. Gladstone was now Prime Minister and Lord Salisbury had been replaced at the Foreign Office by Lord Granville. Fanny wondered if Lambton would be able to arrange for her to have a conversation with the new Foreign Secretary.

She reached London in May. It seemed to her to be far more crowded than she remembered it. The cabs, the drays, the buses, the elegant hansoms, the boys on their tall penny-farthings brushed past each other. It was far less light-hearted than the river at Bangkok. There was no laughter. Horses pranced and neighed, messenger boys in small pillbox hats dashed perilously across the streets, threading their way past restive horses. Beggars leaned against the walls holding trays of matches. Blind men tapped their way along the pavements. There was a great deal of shabbiness and poverty.

She found a letter from Lambton awaiting her. He was eager to see her and they arranged to lunch together. After they had referred briefly to the tragic events Fanny had lived through since their last meeting, she said: " Tell me, is Lord Granville well in with the new Prime Minister? "

" Very well in. His nephew George Leveson-Gower is Gladstone's Parliamentary Private Secretary."

Fanny seemed pleased.

Lambton was perplexed and asked her why she was so concerned with the Foreign Secretary.

" What has happened would *never* have happened if Siam was governed as—as—let us say India is," she replied.

Lambton looked at her with a startled expression. " You are not suggesting that we should send an expeditionary force and seize Siam, are you? " he asked.

" That is exactly what I am suggesting," she answered.

" But, Fanny . . ."

" We've done it all over the world. Just look at the red patches on your map."

" History does not support you," he said. " The circumstances are not comparable."

" What I am suggesting is that we should take over Siam, set up a good government . . ." Fanny went on. " Think of the advantages which would come to the people."

" They might not see it in that light. The Indians do not." He laughed.

Fanny went straight to the point. " Could you arrange for me to see Lord Granville? " she asked.

" But he'll blow up if you start suggesting to him that we should annex Siam."

" I won't. I shall tell him what's going on there—the sort of things he won't read about in his official documents. Do you know," she went on, " that Preecha's father and his two brothers are still in gaol, and that all their property has been confiscated. Don't you think that Siamese justice needs to be reformed? "

" I will try to get you an interview with Lord Granville," he said.

A week later Fanny's brother Tom came down from Oxford. She was happy to see him again. He had hardly grown and, save for his moustache, still looked the schoolboy she remembered. There was a Siamese look about him.

They talked of Mamma, of Caroline and Louis, of Papa and about the children, and about Oxford. He had never been very studious, and was vague about his future. His house-master at Haileybury, Carmell Price, had suggested, he told Fanny, that he should go to New Zealand and as their cousins, Walter and Berry Madden, were already there, he was thinking of joining them.

" Does that mean neither Mamma nor Caroline are ever going to see you again? " Fanny asked.

" I could visit them," he replied.

Fanny wondered whether he ever would. She reflected

bitterly that there seemed to be no end to the misery which she and Preecha had, through their love for each other, spread about them.

To try and cheer Fanny up Lambton took her to Ascot. But it was a sombre affair. The court was in mourning because of the death of the Empress of Russia, and by the Queen's command all those with tickets for the Royal Enclosure were required to dress in black. The tall hats of the men were wound in crêpe. The women wore high-necked dresses and tiny black hats.

There were heavy showers of rain with only fitful sunshine. But when Lambton said to her, " I've arranged for you to go and see Lord Granville next Monday afternoon at three o'clock," she no longer observed her surroundings, her mind was busy imagining the interview.

When the day came, Lord Granville received her with great courtesy. He said: " I've been studying the documents concerning your husband's death. I offer you my heartfelt sympathy."

She inclined her head in acknowledgment. He went on: " Unfortunately it's too late to take action now. Nor, indeed, could I have done more than Lord Salisbury did had I been in office at the time."

" Is it your opinion that the Foreign Office could have done nothing to prevent my husband's murder? " Fanny fixed him with her eyes.

Granville looked down at his desk.

She went on: " Whatever your answer to that question to-day, my concern is with the future. Can we not prevent such a crime occurring again? "

" Our authority, Baroness, can only be exercised on behalf of a British subject. Unhappily, your husband was not British, or even employed in any capacity by the British. Had he been, I assure you that he would have been alive to-day."

" But I am British," Fanny retorted. " Are foreign govern-
ments to be allowed full licence to persecute English women
and to murder their husbands? You knew Lord Palmerston.
Surely he would have acted differently."

Lord Granville stroked his upper lip. " Possibly he would
have," he said, " but it might have led to war."

" His threats hardly ever led to war," Fanny objected.

Lord Granville's expression was warm and friendly as he
replied: " We had too many wars on our hands at the time,
Baroness, to take that risk."

" But those wars are won now."

" Not all of them. But am I right in thinking you want us
to make war on Siam? "

" Our victory could not bring my husband back to life, but
you did fight the recent election for justice and fair play in *all*
parts of the world."

The Foreign Minister smiled. " You would make an
admirable advocate in a court of law. But unfortunately you
are asking us to do something we cannot do."

She was silent for a moment, then she said thrustingly:
" Would you be prepared to let the French take Siam instead? "

" What makes you imagine they will? "

" If you observe their moves, Lord Granville, you will see
how they have been forcing their way nearer and nearer the
eastern frontier. They have already taken Annam, Cochin-
China and Cambodia."

He shook his head. " The French wouldn't dare. They
know that they would have to reckon with us if they tried to
invade Siam." He rose, indicating that their interview was at
an end. " If at any time I can help—short of going to war, of
course—please call on me."

He held out his hand.

Frustrated in her main objective, Fanny set about looking for
a governess for the children. She had not given up her plans,

and since futhering them would keep her away from Biarritz, the governess must be a very responsible person. Through Lambton's lawyer Theodore McKenna she heard of a Miss Bindloss, and an interview was arranged. When she arrived, Miss Bindloss proved to be about twenty-nine and of a pleasing appearance. She said she loved children and got on well with them.

Fanny asked her if she were prepared to be solely in charge of Arun, Trakun and Spencer.

" That's the sort of job I've just been doing," replied Miss Bindloss. " I had two children completely in my care until quite recently."

" Were they orphans? " Fanny inquired.

" No, but their mother, Ellen Terry, went back to the stage," said Miss Bindloss with a certain pride.

" I should tell you that my two stepchildren are Siamese, and that if you take the post you will be obliged to go abroad —for they are with my father at Biarritz."

It appeared that Miss Bindloss had held a post abroad before she went to the Terry family, and that Biarritz held no terrors for her. She left England on the following Monday.

Chapter Two

MISS BINDLOSS proved extremely capable, so not long after her arrival Knox decided to leave the children in her care and join Fanny in England. He was anxious to find out what she was up to, for he knew that she had some plan of action in mind.

He gained no inkling of what her activities had been until one day, when they were lunching with Lambton, Fanny said:

" Edward, has Lord Granville begun to realise the necessity of dealing firmly with Siam? "

" What *have* you been trying to do, Fanny? " Knox asked brusquely.

" She's been to see the Secretary of State," Lambton explained. " She wants him to start a war."

Knox was alarmed. " A war? " he shouted angrily.

Smiling, Fanny turned to Lambton and said: " Papa needn't be so shocked, for he himself planned to raise the standard of revolt in Bangkok." She paused and glanced at her father. He looked very uncomfortable, but she did not spare him.

" The gunboat was there. The King wanted to get rid of the Regent and become independent, and Papa felt he had only to give the signal. I was very proud of you, Papa. The pity was that you didn't carry it through."

" That was quite different. I was trying to save a life . . ." said Knox with some embarrassment.

" I am trying to save many, many lives—and I shall find a way." Fanny's lips parted and she smiled. " After all, I am your daughter," she concluded.

The next day a telegram announced that Caroline had given birth to a son, who was to be called Thomas George Knox. This news pleased Knox immensely. It was followed by a letter from which they learned that Mrs. Knox had gone to live at Chiengmai with Caroline. She wrote that all the furniture had been put in store. In a postscript she added: " I've had the family portrait of the Three Graces safely packed so that it won't get scratched, for one day when we have a home again, we shall hang it up in our drawing-room."

Knox had doubts.

" I can't understand your mother," he said. " She seems so westernised—thinks, talks and behaves like the rest of us. But," he added sadly, " I do not believe that she will ever join us in the West, and I cannot return to Siam."

It rammed home the realisation that she had made a mess not only of her own life but of her parents' lives too.

The season was over, but Fanny remained on in London, and so did Lambton. One day they found that there were only a few people lunching in the usually crowded restaurant.

" All Whitehall must be empty," Fanny remarked.

" Not the Foreign Office. The S. of S. is still in town," replied Lambton.

" What's keeping Lord Granville in London? "

" The war in Afghanistan—it's not going at all well. You see, Fanny," he went on, " wars don't always go well. They are difficult, bloody, damnable. But sometimes one can't avoid them . . ."

" And yet, in spite of all you say, sometimes one should plunge into them," she broke in.

His eyes narrowed. He looked very grave. " Fanny," he said, " may I tell you what I am thinking? "

" Of course." She wondered what he was going to say.

" You've been through a dreadful ordeal. I can quite understand your wanting Granville to do something. But if you were

316

honest with yourself you would recognise that what you really want is vengeance."

She replied: "You are wondering why I am so obsessed with this. What I resent is that they should take on themselves the prerogative of the Almighty—no, of the devil, for the Almighty is just, and this was most cruel, most vile. We had had only a few weeks together. We had all our lives before us."

He placed his hand tenderly on hers. He saw that there were tears in her eyes. She put her knife and fork together. Most of her sole had been left untouched.

" I'd like some coffee," she said. Lambton ordered it.

" Your duck, sir," the waiter prompted.

" No—just some coffee," Lambton replied.

Trying to give the conversation another turn, Fanny asked him how long he would be staying in London.

" I am expected in Scotland for the Twelfth."

" I see." She felt that she would miss him.

" But I wrote and told my mother that I might not get there until later. Will you be staying here for a while? "

" Yes. I want to get some toys for the children."

" I don't suppose you'll need any help. You are much nearer their age than I am," he said.

" At this moment I feel a thousand years old," she answered.

Lambton did not help her to buy the toys, but she saw him quite often. There was no doubt that his presence was comforting to her.

One evening he took her to a party at his lawyer's to meet Ellen Terry. It was well after three o'clock when they left. The first light of dawn was creeping slowly across the unclouded sky, and the air was warm.

Lambton asked the man at the door to fetch a hansom. As they clopped along the empty streets, he took her hand in his.

" The beginning of a new day. It goes on, indifferent to

what we do. And we have to do the same," he said. " Begin again."

He waited for her response, but she said nothing. He stroked her fingers gently and looked at her. He could see her pale face and her sad eyes clearly in the growing light. Her expression remained impassive.

After a long silence, he said: " I think you know what I feel about you. I've been in love with you since that night when we were in the ship going out to Bangkok and we walked on to the deck and stood by the rails and looked at the stars."

" I'm afraid I was rather a flirt then."

" But I think you liked me. Indeed, I feel that you still do."

" Yes, Edward. You are kind and understanding. But if this is a proposal . . ."

" I am not proposing now, because I feel the answer would be No. But perhaps in the future you might think about it, will you? "

" You say you don't want my answer now. But it would be unfair not to give it. Edward dear, I mean this. I like you very, very much, and I think you could make me happy, in so far as anyone could. You are a little like Preecha—you are gentle, you have ideals . . ."

" But——? " he asked nervously.

" I have so much I want to do—I couldn't expect you to wait . . ."

" So you still mean to go on with it? "

" I must, Edward."

She noticed a flicker of annoyance in his eyes.

" I won't discuss it," she said, " for we would not agree."

" Very well," he replied. " But afterwards? There will be another day. You can't hold back the dawn."

" That's looking too far into the future, Edward."

" I shall wait."

She kissed him.

The next day Fanny decided to go back to Biarritz. She felt that there was nothing more she could do in London to forward her plan; she longed to see the children and she believed that to leave London would be kinder to Lambton. She had a long wait at Victoria Station for her train, and there she scribbled a brief note to him. " I am just off to Biarritz. I shall be at the Villa des Lauriers, 11 rue Leroy, as before.—Fanny."

Lambton was greatly disturbed when he received it. He wondered if what he had said in the cab had hastened her departure. Perhaps he had been a little brusque in discussing her plan. . . . Quite obviously it had become an obsession and she could not be dissuaded.

After much deliberation he wrote to her: " Why this sudden departure? Was it because of me? I sincerely hope I said nothing to upset you. Believe me, it is the last thing I would want to do. I want to help you—that is the one thing uppermost in my "—he hesitated for a moment, then added—" in my heart.

" You will find it difficult to believe this, in view of what I have said about Siam. I promise you that I shall be sympathetic in future. Would it be of any use if I came to Biarritz? Your letter was so brief and so abrupt. With love—if I dare say so —your devoted Edward."

Biarritz in August was very quiet. The visitors would not return until the autumn. The streets were practically empty. Her mornings were spent with the children at the small, sheltered Port Vieux, where they saw French women in the latest *toilettes de bains*, bobbing about in the water with cork belts and bladders strapped round them. Spencer crawled about the sands under the cautious eye of Miss Bindloss, while Trakun and Arun, with the love of swimming that all Siamese children have, dived and somersaulted in the water.

Miss Bindloss had determined that all the children, and Oun too, should be brought up as good Christians. She spent part of each day teaching them the Catechism and telling them stories from the Bible. In the evenings, before being put to bed, they were made to sing hymns and say their prayers. Fanny had no sooner returned than Miss Bindloss began asking her to have the children christened.

"We had a priest to bless Spencer when he was only a few weeks old," Fanny replied.

"He ought to be properly christened," Miss Bindloss insisted.

Fanny acquiesced. She took the three children to the Church of St. Andrée and, with her father's brother, Colonel Beresford Knox, and Captain Bellairs as godfathers, they were baptized. Trakun was christened Olivia Frances, Arun and Spencer kept their own names.

"What about Oun?" Miss Bindloss asked. "We're not going to leave her out, are we?"

"We have no right to make her a Christian unless she wants to become one," Fanny objected, and turning to her, asked: "Do you want to be christened, Oun?"

Oun shook her hand and her head.

Lambton's letter brought Fanny some comfort. She had thought of him often. But marriage? There would be many advantages in being married to a charming, devoted, protective man like Edward. There would be an end to her financial anxieties. She had already made inroads into her marriage settlement of five thousand pounds, and when that was used up what would she do? Her jewels would keep them for a while —but afterwards? The attraction to marriage with Edward was great, but the purpose in her was too strong. She had to go on along paths which it would be impossible for Edward to follow.

Chapter Three

FANNY was determined to induce the French to take over Siam. To do this she realised that she must go to Paris, but who was she to see when she got there? She knew no one in the French Government. A letter from Edward to the Quai d'Orsay would, of course, open many doors. But she dared not approach him again. She could hear his stern, disapproving voice. " What! Ask the French to annex Siam? It would most seriously affect the interests of Great Britain. Siam is a valuable market. I am surprised at you, Fanny, for even entertaining such a thought." Papa would be furious, too. And yet she felt it would be criminally callous to leave the Siamese people at the mercy of the cruel, arbitrary whims of the Regent—so what other alternative had she?

But to whom was she to go? She read the French newspapers and saw that the French Government was unstable. There were too many political parties, each divided within itself. There were endless feuds. Changes in the Government in September led to the appointment of a new Foreign Minister, M. Barthelemy St. Hilaire. But by the time she got to Paris, who could say whether he would still be in office?

One evening at the casino Fanny met Madame Chalais, an ageing but still beautiful French woman. Until the death of her husband she had lived in Saigon; then she had come to Biarritz, where she had bought a large villa. Her one interest in life now was her son Charles.

Not long after Fanny had made friends with Madame Chalais, Charles arrived to visit his mother. Fanny had expected to see a slender, pampered mother's darling, but the young man was tall, burly and extremely attractive. He had fair hair, bright-blue eyes and a gaiety of spirit and a tendency to tease which attracted her. His left arm hung in a sling, and Fanny learned later that it had been broken in a riot. For some months France had been greatly agitated by the Government's attempt to expel the religious orders. Hostile demonstrations had taken place in Lyons and Nîmes, Marseilles and Toulouse, and Charles Chalais with his love of excitement had gone down to Lyons to join in the fray. He had made a lucky escape over the roof-tops when chased by the police.

" I would not have thought that you were very religious," Fanny said with some surprise, when he told her of the incident.

" I am not. But I'm against interfering with the liberty of the priests. The decree is arbitrary, and therefore odious. I suppose I was born too late. I missed the Franco-Prussian war. It wasn't a good war. But—well, anything's better than these decrees and persecutions."

" Are you looking for a war? " she asked.

" No. Why? You got one up your sleeve? "

" Not exactly," Fanny replied. " But if you have any influence in the Quai d'Orsay you might tell them that France could have Siam for the asking."

He made a disdainful grimace.

" I know nobody there," he said. " Nor do I want to. All they think about is being seen at the opera with a new mistress each week. We have no man in the Government of the calibre of Gambetta. He has got great courage." Charles's eyes were alight with admiration. " If he comes to power, he might be interested in your suggestion. Of course, he is to the left and anti-imperialist, but like many left-wingers, if the annexation could be presented as a civilising movement, it might appeal to him. Why don't you come to Paris? I might be able to arrange a meeting."

" I'll come," Fanny said.

" And while you are there, I'd like you to meet Corinne," he added.

Fanny did not pursue this remark, but told Charles the story of her marriage to Preecha. " The country has to be taken over," she concluded. " I want other women to be spared the anguish I've been through. I will not rest until I have achieved this."

Charles was moved and excited. To Fanny he seemed the only man who was prepared to take her seriously. He left for Paris soon afterwards, and returned to Biarritz shortly before Christmas. When they met she questioned him anxiously.

" I talked to one or two friends about your plan," he replied. " They are not prepared to do anything." He laughed. " I'll tell you what," he went on, slipping his arm through hers. " Let's go out to Siam—just you and I—and conquer the country ourselves."

Fanny agreed that nothing would please her better, but pointed out that this plan wasn't a very practical one. However, they had endless discussions about the possibility of contriving some incident which would compel the French Government to take action in Siam, and Charles, who was by nature an adventurer and enjoyed plotting, found the topic fascinating. He was enjoying Fanny's company very much indeed and she was happy to find a companion who gave her not only sympathy but also hope. When he returned to Paris, he made Fanny promise that she would join him there before long.

She arrived in Paris on the 12th March, 1881, and stayed at the Hotel Windsor in the Rue de Rivoli.

It was six years since she had been there. Paris seemed to have changed very little. The Champs-Élysées was filled with elegant phaetons and landaus with high-stepping horses, in which women carrying gay, coloured parasols were seated.

Charles called early on the evening of her arrival, bringing
Corinne with him. She was dark, slight and very striking. Her
eyes were unusually wide apart. Above her pale face, her jet-
black hair was piled high. Her manner was casual.

She was an artist's model, had posed for Degas when she was
only thirteen, and was very proud of being the third girl from
the left in one of his ballet pictures. She spent her days posing
in one or other of the ateliers, and her evenings going with
Charles from café to café so that she should be seen by artists
and get more engagements.

They discussed how Fanny could obtain an interview with
some important member of the French Government. Charles's
contacts were not very promising ; he moved in a world of
artists and not of politicians. Nevertheless, he did in the end
succeed in taking her to a party at which one of Gambetta's
secretaries was present. True, Gambetta was not in office, but
who could tell when he might be, and he was certainly the type
of man whom no risk appalled. Also, it was the business of his
secretaries to be extremely well informed about the views of
the members of the present Ministry and the public.

When Fanny first began to talk of politics to him, the young
man expressed a conventional surprise that the subject should
interest a pretty young woman. But when she continued, he
admitted that Charles had told him of the tragedy of Preecha's
death and something of her ambition to rid Siam of the
Regent's tyranny. Arguing vigorously about the misery of the
Siamese people, the duty of the Western powers to come to
their aid and the uniquely advantageous position of the French
forces in Annam, Cochin-China and Cambodia, she brought
him to the point of saying:

" Baroness, not only I but many French politicians are aware
of the civilising mission we might have in respect of Siam and
of the economic advantages that might accrue to us if we
annexed the country—but—we cannot march in without a

pretext. There would need to be at least a frontier incident involving French nationals." He said this almost as a joke— but Charles noticed the intense concentration in Fanny's expression as she asked:

" What do you mean by a frontier incident? "

" Oh . . . the crossing of the Cambodian frontier by armed Siamese, or the arrest of French nationals by the Siamese. After this, notes would be exchanged and even if there were an apology the Government could always pick holes in it and act." He spoke lightly and was startled by the emotion in Fanny's voice as she asked:

" But would France act? "

Briskly he replied: " Baroness, I trust you are not considering instigating an incident? Remember you are not French, so we could do nothing about it."

" I realise that," she answered. The reply did not put him at ease; it seemed to contain a threat.

That evening, sitting in a café near St. Germain des Prés with Charles, Corinne and a friend of his called Michel, who was a painter, Fanny said cautiously: " You know my plans. Well, I've come to the conclusion that no one will help me. So I must take action myself. Would you three come with me to the East if I decided to go? "

" Are you going to raise an army and march into Siam? " Charles inquired. He looked at Corinne, then at Michel, and said: " By God, I will! What about you, Michel? You could paint better pictures there than you've ever painted in your life before."

Michel was short and square; he had quick jerky movements. When he dived into his pockets for cigarettes it was almost as though he were wrestling with himself. " It would cost a lot to get there," he said. " Otherwise I've no objection, for I would certainly be able to paint some really remarkable pictures—the women with their bared breasts, the bustle of the bazaars. . . . I could have the whole of the Petit Salon to myself when I came home."

Charles turned to Corinne, and said in a lordly manner: " I'm taking you."

She raised her eyebrows and looked at him. " And what if I say I don't want to go? "

" You'll come just the same," Charles said.

Fanny laughed.

" I'd like to come," said Michel, "but——"

" If you need money," Fanny interrupted, " I will see what I can do. You can pay it back after your show."

They began to discuss the journey. Fanny said that they would go first to Saigon, and from there travel by river steamer along the Mekong to Pnom Penh, the capital of Cambodia. There they would have to engage a party of bearers to carry their tents and get a contractor to provide some elephants.

" And we shall need an escort of armed men," she added, " for it will be a rough and difficult journey to the Siamese frontier."

" To the frontier! " exclaimed Charles. " Are we going into battle? "

" Are you afraid? " Fanny asked.

" No, but there's Corinne to consider."

" Oh," said Corinne. " So I am to be considered? "

Charles pinched her cheek, saying: " I'll look after you."

Fanny was thinking: that makes four, and three are French.

Michel, his face flushed with excitement, exclaimed: " I am itching to start. I shall introduce a new quality of light into my work."

Charles was excited too. Only Corinne remained apparently languid and indifferent. " How long are we to be away? " she asked.

" Some months," Fanny said. " It will take six weeks to get to Saigon. Then there's the journey to the frontier." She fell silent until Michel called "Fanny "—as though to bring her out of her dream—" when are we going to start? "

" Towards the end of the year."

" Why wait so long? " he asked.

" Gambetta might be in office by then," she answered.

On the Saturday morning she caught the train back to Biarritz, feeling much more hopeful.

Chapter Four

WHEN FANNY arrived in Biarritz her father wanted to know what had detained her in Paris for so long. Her answers were evasive. He told her that he thought she should now settle down and keep to a strict budget, and noticed that her expression was resentful when he made this suggestion.

" Tell me then, what are you planning to do? "

He waited.

She made a vague gesture. " Papa . . ."

" Yes? "

She felt she couldn't tell him anything. She shook her head. The merest hint and Papa would guess all the rest.

Knox looked fixedly at her. " If you can't tell me, then it's something you ought not to do. I suppose Charles is mixed up in this. I've always thought him rather mad, and I'm beginning to think you are too. . . . I hope you are not going to do something against the interests of our country."

" I am working in the interests of Siam," she said defiantly.

" If you strengthen France's position out there, then you are working against Britain."

" Do you imagine Charles and I are going to conquer Siam single-handed? " she replied crossly.

" So you *are* planning to go out there, are you? "

" I always planned to go back. I told you that the moment I got home."

He looked at her, then turned and walked out of the room.

Gould arrived the next evening. He was on his way home on leave. Fanny, who was still in Paris when the telegram announcing his visit came, was startled to see him at the door of the villa. It was eighteen months since she had said good-bye to him at the Consulate in Bangkok.

It was a warm-hearted reunion. She had much to be grateful to him for. Arun and Trakun danced round him. He took Spencer on his knee. Oun, reverting to the Siamese custom, surprised Miss Bindloss by greeting him with the palms of her hands joined together in a *wei*, to which Gould responded with equal deference.

Knox and he talked a great deal about the old days. Siamese words kept drifting into the conversation, making Miss Bindloss feel that the villa had suddenly become quite oriental and heathen. Fanny, less interested in the past than in what was happening now, plied Gould with questions about the Regent and the King, and especially about Phya Kesab and Preecha's two brothers.

" They are still in gaol," Gould said, shaking his head sadly. " There has been no trial. No charges have been brought against any of them."

" Isn't anyone trying to do anything for them? " she asked. " They had many powerful friends, not to mention the King."

" No one dares raise his voice. I tried to get some of them to draw up a petition for their release. But they knew it would be their turn next if they did."

Fanny exploded. " And Papa feels that Siam should be left to go on like this. Everyone trembling with fear lest they rouse the Regent's wrath. How can we look on with indifference? "

" Terrible things are happening in a lot of countries," said Knox. " What can we do about it? "

" We can't interfere in the internal affairs of another nation," Gould pointed out.

" We must," Fanny retorted.

" All the world over? " Knox asked.

" We can only alleviate the suffering of which we are aware,"
Fanny answered.

" She has some hare-brained scheme," Knox explained, " for
interfering in the affairs of Siam. Heaven only knows what it
is. She wanted Granville to send an army into the country to
take it over. Now she's been to Paris, so I suppose she wants
the French to do it, since Granville won't."

" The French have their hands pretty full at the moment,"
Gould said. " They are not likely to embark on anything more.
And, Fanny, I beg you to keep out of anything of this sort,
because the Regent's only waiting for an excuse."

" To get me? " she asked. " The children are safe."

Gould shook his head and looked at Knox.

Fanny left them, for she had letters to write, far too many
for her liking. Mamma had to be written to as well as Caroline
and Tom. There were letters from Lambton awaiting an
answer, and she must also write to Charles.

She had a date in mind for their departure—the middle of
January, at the very latest. She intended to go to Paris again
before then, and possibly also to London. It might be the last
time that she would be seeing these places and her friends.

She had written to the Messageries Maritimes Company at
Marseilles and booked passages for herself and the other three.
So now she wrote to urge Charles to see that all would be ready
by that date. " We have only a few months left," she wrote.
" I shall be in Paris at the end of November, but only for a
few days. We can then work out such details as have still to
be settled."

Charles came to Biarritz at the end of October, and they
travelled back to Paris together. She took Spencer and Oun
with her. The child was two now, and in view of her impending
departure she wanted to be as much with him as she could.

She joined Charles and Corinne and Michel for dinner. It
was chilly and they sat indoors in a café near St. Germain des

Prés. Michel was as enthusiastic as before, but Corinne seemed casual and bored. Fanny felt uneasy. Was it going to work? Would they refuse to go on once they reached Saigon? Michel because he was really only interested in painting; Charles and Corinne because it was a town and offered gayer diversions than they would find up-country.

Fanny thought she had better prepare them for what lay before them, and see how they reacted.

" You've had time to think about our expedition," she said. " Are you prepared to go on with the plan—there will be discomfort, hardship, risks. . . . On the frontier there may even be trouble. We might, for instance, be arrested."

Charles smiled. " It's going to be exciting. Arrest I had not bargained for. And I don't think I'd enjoy it. Still, it may not come to that. We'll come."

The others nodded their heads in not too enthusiastic assent.

" All right," Fanny remarked. " Then we sail on the 17th January from Marseilles."

Two days later she and Spencer and Oun left for London. Lambton met them at Victoria Station. He insisted on taking Spencer from Oun and carrying him to their cab.

" How long do you plan to stay here? " he asked on the way to her hotel in Bloomsbury. " As I haven't seen you for more than a year, even a crumb will be most gratefully accepted."

She was sorry. The tenderness in her eyes revealed it.

" Edward, please don't think I've been trying to avoid being with you. I wouldn't have written to you if I were. But let's agree that we won't talk again about marriage. I'm deeply grateful, as you know, but it can't be—not for a long time, if ever."

He frowned. " Why do you add 'if ever'? "

" We don't any of us know what's going to happen in the future."

" You have plans, I suppose? " he asked.

" Yes."

" You'd rather not discuss them? "

" No." Then, noticing his embarrassment, she added: " It isn't that I don't trust you. But all that is settled is that I'm going out East again in January."

" Would you like to tell me *something* of what you plan to do when you get there? "

" No. Edward, don't let's discuss that either. Will you, please? "

They went to a theatre and had supper afterwards. Their talk was confined to things that he had been doing.

Fanny called the next day at Coutts Bank in the Strand. She wanted to see how her account stood and was appalled to find that she had only £2,300 left. She couldn't understand it. How had she managed to get through more than half her capital in so short a time?

She had brought most of her jewels with her in a brown Gladstone bag. " I wanted to hand these to you for safe keeping," she said, " but I think perhaps you'd better try and sell them."

" We could have them valued by a reliable man," the manager suggested.

She agreed, and asked if this could be done immediately.

He returned after a time and informed her that they were worth something in the region of £1,250.

" You'd better sell them and credit my account with whatever they fetch," she said.

At least this would raise her balance to about £3,500. It would, she hoped, see her through what she was about to undertake.

Fanny was greatly heartened on leaving the bank to learn from the newspapers that Gambetta had been invited by the French President to form a new Government. So at last he was in power. She regarded this as an encouraging step, perhaps the intervention of fate to ensure the success of her plan.

She paid a short visit to her relations in Ireland and returned to Biarritz early in December.

Knox, aware that the time for her departure was drawing near, said as they sat alone in the front parlour one evening: " You don't realise the sort of fire you're playing with, Fanny. Have you considered what will happen to you if things go wrong? I can't stop you—if I could I would. But just remember this. The Regent is still in power out there, and he will pull every string he can to stop you—and to get you——"

" But I'm not going to Siam," she said.

" Maybe not to begin with. But if you get into Cambodia, as I think you plan to do, remember that there are treaties between Siam and King Norodom. One word from the Regent and you will be stumped. And he'll say the word too, you'll see. And if by some mischance, you happen to fall into his hands, then heaven help you, for neither Gould nor I will be able to. You are a British subject, but Britain is not likely to go to war over the folly of a silly girl who ought to know better."

" Thank you, Papa, for the warning," she replied. " I promise you that I'll take all the care I can to keep out of his clutches."

" But nothing will stop you? " he asked.

" Nothing," she said.

Chapter Five

FANNY LEFT for Marseilles on the 16th January. When she met the others on board the *Oxus* a few hours before sailing, it seemed to her that they had all brought too much with them. Michel had two large cases packed with canvases and paints. Corinne had more dresses than she was likely to need; but there was one item, most necessary in her view, that was missing.

Taking Charles aside, Fanny said: " We ought to take some guns with us."

" Rifles? " he asked in surprise.

" Yes, rifles. There may be all sorts of restrictions on buying them in Saigon, so we'd better take some with us."

Charles agreed, and they both went ashore and without much difficulty, though at considerable expense, made their purchases and returned with six Snider rifles, two pistols and a supply of ammunition.

For Fanny the voyage to Singapore was full of memories. It was her third passage through the Suez Canal (it had not been opened the first time she went home). In particular she kept recalling the evenings she had spent with Lambton on her last trip out.

As their ship docked in Singapore, at the very dock from which she had escaped with the children less than two and a half years before, she saw the *Chow Phya* getting ready to leave for Bangkok. It was the boat in which Anna and Louis had travelled from Singapore twenty years before with Captain Orton. Fanny longed to get aboard, but she had to wait and take the longer, more difficult and more dangerous, route back.

The *Oxus* left for Saigon early next morning. The journey was comparatively short. But the weather now became stifling. The nights were airless and they slept on deck in long cane chairs.

Saigon enchanted Charles, Michel and Corinne. With its wide boulevards and brilliantly lighted cafés with marble-topped tables, it reminded them of a French provincial town, and many of the newspapers on sale in the streets were written in French too. But it was France with an exciting difference, exemplified by the national dress worn by the women, with its flowing panels and conical straw hats tied under the chin with gay ribbons, and by the smart yellow rickshaws.

Fanny herself did not like the town, and compared it unfavourably with Bangkok. Instead of canals there were dirty roads, pitted with ruts, and the bustling traffic filled her lungs with dust. In place of the tiered, tiled, triangular roofs of Bangkok, fashioned in the shape of the squatting Buddha, the large public buildings, the offices and the shops were all modern and very French looking. The inhabitants of the centre of the town consisted of a sprinkling of French officials and businessmen and many Cochinese, Annamese and Tonkinoise; the adjoining suburb of Cholon was completely Chinese and hung with paper signs and lanterns. She was eager to leave it as quickly as possible, but she needed time to make a number of necessary arrangements. First she hired a river steamer to take them up the Mekong into Cambodia; then she bought food and engaged servants.

A week later they started off.

Fanny could now relax for a short time. She opened a newspaper she had bought in the streets of Saigon, and was startled to read that Gambetta's government had already fallen. It had lasted for only sixty-six days. This was a severe blow to her hopes, but it was now too late to turn back.

The Mekong was much wider than the Menam, indeed it is one of the largest rivers in the world, but to Fanny it seemed far less attractive, for it lacked the laughter and the gaiety of the river at Bangkok. Michel, however, was not so critical, and at every bend of the winding river shouted with delight and soon got busy making sketches of thatched huts, bare-breasted women, naked children splashing in the water, against a background of tall palm trees and jungle.

There were only two cabins on the steam launch. The deck was small and the saloon cramped. It took them two and a half days to reach Pnom Penh, the straggling, dusty capital of Cambodia. Here again Michel found plenty to sketch; he was particularly attracted by the houses, which rose on stilts out of the swamp.

The hotel they stayed in was small and uncomfortable. The floors were bare, the beds hard and lumpy, the mosquito nets torn and dirty. There were lizards on the walls and cockroaches raced across the floor. Corinne deeply regretted leaving Saigon, where they had lived in adequate comfort, and Michel and Charles were also sufficiently disgusted.

Fanny was anxious to go on as soon as possible, but coolies and elephants had to be hired and some supplies laid on.

" We shall have to spend a day in the bazaars," she told Charles. " For once we leave Pnom Penh we shall really be in the wilds."

Charles asked how far the launch would still take them and when they would have to disembark and meet the elephants and coolies.

Fanny took out her map and spread it across the table. " From Pnom Penh," she said, " we travel northwards along the river Tonle Sap, to the great inland lake, the far end of which juts into Siam. We shall go ashore at Kanchor, about thirty miles from the frontier, then we shall move in the

Fanny's son, Spencer

The shrine erected in memory of Fanny's husband

The first offices of Louis T. Leonowens, Ltd., in Bangkok

Louis Leonowens in his first motor car

direction of Battambang. Beyond that is Kabin—then Prachin."

" And then we seize the palace at Prachin and proclaim you Governor? " Charles laughed.

" Things will happen long before we get to Battambang, let alone Prachin," Fanny replied gravely.

Inquiries in the bazaar led them to a contractor named Chup. He said that they would need three elephants and twenty men, and that some of the men would need to be armed, since they might be waylaid by bandits. He would buy spears and stout sticks in the bazaars; more rifles would have been useful but would be unobtainable, for the French Government had become very strict about the sale of arms. Chup demanded to be paid in advance. After receiving it, he said: " I shall meet you at Kanchor in ten days' time with the elephants and the men."

One afternoon, in the busy open market, Fanny caught sight of Prince Poh Duan, one of King Norodom's sons; he was riding by on a grey horse. She hurried into the covered section of the bazaar, for she had met him quite often at receptions in Bangkok and was on friendly terms with him. Now the last thing she wanted was to be recognised and questioned. " But he might help us," Charles suggested.

" It's better that nobody should know I am here. I only pray he hasn't seen and recognised me."

Michel, whose high spirits seemed inexhaustible, announced as the time drew near for their departure, that he would prefer not to go on, and was instantly supported by Corinne.

So, on their last night, with the spears stowed away and their elephants and coolies awaiting them at Kanchor, the whole project was brought to the verge of abandonment. After a long, angry argument Fanny said:

" You do what you like. I'm going on, even if I have to go alone."

Charles raised his hand to quiet her. " I'm coming with you. As for Corinne and Michel, they can go to the devil."

He stormed out of the room, and the party broke up.

When Fanny later went to the bedroom which she shared with Corinne, she found her lying on the bed sobbing. After gazing at her for a while, Fanny decided to get on with her packing.

About an hour later Corinne rose and began to pack too.

" I suppose these shoes won't be much good in the jungle," she said, holding up a pair of high-heeled shoes.

" No," said Fanny. She smiled.

Next morning, Michel joined them and they went off to their river steamer together.

The boat turned out of the large but shrunken inland lake and nosed its way to the mud-flats at the mouth of the River Stung Pursat, where it pulled up at the small jetty of Kanchor. Here they disembarked.

Fanny wanted the launch to wait a day or two in case the contractor had been delayed. She knew how unreliable such middle-men could be. But the man in charge of the boat refused to wait. He said he had another job to get back to at Saigon and was already behind schedule.

Kanchor was little more than an overgrown village of rough mud huts, all built on stilts. Around them stretched vast rice fields, bone dry at this season, waiting for the coming of the rains.

Fanny collected some coolies to unload their luggage, and walked into the town with the others; there was no sign of the contractor or of the elephants. Able to make herself understood, for the language here bore some resemblance to Siamese, she could learn nothing of Chup's whereabouts. They said that he had been there a few days earlier but had then gone inland.

This was a serious setback. They might have to wait for days. They would have to pitch their tents just outside the town, or possibly try and find accommodation with the local inhabitants.

She talked to the villagers as they sat gossiping in groups in the shade of the trees, with goats nibbling and hens scurrying around them. They listened and nodded but seemed to understand very little; eventually they led her to a short, bearded man who, though he was dressed like the natives, was plainly a European. He spoke to her in French, which she realised was his native tongue. She asked him how he came to be in such an outlandish place. He told her that he was a priest who had come to Cambodia many years ago. " I live with them and do what I can to help them," he said. " Perhaps I do some good. It is difficult to tell."

He, too, knew the contractor Chup. " He comes here every few weeks. I suggest you wait here until he returns. He is sure to come back, for this is on his route."

Time obviously had ceased to mean anything to Père Jacques.

Fanny realised that, since it was impossible to move without adequate transport, they would have to stay there.

" Couldn't we," she asked, " find another contractor and get some bullock carts and elephants? We cannot remain here indefinitely."

" Your stay will not be indefinite. A week or two, a month at the most. It is not too long to wait."

" But we must get on before the rains come."

The priest shrugged his shoulders. He offered to find somewhere for the women to sleep. He himself had no bed, for he slept on the floor.

In the morning Fanny began her inquiries afresh. She had brought all her money with her, silver coins packed in small metal boxes. She extracted some coins and held them out in her hand, and asked who was prepared to go and look for the contractor.

" Perhaps he has not been able to find the elephants and the coolies," the priest said.

" At least they could tell him to hurry."

" How can he hurry if he hasn't got the elephants or the men? "

So resigned an attitude got on Fanny's nerves. " But there are elephants all over the place, Father," she complained.

He made a gesture of dismissal. " They are wild. They wouldn't be of any use to you."

Half a dozen men and women helped themselves to the coins in her extended palm. " We'll go," they said.

Charles surmised that it would prove a fruitless quest. " They only want the money," he said.

Fanny glared at him. She could not endure the delay and the inactivity. Only thirty miles away was the frontier, which she and Preecha had inspected during their brief, interrupted honeymoon. Her thoughts had been with him every mile she had come. The only photograph she had of him was on one side of her locket; on the other was a picture of their son.

She went to the edge of the lake, on which there were many fishing boats, the men leaning from them to catch fish with their bare hands. Egrets and cormorants paddled in the mud and cranes and wild duck flew overhead.

She sat there for some time in angry frustration. There was a temple a few yards away and a spirit shrine, a resting place for " the wandering phantoms." In the distance she could see a large paddle-steamer approaching slowly. As it came nearer, she saw that it was a handsome, elaborately carved and heavily gilded affair. She felt it must belong to the King or to one of the Princes. But what would bring them here at this time of the year, she wondered?

It drew near the shore and a young man, attended by two liveried servants, alighted, looked around him, then walked towards her.

She saw that it was Prince Poh Duan.

" It is a long time since we met in Bangkok," he said, smiling. " You have not forgotten me? "

" No, Your Highness," she replied, " but I am greatly surprised to meet you here and cannot imagine what should have brought you to such a desolate place." She felt that she knew the answer only too well, but she thought that she had better hear it from his lips and know how they stood.

" I saw you in Pnom Penh, in the central market. I wanted to talk to you, but you seemed to be in a hurry."

" You've come a very long way, Your Highness, to verify whether I had returned to the East."

" We already knew you were in Cambodia," he replied.

She was silent for a moment, then, hoping to keep the conversation on a light note, she said:

" Your sorcerers and your witches must have been very busy."

" We were informed by telegram from Bangkok."

" Who would have sent such a message? "

" The Regent. His agents saw you in Singapore—and again in Saigon. They reported that, together with three friends, you had boarded a river steamer and were making for Cambodia."

" What was his purpose in informing you? " she asked.

" He wanted us to keep a sharp lookout in case you should be considering crossing the Siamese frontier. The King wished to prevent you from landing in Pnom Penh, for our relations with Siam are very good. . . . It was I who persuaded my father to do nothing for the time being, since it did not appear to me to be right that such drastic action should be taken against one whose visit might be perfectly innocent and harmless."

" Why then have you come here? " she asked.

He raised a warning hand. " You are closely watched. The elephants, the coolies, the spears, were not reassuring . . ."

" Is the King responsible for the elephants not being here? "

" Yes. He sent a runner after your contractor to tell him not to supply them. By the time the man reached him the elephants had already been engaged."

" Where are they, then? "

" Being dispersed, I trust," he said.

" No! " The exclamation was one of despair. Then she controlled herself and said: " Your Highness's deductions are wrong. One of the members of our party is an artist. He came to paint pictures which he intends to exhibit in Paris."

" And the other two? "

" Charles Chalais has come because he was born in Saigon. His father was a French political officer there. He is interested in Cambodia because it is a French protectorate."

" And the girl? "

" She follows Charles—you can draw your own conclusions. Having explained the nature of our expedition to you, I hope that Your Highness will induce your father to countermand his orders as soon as possible."

He avoided giving an answer. " Where are you staying in this—er—desolate place? " he asked.

" Scattered through the various huts. Your people are kind."

" I hope you will allow the son of their ruler to be kinder." He gestured towards his boat.

" How long do you expect to remain here? " Fanny inquired.

" Until your elephants arrive."

" Oh! Then they will come? " She could hardly believe she had heard aright.

" Certainly—if you will allow me to accompany you."

This was an unexpected turn in the situation.

" You . . . and——? "

" One or two servants."

" Well, if that is the condition . . ."

" You are not very gracious. But I might be of some help to you. I know the country well."

Fanny did not answer.

Chapter Six

FANNY WENT back to the village. She was greatly perturbed. To think that they had come so far and spent so much money ... and now, on the very threshold of putting her plan into operation, she was going to be cheated. . . .

She looked for the others. Corinne, who had taken to dressing as a Cambodian, because it was more comfortable and cooler in this oppressive heat, lay asleep under a tree. Charles, some yards away, was trying to strum on a native guitar with a crowd around him, listening and grinning, Michel among them.

Fanny suggested that they should walk a little way into the jungle, as she wished to talk to them without being overheard. When they had gone some distance she told them of the Prince's arrival, of his offer of hospitality and of his insistence on accompanying them.

Michel was alarmed. Waving his hands, he exclaimed: " If they already know about us in Siam, the Regent will have an armed posse waiting for us. They'll seize us the moment we put one foot across the frontier."

" Splendid! " said Charles. He and Fanny were the only two who knew the aim of the expedition, and that they were courting arrest.

" But I don't want to be locked up," Michel expostulated.

" That's exactly what I've come here for," Charles replied. " Let the Prince come with us," he went on. " We can't stop him, anyway."

" We'd better go to the boat," Fanny said at last. " We

343

might as well wait there till the contractor comes. Let's move in before it gets dark. I can think of no way of stopping the Prince coming with us. What we must try to work out is some way of shaking him off by the time we get to the frontier."

They turned and walked towards the lake.

During dinner it was obvious that the Prince was interested only in Fanny. His eyes hardly left her. This was distressing to Corinne, who had changed into a skirt, rouged her cheeks and piled up her hair on top as she used to in Paris. But beyond the normal courtesies required of a host, the Prince seemed unaware of her presence. He wished to allot the best cabin to Fanny, but she insisted on sharing it with Corinne. They were all up early next morning.

Runners had been sent out in various directions, but it was certain that the contractor would not be found for a day or two, so they had to make the best of each other's company. Corinne was irritable and so was Charles. Fanny was nearly desperate; only Michel was cheerful.

By the time the elephants arrived they were all thoroughly on each other's nerves. They were still on board when the news was brought to them, and rushed on deck in various stages of undress to see the cheering sight. Fanny, with little more than a wrap round her, waved her arms above her head.

The Prince, smiling wryly, asked: " When do you propose to start, Fanny? "

" Now," she said, and rushed back to the cabin to finish dressing.

Measured by the rate at which elephants travel, the frontier was barely two days away. On the Prince's instructions, the contractor had also brought horses, but the pace would be set by the elephants.

On the first day of their journey the Prince rode as close to Fanny as possible, and when she spurred her horse forward to join Charles or Corinne or Michel, he came up too. The three elephants which carried their kit went in front; the coolies, chattering and singing, followed behind the horses.

For some miles they travelled inland, parallel to the River Stung Pursat. The road was a wide, dusty track. The elephants stirred the dust with every step, making them all cough as they rode into the cloud.

At Pursat, bigger than Kanchor but scarcely a town, they turned off, taking an equally dusty track which led to the frontier. Soon after midday they halted for the elephants to rest in the cool of the immense trees, then they moved on again, travelling until well after ten at night.

Then the coolies pitched their tents and they divided up, Corinne with Fanny, Michel with Charles. The Prince had a bright scarlet-and-gold tent to himself and two personal servants to attend to his needs.

A second heavy-going day followed.

That night, as their tents were being pitched by the Kampong Prak river, very near the Siamese frontier, Prince Poh Duan said to Fanny: " Now that we are almost in Siam, perhaps you could tell me what you propose to do."

" Your Highness has been extremely kind," she replied. " Your thoughtfulness, and your servants, have taken the edges off our rough journey. We are all most grateful to you. But as to my plan, I'm afraid you would not believe me when I tell you that I haven't got one. Our purpose is to get into Siam. You may ask ' Why then come this way when the other would have been shorter and easier? ' "

" That is not a question I shall ask you," replied the Prince, " for I know the answer. This way leads straight into your late husband's province. Do you propose when you get there to rouse those who knew and loved him? "

" That would not, you will agree, be a very practical plan," she fenced.

" Not very, I'm afraid. But you have some Snider rifles."

"You have had our baggage searched," she said angrily.

"I needed to know something of your intentions." He shook his head sadly. "The Regent would put down any rising in a matter of hours—like that." He flicked his fingers. "I suggest that you throw away those rifles, or let me have them. If they are found in your possession, they'll arrest you."

"Me—or all of us?" Fanny asked anxiously.

"All of you, I suppose. Will you let me take care of those rifles for you?"

"No, Your Highness," she said. "We may need them against bandits—or—or—tigers."

"Up to the frontier—that is to say, for the next four or five miles—I can protect you. Beyond that—I can do nothing. I hope you have considered this?"

"I have," Fanny replied. "What I had never supposed was that I should have your help up to the frontier."

Their camp was in the forest. The trees rose to a great height above them and there was a tangle of undergrowth all round. Fanny left the Prince and went to find Charles. He was sitting with his back to a tree, and she sat down on the hard, dry earth beside him.

"I have been trying to think how we can get away from the Prince," she said. "We *must*. I think we had better start very early to-morrow, while he is still asleep. The frontier is not very far from here. We could slip away separately, one by one. You tell Michel and I'll tell Corinne. I have a pistol. You have one too. We shall have to forget about the rifles. It will be impossible to get at the baggage without waking up the coolies, so we shall have to do without them."

She unwound her arms from her knees and threw a twig at some small animal that had scurried past in the darkness.

"I think," she went on, "that we should travel diagonally and make for another part of the frontier; he is sure to look for us at the nearest boundary. If he appeared, the Siamese would do nothing; they don't want to have bad relations with Cambodia."

" What time do you suggest we start? " Charles asked.

" In about four hours."

He stretched and yawned.

" Not so loud," she cautioned him.

" I'm tired," he replied. " Where shall we start from? "

" Here," she said.

He stretched again. " I'm going to bed to get what sleep I can," he said.

" It's too hot. I shouldn't be able to sleep. But you go," Fanny answered.

" And leave you alone here? "

" Why not? " she asked.

" Well—snakes, for one thing."

" They won't bite unless they are attacked. In any case, they can slip in under the canvas of a tent."

Charles made a face, stifled a yawn and slowly walked away.

Fanny sat in the forest for some time. She was very wide awake. She kept on wondering what would happen when they got to the frontier. If they were arrested, would the French intervene now that Gambetta was no longer in power? And even if the French were angry, what would they do? Would they only protest, or would they move into Siam, as they had moved into Cambodia? For all the brave and defiant spirit that had sustained her so far, now that the moment was near, she felt very nervous. She asked herself: What would Preecha have advised? At moments she imagined that she could hear him saying: " You will be freeing my people from subjection, Fanny, and they are your people too. Don't forget that." She seemed to hear it, but it didn't ring quite true. She told herself that all she wanted was the good of the people of Siam, but would Preecha believe her; were her motives so pure?

She pressed her head against her knees. " Oh, God! Am

347

I doing right? " she moaned. After a while she raised her head. Her lips were firmly set. She must go on. She *couldn't* allow the Regent and his vicious henchmen to go on with their diabolical machinations. They were murderers. She owed it to the people, to his people, that such things should never happen again—ever.

She held the locket in her hands, but the thickly-leaved branches of the tall trees cut off the pale moonlight and she could barely see the pictures of Preecha and their son. More than ever she felt certain that what she was doing was right.

She looked at her watch again. It was barely an hour since Charles had left her. She had dragged him into danger. Perhaps it did not matter. He liked excitement, even went out to seek it. But poor Michel had had his fill of danger during the war. He did not want any more excitement. He had only come to paint. And as for Corinne—she was sure that Corinne had hated every moment of the journey, anyhow since they had left Saigon. She had only come because Charles in his high-handed way had told her to, and because she wanted to be with him.

Fanny wondered if she herself had not been high-handed. In her determination to get even with the Regent, she had swept these three into her adventure. Charles at least had known from the outset what he might have to face, but the others had no idea of what the dangers were. She had told them that it would be rough and difficult and had hinted that there might even be danger, but she had not been open with them and in her innermost consciousness she began to feel that in her blind, unyielding resolve she had been as ruthless as the Regent.

She covered her face with her hands. The hard gold of the locket pressed against her forehead, moist in the heat of the stifling, airless night. With her eyes closed, she could see Preecha more clearly; she felt closer to him. Now, she believed that she saw a disappointed look in his gentle eyes, heard him ask:

348

" What good can come of revenge? " " I can't give up, I can't give up! " she cried out to him. But she knew that it was hatred and bitterness that was driving her on. Perhaps it was Preecha who had been trying to stop her at every turn, bringing all her plans to naught. She wished she could be like him. If they had been together a little longer, perhaps in time his gentle influence might have guided and helped her. But her spirit had been roused and her will was too strong to submit in meekness. " It is for your father and your brothers, who are still in gaol, and for our children and their children that I am doing this," she argued.

She wept for a while. Then she thought she heard something stirring near her. The sound was unlike any other common to the night. She listened, but all was still. Then a large bird fluttered with a cry out of the branches overhead, and something scurried across her foot and disappeared into the darkness.

Suddenly she felt a pair of human hands clasp her firmly by the arms. A gag was pressed against her mouth, then other arms lifted her up and bore her off. She saw that there were half a dozen men around her. They carried her through the forest, tiptoeing across the dry, fallen leaves. She struggled to get free, but their grip on her was too firm and she could make no more than a muffled, gurgling sound.

For a mile or more they carried her to where an elephant and some horses were waiting under the trees. One of the men leapt on to the foremost horse and made off. The others raised her on to the back of the elephant, and the small procession swayed slowly towards the Siamese frontier.

She understood every word they said to each other, and knew she was a prisoner of the Regent. On the backs of the horses walking beside her elephant were stacked the rifles she had bought in Marseilles and the spears she had bought in the alleys off the bazaar in Pnom Penh.

Chapter Seven

THE CAPTURE was effected so swiftly and so silently that none of the others was aware of it. More than an hour later, Corinne, seeing that Fanny had not yet returned, went to Charles's tent and called to him.

" Where's Fanny? " she asked. " I'm worried about her."

He rubbed his eyes, yawned and, coming out of his tent, pointed into the distance. " She must have fallen asleep in the forest."

They walked to the spot where Charles had left her and, not seeing her, began to shout her name.

" Are you sure this is the spot? " Corinne asked anxiously.

" Look—this is where we sat. You can still see our footprints. Wait a minute. What's this? " He picked up the locket. " And here—the marks of many feet. Oh, God! There's been a raid. They've carried her off! "

Corinne and Charles rushed back to their encampment, calling loudly. The Prince was at the door of his tent when they reached it.

" What is the matter? " he asked.

" Fanny," said Charles breathlessly. " She's been kidnapped."

" Kidnapped? It is impossible, for we are in Cambodia still. They wouldn't dare come into my country and carry off one of my guests. Let us go and look for her. She may have been attacked by a wild elephant—or a tiger."

A clamour among the coolies now revealed that the rifles and

350

the spears had disappeared. This was plainly not the work of elephants or tigers.

" We must go after them," cried the Prince angrily. " I shall cross their frontier if necessary. I mean to get her back at all costs."

By the time they set out, the raiding party were well on the other side of the frontier, and Fanny's gag and the ropes which bound her had been removed.

As she jogged along on the back of the enormous elephant, with two men, both armed, seated beside her and two others on horseback, also armed, riding alongside the elephant, the mahout talked freely to her. They had received instructions, he said, from the Government in Bangkok. They had been told to come and get her. The man who had ridden off on the pony had gone to Battambang to despatch a telegram announcing her capture and stating that they were now on their way to Bangkok.

Fanny felt certain that Poh Duan would try to rescue her. But she wondered if he would dare pursue her across the frontier. Hopefully she looked back again and again along the road they had come, but she saw no tell-tale clouds of dust.

During the hottest part of the day they halted for a while, then as the scorching sun began to set, they started off again.

On the third day, in the early morning, she could see ahead of her Kabin, to which she and Preecha had gone on their honeymoon to see his gold mine.

Passers-by turned to look at her as she rode by on the elephant, surprised by her escort of armed guards—surprised, too, to see a white woman in this region. Some joined their hands together and bowed to her. Others exchanged quick whispers; after a time it became obvious that someone must have recognised her and that the rumour of her capture had spread. Would these people, *his* people, attempt to rescue her, she wondered. But how could they, unarmed and unaided?

Surrounded by her guards, she passed through the dusty main street of Kabin, skirted the quarries and the engine-house, and went on towards Prachin. A searing anguish, intense and unbearable, seized her as she lived again the tragic hours of her last coming to Preecha's home.

They were only two hours away from Prachin when night fell. They camped in the open. As she lay under the stars she tossed restlessly and cried at intervals.

Two pairs of guards took it in turns to watch over her. They exchanged glances and shook their heads. What her fate might be after they had brought her to Bangkok they could only guess. But they seemed to be filled with pity for her.

Suddenly in the darkness half a dozen men emerged from behind the trees, fell upon the guards and gagged and bound them. Fanny observed that they offered no resistance, did not put up even a perfunctory struggle, or call to their companions for help.

Taking her gently by the arms, her rescuers led her to some ponies they had brought with them. " For you, my lady," one said, bowing low. They helped her to mount, and together they rode off into the night.

Not until she was well on her way did the guards react. Then they fired a few shots into the air and one of them rode back to Kabin to report that they had been overwhelmed and that in the battle she had escaped.

Her rescuers brought her to Prachin an hour before dawn, and led her to the temple which had been erected in Preecha's honour, an expression of sympathy which the Regent had tolerated to avoid disaffection. To this shrine the people who had known and loved Preecha came on pilgrimage to pay their respects and to express their devotion.

Then, as night fell, disguised once again in saffron robes and with three priests seated beside her in a small country boat, she

The memorial to Louis Leonowens in Bangkok

The alley in which Fanny lived
after her return to Bangkok

The monument
commemorating the
establishment of
democracy in Siam
in 1932—a cause
to which Fanny devoted
her later years

set out for Bangkok. Their intention was to get her to the British Consulate, where they believed she would be safe.

Gould was now the Consul. Could he help her? With the evidence of the seized rifles, the Regent would be able to build up the most fiendish charges. If he spoke of an armed raid intended to raise a rebellion and overthrow the King, could Gould, could the British Government, refuse to surrender her?

The priests brought her to the British Consulate under cover of darkness. Here they left her. She sighed with relief as she stepped on to the familiar landing-stage.

She tiptoed across the dark lawn and up the stairs to the veranda. The night watchman, dozing in a corner, leapt up to give the alarm but, recognising her, *wei*-ed humbly.

From her father's old bedroom, Gould emerged in his night shirt. " Fanny! . . . I can hardly believe my eyes! I had heard terrifying things about you—that you were seized and were being brought under arrest to the Regent."

" I am sorry to involve you in all this," she said. " But just tell me. Will I be safe here? "

" We shall have to see. We don't yet know what the charge is. I intended to protest the moment I had confirmation of your arrest. Let me get you some tea, or better still, some brandy, and I'll have a bed prepared so that you can get some sleep."

While she sipped her drink, she told Gould of all that had happened. She saw a scowl flit across his face from time to time. When she had finished, he said: " Fanny, what made you do it? It wasn't at all a wise thing to do."

" There was no other way. It did not seem wise, but it seemed possible."

" Did you really think it would succeed, Fanny? "

" Yes, or I shouldn't have embarked on it."

He shook his head doubtfully.

" And it might have done," she added. " But, with the coming of Poh Duan everything went wrong."

" Things often do. This was sure to anyway," Gould said. He filled her glass again. " Mind you," he went on, " after what you'd been through, it's not surprising that you'd lost your sense of values." Gould paused and then went on: " Forgive me for talking to you as your father would. I shall ask no more questions. Please stay here—for a while at any rate."

She walked to the edge of the veranda. With her back to him, she gazed out on to the river. Very faintly the dawn had begun to tinge the sky.

She slept until the late afternoon in the room that used to be hers. When she woke up she looked about her. Everything was different. The furniture had been rearranged. The old pictures were no longer on the walls. Then, with the saffron robe in which she had arrived wrapped loosely about her, she called: " Is anyone there? "

Singh came up and bowed low as he salaamed. " Missy Baba! " His face shone with pleasure.

" Are there any clothes I could wear, Singh? A *panaung*—I think I'd prefer that. Could you find me one? "

Gould came out of the study and thudded his way up the stairs.

" Has there been much of a stir about my escape? " she asked him.

" Gossip only. No official intimation."

" Official? " she frowned questioningly. " I would hardly have thought there'd be anything official about that."

" I feared that the Regent might send me a warning to say that if you were recaptured, as he doubtless expects you will be, you would not enjoy the protection normally accorded to a British subject."

" I see," she said gravely.

" One reason for receiving no communication from him may be because he's ill. I have noticed doctors crossing the river constantly . . ."

Singh arrived with a gay *panaung* and a jacket.

She went into her room to get dressed.

Half an hour later Gould saw her walking across the lawn towards the river.

" Don't leave the Consulate," he called anxiously.

She turned and looked up at him.

" One step outside these grounds and they'll get you."

She looked a little less tired, but round her mouth and eyes there were traces which bore witness to the great strain she had been under. She waved her hand in acknowledgment and walked on towards the landing-stage.

" Not too near the water, Fanny." Gould hurried down the stairs after her. " One swoop from the Regent's men and you'll find yourself a prisoner again."

She laughed. The river seemed different. All was still.

" Why is everything so quiet? " she asked. " What has happened? The gaiety, the laughter has gone from the river. Why this extraordinary hush? Look, the shops are being shut in the bazaars, and white flags are being run up."

Gould stared across the river towards the Regent's residence. Boats could be seen making for its landing-stage.

He called for Singh, who ran up and salaamed. Pointing, Gould asked: " What has happened? "

" His Excellency Somdetch Chow Phya Suriwong is dead, Sahib," said Singh with an air of satisfaction.

Gould did not doubt the truth of this statement, for the grapevine worked quickly and accurately in Bangkok. In the distance they heard the chanting of prayers. Fanny and Gould looked at each other, then turned and walked back across the lawn.

Chapter Eight

AT DINNER Gould gave Fanny such news as he had of her family. Her mother was still at Chiengmai with Caroline and Louis. Her brother Tom had left for New Zealand. Her father had written that the three children were well.

She wanted to telegraph to her mother, who might have heard rumours and would be very anxious.

"Better not, Fanny," said Gould. "The Regent had a number of faithful henchmen, the Foreign Minister among them."

She was silent. Fate had intervened at last. What the British and the French were unwilling to undertake had been accomplished. The way had been cleared. Her work could now begin. The people, fatalistic by instinct and complacent by temperament, accepted their hardships with hardly a murmur. They must be guided and helped. Who would lead them? The King? He had had ideals planted in his mind by Louis's mother Anna. This was the chance for which he had been waiting. Now he could put in hand all the reforms which were required. But would he? The knife would have to cut deeper than he would be prepared to go.

A few days later, she wrote to the King:

Your Majesty—I have returned to Bangkok. I had always intended to come back, though not in the way I have come.

I am writing to ask if Your Majesty will be so kind as to see me. I am prepared to leave the comparative safety of the British Consulate because I know that you have always been

just. There is much that I should like to talk to you about.—
Fanny Preecha.

The King's reply was brought by hand the next morning.
He suggested she should come at four that afternoon.

When she arrived he greeted her warmly, took both her hands
in his and held them for a while. Then slowly the welcoming
smile faded. He looked at her, and began to pace the room.
She followed him with her eyes. Twice he stopped and cleared
his throat as though about to say something, but turned and
walked on.

" I should have asked you to sit down," he said suddenly.
" I am sorry." He indicated a chair in the small drawing-room.

He came up and stood beside her, and in a gentle voice said:
" Fanny. He was my friend. Five times I refused, but . . ."
He made a despairing gesture. " They had made up their
minds. I could do *nothing*." He saw the corners of her mouth
harden. " If you reflect, you will realise what they would have
done if I had continued to refuse."

" I don't," she said, looking fixedly at him.

" Another King would have signed it," he said.

" Did it mean so much to the country, then, to kill Preecha? "

" Not to the country," the King replied, " but to one man
it meant everything. I cannot restore him to you. But I have
already given the order for the release of his father and his
two brothers and the return of their confiscated wealth to
them."

She inclined her head in acknowledgment. Then she said:
" Is it not monstrous that *one man* should have so much power
and should cause so much suffering? "

" Yes. But in fairness this must be said too. He did much for
the country. He was a *very* great man. Together with my father
he forged the links with Western civilisation. I personally owe
an irredeemable debt to his family, for it was he who helped

my father to regain his throne, which had been usurped from him."

" I know. But . . ."

Changing the subject, the King asked: " Are you going to settle in Siam? "

" Yes, I am going to live here, Your Majesty," she said.

" I am pleased to hear you say so."

" Perhaps Your Majesty will not be so pleased when you hear what I plan to do."

He smiled. " Tell me."

" There is a need for sweeping reforms."

" I know this, and in the few days in which I have been able to exercise true power I've abolished the old habit of lowering the forehead to the ground and crawling. You may have noticed when you arrived that the servants walked upright and merely bowed. More than this, I plan to abolish slavery. In future nobody will be allowed to have slaves."

" Your Majesty has indeed deserved well of your people."

" You can attribute this to the influence of Louis's mother Anna Leonowens. All her talks about Wilberforce and about the American Civil War are bearing fruit. But these reforms cannot be put through overnight. Freeing the slaves, for example, will affect a lot of people—the owners as well as the slaves. So it will have to come gradually."

Fanny nodded. The King continued:

" When I heard that you wanted to see me I thought that you might want to ask me about the position of your husband's estate. It was confiscated by the State. All the land has been sold and the money has been applied to various purposes. The situation of his father and his brothers is quite different, for their property was merely sequestrated and held; the possibility of returning it to them was allowed for. But for Preecha's children—I shall do something for them, you may rest assured of that. Will they join you here? "

" Certainly."

" I am glad. It will make their grandfather very happy to have them near him."

Fanny knew that she was being dismissed, but she had one more thing to say, something that in fairness she must say because it was important and because it might change the King's attitude towards her. So rather breathlessly she burst out:

" What is the good of freeing the slaves if even the free men have no rights? "

The King looked startled. " What do you mean? " he asked.

" I mean justice—fair trials."

He nodded slowly. " You are thinking of what happened to Preecha."

" And not only to him but to others, equally innocent."

" I intend to reform the judicature. In future there will be fair trials, with witnesses freely heard."

" But, Your Majesty, this will not be enough unless you cut to the very roots."

" What do you mean by the roots? "

" The system which gives so much power to one man—the power of life and death over the people—the power of absolute monarchy which can at any moment turn to tyranny."

" You want to get rid of me? " The King laughed.

" Not you, Your Majesty, because you are fair-minded and just. But others have done murder in your name—have forced you to bow to their will."

" It could never happen again."

" Not if another minister in the reign of *another* King——? "

He shook his head.

" It could," she insisted. " And that is what I am going to try and prevent."

" You will not succeed," the King replied. " Don't go too

far, Fanny, in promoting subversive elements, for if you fall foul of the law I may not be able to help you. You cannot expect me to look on idly while you try to undermine my authority."

The King rose and held out his hand, then he walked with her to the door.

Chapter Nine

Fanny arrived in Chiengmai in the middle of the rainy season. The rivers were in flood and the journey took longer than she expected—nearly five weeks. Louis's servants escorted her to the large new house he had recently built. He was certainly living in affluence.

Caroline was well, but Mamma looked old and drawn. Louis had begun to put on weight and had allowed his moustache to grow long enough to twirl.

Her nephew Thomas George Knox Leonowens, called George, was just over two, some months younger than Spencer, but he was so very much bigger.

It was odd to hear Mamma called " M'lady " by those who spoke English. She hugged Fanny again and led her to a chair. " It is going to take you a year to tell me all you have been doing, so you'd better begin now," she said.

" Where shall I begin? " Fanny asked, smiling.

" At the beginning, of course—three years ago." But she kept on interrupting. She asked questions about Papa and the children. " It must be very cold in Biarritz in the winter. Papa used to catch cold so easily. I am going to join him one day, but I don't like the cold—and I don't think I shall like the life."

She asked about Lambton, for she had never given up the hope that Fanny might marry again.

" I saw quite a lot of him in London," Fanny told her. " He again asked me to marry him, but——"

" But? "

" I have asked him to wait."

Mamma was plainly distressed. " You think it's like having credit in the bank, something you can draw on later. But it isn't like that, not at all. Men get tired of waiting and they go off with someone else."

Alone with Caroline after Fanny had gone to bed, Lady Knox said:

" You haven't heard all she has to tell, but from what she's told me and what your father's written about her, I am convinced that the diabolical things they did to Preecha have had a shocking effect on her. She is very unbalanced still. Goodness knows what further trouble she will bring on herself, trying to start wars and revolutions. She ought to settle down and have more children."

Caroline agreed.

Quite suddenly one morning, without any warning, Fanny began to pack. Caroline and Louis had hoped that she would make her home with them. But Fanny was eager to get back to Bangkok. She had work to do, she said, and would not be dissuaded.

Ever since that night in Cambodia when Fanny had sat thinking under the trees, she had begun to recognise that revenge was not enough. It achieved nothing. There were other and far better ways of helping the people. That was how Preecha would have felt. Perhaps that was what he had been trying to tell her that night. While still retaining her ultimate goal, which was the abolition of the absolute monarchy, her chief desire was to serve the people.

Mamma, worried as to what Fanny might do, insisted on going back with her. Comfortable and happy though she was with her daughter Caroline, her son-in-law and grandchild, she began to pack too. " You can't have very much money left," she told Fanny. " What Papa sends me will be a great help. We shall try and manage on that together."

They rented a house in an alleyway off the New Road. It

ran at the side of the Hong Kong and Shanghai Bank and was just round the corner from the British Consulate.

The house was small and cramped. They had great difficulty in getting all the furniture into it. Lady Knox insisted that the Reynolds family portrait should have the place of honour in the sitting-room, where it filled almost an entire wall. There was no room for the piano, so it had to be sold.

Fanny was sad that they could not see the river. Across the narrow alleyway was a line of wooden houses, some ramshackle like their own but all wearing a proud air. She felt that Mamma's doubts about her finances were unfounded. Coutts had sold the jewels she had taken to England, so there must be some money left, and there were still a brooch and a ring or two which she had left behind in Biarritz and had asked Miss Bindloss to bring out with her when she came with the children. But a statement from the bank revealed later that in fact she had barely a hundred pounds left.

During the three years she had been away from Bangkok many new roads had been built, and bridges now crossed nearly every canal, so that one could travel everywhere by rickshaw and in box-gharries drawn by ponies. Some of the Regent's work had certainly borne good fruit, though the boatmen grumbled that the introduction of wheels was depriving them of their livelihood.

One of Fanny's greatest satisfactions was that she was now living among the people. She visited them and discussed their problems with them. If they grumbled over passing annoyances she tried to console them, but where she detected a real injustice she probed further.

A letter from her father, after telling her that "the Princess Frederica of Hanover was asking after you and wondered when you would be returning," and that "the Grand Duke Constantine of Russia was most dejected when I told him you had gone back to the East," ended with one of his lectures. " I do beg of you, Fanny, not to embark on still another silly project. You will achieve nothing, but will only bring the name of Knox into further disrepute. . . ."

He ended by saying: "I should tell you that Madame Chalais has not ceased talking about your mad adventure and blames you for her son's marriage in Saigon to a girl called Corinne. Madame Chalais fears she may be an Annamese or a Cochin-Chinese!"

There was a P.S. " Lambton wrote inquiring as to your whereabouts. I told him I would let him know as soon as I had any definite news myself."

Phya Kesab, over seventy now, had recovered from his long imprisonment and had begun to put on a little weight. Whenever Fanny arrived, Preecha's brothers always hurried out to greet her. It touched her that they should be so warm and affectionate, although her marriage had brought them so much suffering.

Invariably Kesab asked after the children. " When will they come? We want to see them."

" I have written, Phya Kesab. I want them here too." Her eyes filled with tears. " It is so long since I saw them."

The delay, it emerged later, was due to her father's financial circumstances. Helping his son Tom to get to New Zealand had cost him a lot of money, and he kept receiving repeated demands for help while Tom tried to find a suitable job there. Sir Thomas, for reasons of economy, had moved from Biarritz to Pau, where the cost of living was a great deal lower. His health too had been troubling him of late. " I continue to suffer from the stomach disorders," he said in one of his letters to Fanny. " But I would prefer that you do not mention my ailments to your mother, especially as I am now much better after taking the waters at Eaux Chaudes.

" With regard to the children's journey to Siam, since neither you nor I can raise the money for their fares, which

364

will cost a great deal, particularly since they must be accompanied by someone like Miss Bindloss, whose return passage will need to be paid, I have thought it best to write to the Siamese Legation in Paris to ask if they can help. Considering that none of this would have arisen had it not been for the action taken by the Siamese Government against your husband, yourself and the children, it seems to me only just that they should now be responsible for the cost of their return to their country."

This the Siamese Government undertook to meet, and on the 26th September Miss Bindloss and the three children at last arrived in Bangkok. Oun did not return, but had gone to Paris to work at the Siamese Legation.

Fanny's house being too small, Trakun and Arun went to live with Kesab on the family estate. Spencer stayed with Fanny.

Miss Bindloss, as she recorded in her diary, " wept when I had to say good-bye to the children, whom I had learned to love."

Chapter Ten

Living in close proximity to the poor people of Bangkok, Fanny discovered that they were not as well fed or as happy as Mamma had imagined. Beneath their gaiety and their laughter there was an abiding anxiety. Many were desperately short of money. In order to buy food for their children they were often obliged to pawn such pitiful possessions as could be spared.

The debts often amounted to only small sums, yet when the weekly interest fell into arrears, the moneylenders took the law into their own hands and carried off everything belonging to the debtor. Such high-handedness infuriated Fanny. It was cruel and illegal and she urged the victims to resist.

" I shall fight for you," she said.

The judges were startled when they saw her enter the court accompanied by the debtor's entire family and a horde of neighbours, who had come out of curiosity. Fanny pleaded with vigour, but the dice were loaded against her. Witnesses, hired and coached by the moneylender, were prepared to testify to any falsehood, just as had happened when Preecha was tried. How could she succeed against them?

Her chance came when an elderly man named Sut Chai, who lived at the far end of the alleyway, received a peremptory demand for the return of some money which he swore he had never borrowed. The sum involved was fifty ticals, about five pounds. It was far beyond anything the old man possessed. With tears coursing down his wrinkled cheeks, he told Fanny that he had never at any time borrowed money from this man.

Fanny was convinced that Sut Chai was telling the truth. " We will fight," she said.

Very little reflection was required for her to see the difficulties with which she would be faced. There would be witnesses who would say that they saw the sum being counted out into the palm of Sut Chai's hand.

" These men will receive a share of the money," said Sut Chai. " And I have no witnesses. How can anyone testify to my *not* having borrowed the money? "

Fanny saw the difficulty. How could she bribe witnesses to testify that *at no time*, not even when they were *not* there, was any money lent to Sut Chai? If a date had been mentioned, or a time . . . But it seemed impossible to prove something negative. Fanny turned it over and over in her mind. At last she thought of a plan, and said to Sut Chai: " We must fight this man with his own weapons. Get together as many friends as you can. We will take them to the court to testify that they saw you repay the money—*in full*. They were present. They saw you repay it."

" But I never borrowed it," protested Sut Chai.

" That does not matter," said Fanny.

There was a stir in court when the moneylender saw that Sut Chai had witnesses. One by one Fanny called them to the box to give their evidence. The moneylender shouted angrily: " They were not there. I have never seen these people before."

Nevertheless, each in turn asserted that they had seen Sut Chai repay the loan.

When the verdict was announced in favour of Sut Chai, the moneylender waved his arms wildly, shouting: " I shall know how to deal with these people."

The judge, rising from the mat on which he reclined, spat out the betel nut he was chewing and, raising his hand for silence, said: " I warn this man that if he carries out his threats, either directly or indirectly, he will be dealt with by the court."

The case was a triumph for Fanny. People came constantly to her house to seek her help. She weighed the merits of each case. Some were trivial and were settled in her own drawing-room. But she felt that if a true reform were to be achieved, her campaign would have to be widened. She began to write articles in the newspapers, exposing the corruption of the judicature and calling for a radical reform in the administration of the law.

" Siam possesses an admirable code of laws—on paper," she wrote. " In the main, the laws are just, but in their application they are often cruel, inhuman and barbarous."

She quoted numerous instances of delays in the hearing of cases. " Men, awaiting trial, have been left forgotten in the gaols, sometimes for years, unbelievable though this may seem." She exposed the bribery "not only of witnesses and of the police, but even of the judges" that was being practised.

Each week she made a fresh onslaught. Friends warned her that those in authority would soon find a way of silencing her. It was not difficult to invent charges, and witnesses, as she now knew, were easily come by.

Their warnings had no effect on Fanny. She continued her weekly denunciations in the Press and went to the courts to fight for those who, being accused, had the right, she insisted, to be heard. There were few people in Bangkok who did not know of her, indeed, her fame had reached the remoter parts of the country. " Even here they talk of you," Caroline wrote from Chiengmai.

But while the Siamese and the Chinese greeted her enthusiastically in the streets and the bazaars and cheered as they passed by in their boats and barges, the Europeans regarded her activities very differently.

Lady Knox was most unhappy as a result of all this. She found the continuous coming and going of Fanny's visitors, the chatter and the arguments which went on far into the night, most unpleasant. She often spoke of going to join her husband at Pau, but she never made any plans to go.

In the spring of 1885 Lambton arrived in Bangkok. Fanny was immensely pleased to see him. He looked about the small, cluttered drawing-room. There were clients in every chair, many were seated on the floor. Papers and files covered all the tables.

" I'm going to take you away from all this," he said, " even if it's only for a little while. I'm staying at the Oriental. Will you come and dine with me there? "

" Yes," she said eagerly. " I'll be about an hour. I have some work to do till then."

Lambton sat and watched while she talked first to one, then to another of those around her, with just an occasional word tossed to him.

At dinner he said: " I perceive that you are enjoying yourself very much, Fanny."

" Things are beginning to come right, Edward," she said. " It will take time—a long time, I think. But I feel I shall achieve what I am trying to do."

" What is your present goal—a revolution? "

She noticed his half-smile and answered with emphasis: " A peaceful revolution, I hope. A series of reforms. I have started with the law, because that affected me most closely."

He nodded slowly. She thought he was looking older. He was greying at the temples. " I suppose it would be ludicrous for me to mention that we once talked of the possibility of marriage—sometime in the remote future? "

Gently she put her hand on his. " I know, Edward. But as you see . . . by the time all this is done I shall be very old. I'm not young now. I shall be thirty soon."

He found it difficult to believe. She still looked so very young, little more than a schoolgirl.

" You think I'm wasting my time? " she asked.

He buttered some bread. "No; I think you will succeed, Fanny—with some of your reforms, at any rate. You have a great deal of determination."

"They used to call it obstinacy. I got smacked for it often." She half-closed her eyes and was quiet for a moment. "I suppose in a way I am doing this for Preecha. But I'm also doing it because it is something that must be done. Millions of people will one day be the better for it."

"I shall wait for you, Fanny," Lambton said.

"I am touched," she replied. "But you should not wait. It is likely to be not only long but fruitless."

They met again the night before Lambton left for Chiengmai. He had been to see the King.

"I was agreeably impressed," he told her. "He spoke of you. He said he was sorry you had detached yourself from the social life, of which you had been such an ornament—his word. And then, almost echoing De Quincy, he said: ' The work on which she is now engaged has divided her from those with whom she once dined and danced and looked on as her friends. She will achieve nothing.' On that last point I disagree with His Majesty."

Chapter Eleven

THE KING, in his desire to make amends for the wrong done to Preecha, had asked Phya Kesab if Trakun, who was now fourteen, could join the Court as one of the ladies-in-waiting. A regular income from the Privy Purse was accorded both to her and to her brother Arun.

Trakun was not strictly pretty, but she had great charm and vivacity, which even at that early age attracted many suitors. When she was fifteen she married her first cousin Bhubarn, Pet Pichai's son. The wedding was solemnised on the family estate, and the King honoured them by attending and personally anointing the hands of the young couple.

A letter from Papa in July informed her that he was now at Eaux Chaudes, where he had taken two small but comfortable rooms at the Hotel Baudot. Mamma must have received a similar letter, for she was greatly disturbed. " I must go and join him. He needs me," she said. " He has to have a nurse now "—a fact he had not mentioned to Fanny.

Lady Knox went to the British Consulate to make plans for her immediate departure. She booked a passage, she began to pack.

The night before the ship was due to sail, a cable arrived saying that Papa had died.

Lady Knox collapsed in the drawing-room and Fanny, with the aid of the maid, carried her up to her bedroom.

Mamma remained in bed for many weeks, weeping constantly. Caroline telegraphed to ask if her condition was critical. The doctor said it was not.

371

Early in the new year Caroline came with Louis and little George to see her. It was while they were still there that Lady Knox passed away in her sleep.

The loss of both her parents within a few months of each other left Fanny with a deep feeling of guilt as well as of grief. For whereas they had filled her childhood with happiness, she had saddened their last years. She tried to console herself by dwelling on the far-reaching consequences of her work, but she could not rid her mind of self-reproach.

She found it a struggle now to make ends meet. Neither Papa nor Mamma was able to leave her any money. The jewels Mamma had were divided equally between Fanny and Caroline. Fanny sold hers in order to help neighbours in need. She let off all the rooms in the house except one: in that she lived and worked. She also took on translation work for the big European commercial houses. It brought in a little money, which she supplemented by teaching English to a few private pupils.

Her energy seemed to be inexhaustible, for without relaxing her vigorous campaign for reforms in the administration of justice, she began a fresh agitation for an improvement in the system of education.

She pointed out in her articles that, whilst some boys went to the monastic schools, they only attended when their parents pleased: there was neither direction nor supervision. Girls received no education at all. She urged the King to follow the great example of his father, King Mongkut. "Since Anna Leonowens's departure in 1867, over twenty years ago, the hope that modern schools would be opened in Bangkok and in the provincial cities to supplement the good work being done by the American mission schools, has met with nothing but frustration and disappointment."

One morning, to her great surprise, Prince Damrong called to see her in her small room. It was many years since they had seen each other. She wondered what he had come to say, for she realised that this was no social call.

" The King has the improvement of education very much at heart," he said, " and he has entrusted to me the task of examining and reporting on what should be done. I plan to visit schools in England and in some of the chief cities in Europe, in order to examine the different methods of education. Much will be done when I return, but it will take time."

Fanny still felt she was not doing enough. Bangkok had been growing rapidly. There were new factories, new mills, new shipping companies, many new industries. Fresh labour was pouring into the town, but no provision had been made for the accommodation and the welfare of the workers brought in from the provinces. Many slept in the streets. Others huddled together a dozen or more to a boat. Very few of them got the wages promised to them by the contractors. There were commissions and deductions of various kinds, so that the sum they eventually received was pitifully small. Many were callously dismissed and replaced by newcomers without any provision being made for sending them back to their homes, and they were left to beg for food in the streets. Something would have to be done to help them. She had known how in England, for half a century or more, the workers had banded themselves together in order to fight the appalling conditions imposed on them by their employers. She wanted the Siamese workers to follow their example. She talked to them about unions, and after much careful planning an organisation called a Private Society was formed. In effect it was a trade union.

There were many Chinese secret societies in Siam at the time—some, like the Mafia, intent only on revenge; others engaged in a variety of criminal activities. Fanny was determined that there should be no confusion between these societies and her union, either in the minds of its members or in that

373

of the authorities. She imposed the strictest discipline, but in spite of her precautions, she was always afraid that members of the criminal gangs might infiltrate into her society. That this had occurred was shown when a dispute between the rickshaw coolies and their employers, which could have been settled by negotiation, led, while talks were still in progress, to an outbreak of rioting. Shops were raided, many people were injured, and a number of arrests were made. Fanny immediately summoned a meeting of the society's stewards and upbraided them severely.

Further rioting occurred a few months later. Fanny was passing through the street at the time, and tried to stop the rioters. In the general confusion, she was arrested. She was hustled into a crowded cell together with a number of other women, many of them prostitutes.

When the King learned that she was in prison, he ordered her immediate release. This experience provided her with material for several articles on the appalling conditions prevailing in the prisons.

On the anniversary of Preecha's death she sometimes went to Prachin to pay tribute in the temple raised above his grave. As a rule, Preecha's brothers, Pet Pichai and Aphilla, Trakun and her husband, Arun and Spencer accompanied her in Kesab's houseboat.

As they neared the landing-stage in front of Government House they invariably found a long line of people moving slowly towards the shrine by the temple. Here each in turn would lay his offering of flowers and fruit, and then kneel and pray for a while. They would then go on to the large courtyard in front of the school which Preecha had built. Here there was always a large crowd. Many stood, many more sat on the earth, watching a play in which the teachers and the priests, as well as the people, took part.

The Abbot, clad in his saffron robes, usually supplied the commentary. He told those assembled before him:

" This play shows the true story of Phra Preecha, a saint who lived in our midst and was loved and revered by us all. May his dedication to the service of the people and his tender solicitude for the humblest among us, be an example and an inspiration."

Preecha was portrayed in his early boyhood and his pious youth. Other scenes illustrated innumerable acts of service and sacrifice while he was Governor, the building of the temple and the school, his marriage to Fanny, his arrest, the false charges brought against him, the appeal of the people of Prachin to the Regent and the King, and his execution.

When the play ended, the Abbot said: " He will live on; by his example many yet unborn will learn to live better lives."

Chapter Twelve

TOWARDS the end of 1892 Caroline came to Bangkok for Christmas with her two children—a girl, named Anna Harriette Leonowens, after her famous grandmother, had been born two years before. They stayed at the Oriental Hotel, since Fanny could not put them up.

It was a most enjoyable reunion. But by the end of the festive season Caroline fell ill. The doctor said that she was suffering from a stomach disorder, brought on by the rich food she had had at Christmas. As she did not get better, and had to stay in Bangkok, Louis came hurrying down to join her. He was horrified at her appearance.

"Fetch another doctor—fetch a dozen doctors," he shouted.

Consultations were held. The doctors prescribed a more rigorous diet and Caroline began to respond to the treatment. Recalling that it would at best be some months before his wife could travel, Louis directed his keen business eye to the needs and opportunities he saw around him. First he opened a small general store in Bangkok, then he bought the Oriental Hotel. To mark this acquisition with a characteristic flourish, he rode his horse up the front steps into the drawing-room of the hotel.

His love of ostentation led him into other odd excesses. One day he gave a luncheon party in the middle of New Road, just behind the hotel. A long table was taken out into the street and laid for thirty guests, and a sumptuous meal was served by the hotel waiters. A cordon of men formed a ring around them to keep off the traffic.

Fanny, walking past on her way to a case in the law courts,

376

stopped and shook her head. " Louis, you must be mad," she cried, " with Caroline so ill . . ."

" She's recovering," he replied. " That is why we are celebrating."

But Caroline did not recover. The illness recurred and the doctors decided to operate. After the operation she developed pneumonia and on the 19th May, 1893, she died.

The funeral took place two days later, in the cemetery not far from the little church in which she and Louis were married. Fanny went with Louis and held George by one hand and little Anna by the other; Spencer walked behind them.

Walking between the graves, they passed a large and impressive monument in honour of Alabaster, who had died nine years earlier. Inside, Fanny noticed, it bore several quotations from the Scriptures. She was able to read only one of them as she went past: " Thou good and faithful servant, thou hast been faithful over a few things . . . Matthew, Chapter 25, verse 21." This was the man who had been responsible for so many of her misfortunes. He had indeed served the Regent well. But the Regent had died before him. Who, then, she wondered, had erected so magnificent a monument to his memory?

Two weeks later Louis left with his children for England. He had decided to take them to Canada, where his mother had been living for the past fifteen years with her daughter Avis, who had married a Scottish banker, named Thomas Fyshe. He felt his children would be best looked after in their home in Halifax.

He was away for six months. On his return he spent a week in Bangkok, staying at his hotel.

" I have some business to attend to," he told Fanny as they dined together there, " but the real reason for my being here, Fanny, is to talk to you, and I think you can guess what I'm going to say."

She wondered how she could stop him putting it into words. " Louis, dear . . ."

" Please," he interrupted, " let me go on. I know you have your work to do. . . ."

She was about to speak again, but he stopped her. " Isn't it time you thought of yourself—and of me? I need you, Fanny. I have never had a strong character and left to myself I shall certainly fall into bad ways. Won't you take me on as a person who needs to be helped just as much as any Siamese."

" I'd like to help you, Louis, dear," she said, " but——"

" Your work," he said, tightening his lips.

" You may sneer at it, Louis, but it is necessary and it is helping people—a great many people."

" To you," he said bitterly, " I'm not Louis. I'm just one person as against millions! "

" Are the children happy in Halifax? " she asked.

" Yes. Mamma makes a great fuss of them. But I won't let you change the subject, Fanny. This is no life for you."

" It's the life I want, Louis. It's the life I've chosen. I don't want the luxury that you want to give me."

" You make the life, then, and I'll try to live it with you. I'm prepared even for that."

" You wouldn't be, Louis. You would hate it."

" All right," he said, draining his glass. " I won't ask you again. Three times is enough."

" Thank you, Louis. You won't understand, but——"

" I know, I know," he interrupted. " Your articles, your campaigns, reshaping everything around you . . ."

She rose. " I must get back to my work now."

He took her chin affectionately in his hand. There was a further appeal in his eyes.

She gave him a quick kiss and left.

Arun, now nearly twenty, was writing at the desk in her room when she returned. He took a keen interest in all she was

378

doing and had recently joined the *Siam Observer* as a reporter. He helped her with her social work and she helped him with his writing.

Together they discussed and planned what had still to be done. So many more reforms were needed. " We must get rid of this nepotism," she said. " Some of the King's relatives, like Damrong, are able and public-spirited, but the system's wrong. For every one efficient, honest man you have to put up with ten others who are parasites. This abuse must be dealt with first. To end the absolute monarchy and get a democratic constitution will take many years. You, and other young men like you, will have to carry on and complete my work."

" But you are not old," said Arun.

And indeed Fanny didn't feel old—how could she, when she had just received a proposal?—but, all the same, the years of hard work and privation were beginning to tell on her.

In due course Arun became editor of the *Siam Observer*, and his half-brother Spencer one of his reporters. Spencer had never been strong and caused his mother great anxiety. She was completely devoted to him and broken-hearted when he died, thus severing the closest link she had with Preecha. The world around her was changing and many familiar figures disappeared from the scene.

In 1910 King Chulalongkorn died. Although she had not seen him for many years, Fanny had retained both an affection for him and an intense admiration for his integrity and his progressive outlook.

In Bangkok many of the canals had now been replaced by roads. Large hotels and enormous Government offices had been built. Massive commercial and shipping offices were to be seen at every turn. A great many trees had been cut down. The town was much less green and beautiful. There were fewer birds and no longer any monkeys. Motor-boats chugged noisily along the river, drowning the laughter that was its chief characteristic.

Life was very hard for Fanny as she grew older. She had few friends among the Europeans. Most of them tried to avoid her for fear of being pressed to help in some of her projects. The Siamese aristocracy also avoided her, for they feared to be associated with one who was known to be pledged to democratic government. Phya Kesab, by now very feeble, shook his head when he saw the poverty in which she chose to live. All her jewels and her furniture had been sold, even her bed had gone to help a family in distress and she now slept on a mattress on the floor. The one room which remained to her was bare, save for the family portrait, for which she could find no purchaser. Beneath it, she sat, serenely happy, with students and poor people grouped on the floor around her, talking into the small hours about the future of the country. To achieve their aims they had formed a People's Party. Its members were chiefly young men who hoped to go to a European university to be trained as economists, lawyers and doctors.

Most promising of them all was a youth of eighteen named Prosit. His parents were too poor for him to have any hope of ever reaching Europe. Fanny, seeing the wistful hope in his eyes, often wished she could find some way of helping him. But there was nothing left for her to sell.

Then one morning Trakun arrived with the large brooch of yellow diamonds and emeralds which the Regent had given Fanny after the performance of *The School for Scandal*. It was a shock to Fanny when she saw it and she pushed Trakun's hand aside, saying: " Where did you find that? "

" Grandma gave it to me," the girl replied.

Lady Knox had found it and hidden it, fearing that Fanny would throw it away in disgust. Staring at it now, Fanny suddenly snatched it from Trakun's outstretched hand, saying: " This will pay for Prosit's education. Now he can go to Paris."

She kissed Trakun. " There could have been no better use for it," she said.

When the time came for Prosit to leave, he took both Fanny's hands in his and kissed them. His gratitude was touching, and he vowed that when he returned he would help " to the utmost of my ability and energy to attain the ultimate goal we all have at heart."

Others who went to Europe made a like vow. Most of them she was never to see again.

On Friday, the 17th December, 1925, while hurrying through the streets as though not much time was left, Fanny felt a little faint, and leant against a wall. Shopkeepers, and then customers, rushed out. With the help of many passers-by, all of whom seemed to know Fanny, she was carried to her home and up to her room.

Lying there on the mattress, she slept. She was in her seventieth year and utterly exhausted.

Someone ran to fetch Dr. Carthew. He was the only European she knew now. He sat beside her mattress for some time, and gave her something to drink. He realised there was not much he could do.

Late that night, she opened her eyes and saw Trakun and Arun seated on the floor beside her. They were holding her hands.

She smiled faintly. His children. Then she closed her eyes and died.

Less than seven years later, in June, 1932, Prosit, who had returned from Paris, helped to achieve the *coup d'etat* which limited the powers of the absolute monarchy.

The King, the son of King Chulalongkorn, was on holiday by the sea at Hua Hin. The organisers of the coup assembled all the princes and the high officials in the Throne Hall, and read to them the manifesto issued by the People's Party. It stripped the King of his arbitrary powers. Thereafter the role of the

Sovereign was to be much as that of an English monarch. All the people of Siam were to have equal rights. The Supreme Council and the Privy Council were dissolved. Legislative and executive authority was vested in an elected assembly.

Informed of the ultimatum, the King agreed to its demands, returned to Bangkok, and the next day put them into effect. It was a bloodless revolution, as Fanny had wished.

To mark these momentous changes, an immense monument was erected in Raja Ramnoen Road, the new highway which leads to the Royal Palace. It rises like two gigantic wings and bestrides the roadway. It might well have inscribed upon it:

FANNY KNOX PREECHA—1856-1925

But Fanny's monument is not made of stone and marble. It is a living monument, embodied in the free and happy lives of the people of Siam, whom she had learned to love deeply.

THE FAMILY TREE OF THE KNOX AND LEONOWENS FAMILIES

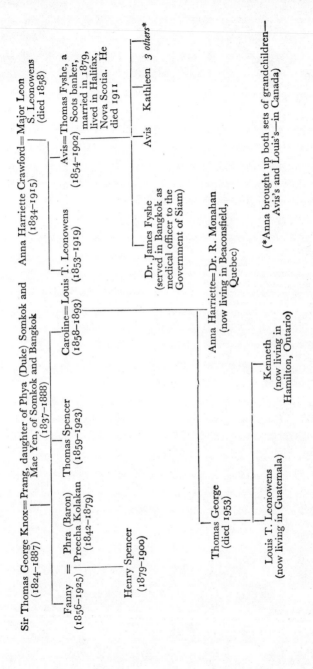

Sir Thomas George Knox = Prang, daughter of Phya (Duke) Somkok and
(1824–1887)   Mae Yen, of Somkok and Bangkok
(1837–1888)

Anna Harriette Crawford = Major Leon
(1834–1915)   S. Leonowens
(died 1858)

Fanny = Phra (Baron)   Thomas Spencer
(1856–1925) Preecha Kolakan (1859–1923)
(1842–1879)

Caroline = Louis T. Leonowens
(1858–1893) (1853–1919)

Avis = Thomas Fyshe, a
(1854–1902) Scots banker,
married in 1879,
lived in Halifax,
Nova Scotia. He
died 1911

Henry Spencer
(1879–1900)

Dr. James Fyshe
(served in Bangkok as
medical officer to the
Government of Siam)

Anna Harriette = Dr. R. Monahan
(now living in Beaconsfield,
Quebec)

Avis   Kathleen *3 others**

Thomas George
(died 1953)

Louis T. Leonowens
(now living in Guatemala)

Kenneth
(now living in
Hamilton, Ontario)

(*Anna brought up both sets of grandchildren—
Avis's and Louis's—in Canada)

6